Barmy

DATE DUE

Victoria Wood

BARMY

The New Victoria Wood Sketch Book
Sketch Book
Featuring 'Acorn Antiques'

METHUEN

by the same author

Lucky Bag: The Victoria Wood Song Book

Up to You, Porky: The Victoria Wood Sketch Book

A Methuen Paperback

First published in Great Britain in 1987
by Methuen London Ltd
This paperback edition published 1988
by Methuen London
Michelin House, 81 Fulham Road, London SW3 6RP
Copyright © Victoria Wood 1987
Printed and bound in Great Britain
by Richard Clay Ltd, Bungay, Suffolk

British Library Cataloguing in Publication Data

Wood, Victoria
    Barmy: the new Victoria Wood sketch book.
    I. Title
    828'.91409   PN6175

    ISBN 0-413-16880-8

To Susie, Ceal, Duncan, and Julie
– for the acting

Contents

List of Illustrations

Preface

Joan	And now it's over to Margery, who's been looking at what's out on the bookstalls this week for those of us who enjoy a jolly good read. *(Strolls over.)* Hello Margery, what's out on the bookstalls this week for those of us who enjoy a jolly good read?
Margery	Hello Joan. Well there's a bumper crop of goodies available, and a varied assortment they are too.
Joan	Golly. For instance.
Margery	*Glamour*, a powerful family saga of a Salford mill girl's rise from the depression-hit thirties to the heights of Hollywood. There's *Saga*, a family story of height-hitting Hollywood glamour and power in the depression, and *Salford*, that's just very depressing.
Joan	And are they full of liberated thirty-five-year-old women doing unspeakably erotic things to bronzed muscly tycoons?
Margery	Yes they are Joan, so to save a lot of tedious explanations I've brought you a book on tapestry.
Joan	Of course not everything in the publishing world is fiction, is it Margery? There's non-fiction for instance.
Margery	That's right Joan. Investigative journalist Campbell Wemyss has brought out *Crippen – Was It Pre-Menstrual Tension?*, and *Country Diary of an Edwardian Lady* lovers will be delighted to hear that there will be a new cake tin out next month.
Joan	And finally and very quickly Margery, comedy.
Margery	Finally and very quickly Joan, the funniest book for years fell into my lap this morning. Devastatingly outspoken, a real rib-tickler but with plenty of pathos as well, it really deserves a much wider audience.
Joan	And that's Victoria Wood's second book of sketches, is it, Margery?
Margery	No, it's your diary Joan, you left it on the incinerator in the second floor Ladies. Bye!
Joan	Bye!

Barmy

Nora

Nora   Hello. Have you ever planted your bulbs out in the Autumn and watched them come up in the Spring? Have you? Lovely, arent' they?

Have you ever been out in the garden just after an April shower, and mmm, breathed in that wonderful fresh smell? It's the grass and the leaves saying thank you, really, isn't it?

And have you ever been up on a step-ladder and lost your balance, and grabbed at a frayed light fitting with your bare hand, and been electrocuted? I have. Ooh, it didn't half sting.

And have you ever tried to lose weight by having your jaws wired together, and found you were up half the night trying to liquidize peanut brittle? My neighbour has.

Because life's not fair, is it? Some of us drink champagne in the fast lane, and some of us eat our sandwiches by the loose chippings on the A597.

Ooh – and it makes me mad when people complain – I mean if it starts to rain what do you do? Stick a brolly up.

And do you know what I'd like to do to these moaners and miserable complainers – stick a brolly up! I would.

No Gossip

Tea shop. Two nice ladies

First lady   Did you go to see 'Macbeth'?

Second lady   Mmmm. Wasn't a patch on 'Brigadoon'. There was some terrible woman who kept washing her hands, saying she'd never get them clean. I felt like shouting out 'Try Swarfega'. We walked out in the end.

First lady   Why?

Second lady   Someone said 'womb'.

First lady   No.

Second lady   Is said to Col – get your duffle – two pounds on a box of Quality Street and someone says womb.

First lady   It's happening all over.

Second lady   Oh I know. In my magazine story last week, an unmarried couple slept together.

First lady   Tuh.

Second lady   I mean, in my day, in a magazine, you didn't have sex, you had a row of dots.

First lady   That's right, three dots.

Second lady   In fact, still if Colin turns to me in the night, I just tap him three times on the shoulder and he goes to sleep quite happily.

First lady   Dot, dot, dot, yes.

Second lady   Except of course the children grew up thinking anything in Braille was pornographic.

First lady   How are the children?

Second lady   Well, Susan's still Assistant Catering Manager at Wilkinsons, and she says, in a couple of years, if she plays her cards right – she could become er, a catering manager's girlfriend.

First lady   Oh, that's good.

Second lady   And of course she's saving up for her bottom drawer.

First lady   Oh, what's she got?

Second lady Just the knobs so far, but – oh, and she failed her test again.

First lady Oh, what on?

Second lady Something and nothing. Not looking in the mirror, and failing to report a couple of accidents.

First lady And is Tony still in the SAS?

Second lady No, he left.

First lady I think you do have to be incredibly tough to stick it; the violence . . .

Second lady And then you see, the balaclava was so itchy. And now he's a lighthouse keeper.

First lady Goodness, that must be a lonely life – doesn't it affect him mentally?

Second lady No, he keeps busy, grows a lot of vegetables. And he's fallen in love with a tomato.

First lady An English tomato?

Second lady Oh yes. He's sent us polaroids, she looks quite nice, still a bit green – but –

First lady Has he got over his divorce?

Second lady I think so. His wife got custody of the stereo and they sold the children.

First lady And do you ever see your daughter-in-law?

Second lady I do, funnily enough – she's our window cleaner.

First lady That's women's lib for you.

Second lady No, she's under a man. He's the skilled half, she just dunks the chammy. Anyway what about you?

First lady Oh me? Same as ever.

Second lady Still on that diet?

First lady Still on my diet, still married to Ken, and still General Secretary of the United Nations.

Second lady No gossip then.

First lady No . . .

Margery and Joan: One

Joan	*(standing by a locked tank of water with a padlocked milk churn inside)* Well, your two minutes is up, Mr Jefferson, and I think we're going to have to leave it there for the time being. We'll possibly pop back a little later and see if Mr Jefferson did in fact manage to extricate himself from that milk churn. Now it's over to Margery to see what she's been getting up to this week. Hello, Margery – how's tricks?
Margery	Tricks? What do you mean?
Joan	I meant how are things going generally, Margery.
Margery	Oh, I thought Trix must be another of your god-awful friends in the Hush Puppies. *(Switching on the studio charm)* Hello, Joan. Now we all know about the frightening side-effects of barbiturate abuse, alcohol dependency and nicotine intake – but have you ever stopped to wonder about the dangers associated with these?

Shakes her closed fist à la nescafé, and opens her palm to the camera.

Joan	Now correct me if I'm wrong, Margery, but you've got a handful of ordinary industrial ball bearings.
Margery	Well you are wrong Joan, and I will correct you. Because what I'm holding is the contents of a standard fifty-gram packet of edible cake decorations.
Joan	Well I know that being hit over the head with an adjustable piano stool can give you a jolly nasty headache – but what's so dangerous about these little things, Margery?
Margery	The danger lies in the shiny metallic coating, Joan – the very sparkle that makes these little bimbos an indispensable part of every festivity and celebration from Christmas Day to Boxing Day.
Joan	And is the coating harmful, Margery?
Margery	No it's not, Joan. *(Picking up one ball)* But were a ball to come

into contact with a filling *(pointing one out)*, which can easily happen in a party situation . . .

Joan Someone showing off . . .

Margery Taking big bites to impress a girl; chewing with their mouth open –

Joan I must admit I've done that.

Margery Yes. The ball *(demonstrating)* makes contact with the filling and yaroo, an electric shock. Now one mild low-grade tingler every so often won't do too much damage – but if you've got a mouth full of fillings *and* a heavy cake eating habit – the sort of person who finds it difficult to refuse cake, or who needs cake to feel relaxed in a social situation – even the kind of compulsive chomper who doesn't eat it in public but takes a piece home wrapped in a serviette – then you could be at risk.

Joan And how can we minimize that risk, Margery?

Margery Just by taking a few simple precautions, Joan. *(Camera pulls back to show her feet encased in huge Wellingtons.)* Rubber footwear *(puts gloves on)*, insulated gloves, keep a fire blanket and portable resuscitator by the cake tin, have the phone number of your next of kin tattooed on an accessible part of your body – and – *(picking up cake and taking huge bite)* Happy Eating.

Music. Fade lights.

Joan I never went back to the man in the milk churn.

Faint sound of ambulance siren.

Margery *(mouth full of cake)* Too late now.

They look round vaguely.

Men Talking

Men in close-up, talking in their own homes.

First man   *(sixties)* It was when I was at Freemans, I'd just started on the shop floor, and I was in the washroom, because you couldn't smoke on the floor, that's right – and my pal Eric said, 'Hey, Monkey' – this is before I was bald – 'Monkey – do you know anything about sex?' I said, 'No, I don't, do you?' And Eric said he didn't, but his brother knew. And his brother was on HMS Hastings, went down in forty-four, no survivors, so we never found out anything about it. Mind you – I suppose if I had got going with sex, I'd never have had this terrific involvement with miniature dynamos . . .

Second man *(forties)* And the children were in bed, and June and I were watching the television – it was a nature thing, something about dangerous butterflies – and June turned the volume down and said, 'I'm having an affair.' Silence. Then I said, 'Who with?' She said, 'You don't know him, he's a carpet salesman.' I said, 'Oh.' She said, 'I've told him he can move in on Tuesday, and can we move the hatstand so he's got somewhere to stack his underlay? Oh, and his name's Rory.' Which it was . . .

Third man *(thirties)* And she got more and more depressed. So I said, 'Look Sheila, if you're that desperate, go back to work and I'll stay at home and look after the baby.' So off she went. And I changed nappies, made the breakfast, did the hoovering, cleaned the cooker, made the beds, went shopping, fed the baby – and by lunchtime I'd had enough. I phoned Sheila at work – I said, 'You'll have to pack your job in, I can't stand it.' It's true.

Today in Hospital

Film. Morning. The front steps of a small hospital. A man is mopping the steps.

Corin	*(Voice Over)* It's seven-thirty in the morning. For some people this will just be an ordinary day, but for others accident or illness will mean they end up spending today in hospital.

TITLE 'TODAY IN HOSPITAL'

Corin hurries up the steps to the cleaner.

Corin	Good morning.
Cleaner	I don't mop steps as a hobby, you know.
Corin	How long have you worked at the hospital?
Cleaner	*(turning away)* They want to bring back National Service, in my opinion.

Corin goes into the hospital.

Casualty. Small and empty except for a young couple, Elaine and Conrad. Corin goes over to the receptionist.

Corin	Is Casualty usually this quiet at this time in the morning?
Receptionist	It's as busy as can be expected, thank you.
Corin	Did you have a busy night?
Receptionist	We had a comfortable night and we're now resting.
Corin	Have you been put under a lot of pressure by the cuts in the National Health Service?

Receptionist	You'll have to talk to the doctor about that, but I'm sure there's nothing to worry about.
Corin	Thank you.

He goes over to Elaine and Conrad.

	May I ask what you're doing here?
Elaine	We've come about the test-tube babies and that.
Conrad	We want a test-tube baby.
Corin	Why, are there problems . . . ?
Elaine	Yes, we've only got a maisonette, so a little tiny test-tube one would be . . .
Corin	No, they grow to a normal size – they're conceived in the test-tube.
Elaine	Well, we'll never both fit in.

Small ward. Consultant sweeps up to woman's bed with group of students.

Corin	*(Voice Over)* It's ten-thirty and time for the consultant's ward round.
Doctor	Good morning, Mrs Jones.
Mrs Jones	Good morning, Doctor.
Doctor	How are we feeling?
Mrs Jones	Not too bad, apart from the agonizing pain.
Doctor	Good, good. You – let's see how much you've picked up. What can you tell me about Mrs Jones?
First student	She's wearing a nightie, Sir.
Doctor	And?
First student	And a bedjacket.
Doctor	You?
Second student	I rather think it's a cardigan.
Doctor	And how would you propose to find out?
Second student	I'd have it X-rayed, Sir.
Doctor	Allinson?
Third student	In view of the danger inherent in repeated X-rays, Sir, I'd prefer to have a period of observation.
Doctor	X-rays, observation – there's a very simple solution to all this. Winstanley?

Fourth student	Ask the patient.
Doctor	Ask the patient! If you want to know something about the patient, ask the patient! Mrs Jones – is that a bedjacket or is it a cardigan?
Mrs Jones	It's a bedjacket, doctor.
Doctor	Gentlemen – it is a bedjacket. Thank you Mrs Jones, and a very good morning to you.

Another ward. Two nurses, Della and Noreen, making a bed.

Corin	What made you want to be a nurse, Della?
Della	It was that telly programme, 'Angels'. Seemed a nice job.
Corin	What particularly attracted you?
Della	The short hours.
Corin	Sorry?
Della	Half an hour, twice a week, seemed too good to be true. Which it was.
Corin	Noreen – what do you like about nursing?
Noreen	The challenge, the teamwork, the sense of responsibility, erm, the feeling that you're helping people, the satisfaction, the nurse–patient relationship and the drugs. Oh – and I quite like the apron.

They smooth the sheets, pleased with the job. An old man's voice comes from under the bed.

Old man	Can I get back in now?
Della	*(shouting down)* No, you stay there Mr Dixon – then the bed stays nice and tidy, all right?
Old man	All right, nurse.

Office of Whizz Kid administrator, very high-tech. He is talking on the phone and checking details on a VDU.

Corin	*(Voice Over)* It's lunchtime, but hospital administrator Kevin Foley wouldn't dream of stopping to eat when there's deals to be done.

Kevin	Mrs Smith? Yes, I'm looking at the figures now – the waiting-list situation – fifteen months for a tonsillectomy, three years for a hip replacement, and five years for two seats in the Upper Circle for 'Cats'. Hip replacement – private? No problem – straight away. In fact there's a special offer this month – buy two hips, get one free. Yes, you can bring your own anaesthetic, though we have to charge corkage. Not at all, nice to do business with you Mrs Smith, *ciaou*.

Puts phone down.

Corin	I hear you've introduced some revolutionary schemes to help the hospital pay for itself?
Kevin	Oh, you heard about that? Yes, I'm glad to say, half of our morgue is now an extremely successful freezer centre.
Corin	Really.
Kevin	Tremendous. You can pop down there, pay your last respects and pick up a very competitive shoulder of lamb at the same time.

Phone rings.

Excuse me.

Recovery room. Noreen shouting at an unconscious man on a trolley.

Corin	*(Voice Over)* It's five-thirty, and here is one of those private patients Kevin Foley is so keen to attract to the hospital. Adam McCalpine is just coming round from the anaesthetic after his operation.
Noreen	Mr McCalpine! Wake up, Mr McCalpine! The operation's over, it's all over, we're taking you back to the ward. Can you hear me?
Man	Mmmm . . .
Noreen	Can you open your eyes for me?
Man	Mmmm . . .
Noreen	And can you give me the number of your Access card?

A corridor. Elaine and Conrad sit outside a door.

Corin	How are you getting on?
Elaine	We've been having tests.
Corin	Fertility?
Elaine	For something, I don't know if it was tility.
Conrad	I had to go in a bathroom with a sexy sort of magazine.
Corin	And how did you get on?
Conrad	I could read most of it.

Hospital entrance. Sirens wailing. Corin stands lit by the blue light of an ambulance. Ambulancemen/women rush by him with a stretcher.

Corin Eleven-thirty, the pubs are shut, in casualty things are hotting up.

Casualty. Corin goes into a curtained-off cubicle where a drunken man is sprawled on the bed.

Corin	Good evening.
Drunken man	That's very nice, very nice, I say good evening, you say good evening, that's all very nice.
Corin	What's wrong with you exactly?
Drunken man	God knows.
Corin	Are you ill?
Drunken man	I'm as fit as a pig – sorry, talking rubbish . . .
Corin	Why have you come to the hospital?
Drunken man	It's a nice little hospital, isn't it? Don't you agree? I think so, nice little marvellous little . . . nurse!

Nurse enters in a rush with a white coat, which she hands to the drunken man who gets off the bed and puts it on.

Nurse Sorry – took me ages to find it.

He follows her out.

Now, suspected fractured skull, cubicle nine . . .

Outside the Hospital. Dawn. Same man mopping steps as before.

Corin *(Voice Over)* Another night is over, and so a new day begins for Kevin and Della and Mrs Jones and Mr McCalpine . . .

Elaine and Conrad come down the steps.

Corin So what happened, in the end?
Elaine We didn't get one.
Corin Didn't get what?
Elaine A baby! They said you've to wait nine months or something – and the things they wanted us to do!
Conrad Sections of intercost, or something.
Elaine It was horrible.
Corin Well, everybody does it, you know.
Elaine They don't! Come on, Conrad.

They walk away. Corin stands looking at the hospital. Man waves his mop.

Man Go on, get out of it! You woolly article!

Kitty: One

Kitty   This wasn't my idea. *(Looks at watch.)* In fact, had it been up to me, I'd have been on my second cream sherry in Kidderminster by now. This lot *(gesturing vaguely and disdainfully around)* – they phoned me up last Thursday. I'd just settled down with a Claire Rayner and a quarter of radishes, so I wasn't best pleased. I said, 'Who is it and keep it brief, because I've a howling draught through my architrave'; and if I'd wanted to freeze to death I'd have gone with Scott to the Antarctic and made a day of it. She said, 'Its Morag from the television programme, do you remember me?' I said, 'Yes, I do; I lent you two cotton buds which I never saw back.' She said, 'I've got the producer for you', so I said, 'I hope you've sealed the envelope properly', which is an old golfing retort of mine. On she comes – the producer – I could hear her boiler-suit creaking even long-distance – 'Is that Kitty?' I said, 'If it's not, this cardigan's a remarkably good fit.' She said, 'Kitty – do you like fun?' I said, 'No, I don't. I had enough of that in 1958 when I got trapped in a lift with a hula-hoop salesman.' She said, 'Would you like to come on our new programme? One of our regulars has a skin complaint and has to spend three months eating peanuts with the light off.'

I said, 'Well, I'm quite pushed busy-wise – I'm doing the costumes for the Rummy Club production of "The Sound of Music", and Helen Murchison's Second Act dirndl is a week's work in itself.' (She claims to be dieting but every time we have 'Doh a Deer a Female Deer' there's a terrible whiff of pear-drops.) But that's by the by-pass.

She said, 'Come to the studios, and we'll thrash it out woman to woman.' Well, she's as much like a woman as Charlie Cairoli, but I just said 'Suit yourself' and rang off.

So I fixed up a lift with Mr Culverhouse in flat nine. Well, he owed me a favour and he has got a very roomy Vauxhall. It was no bother to drop me off because he has an artificial arm from the Western Desert and he was coming through to Roehampton anyway to have his webbing adjusted.

So I turn up – I popped into Marks on my way to return a – well, let's call it an item. I'm ushered into the producer – she hadn't changed – new haircut – if it hadn't been bright blue she'd have been a dead ringer for Stanley Matthews. And she won't wear anything approaching a brassiere – when she plays ping-pong it puts you in mind of something thought up by Barnes Wallis.

Well – she stubs out her Senior Service and she says, 'Kitty, how can we tempt you?' and starts boasting about her big budget. I thought if it's that big, why don't you splash out on some foundation garments but I kept well buttoned. So I stated my terms. One – proper remuneration – I'd seen in the papers about Terry so-called Wogan and his astronomical figure – it wasn't my paper – it was wrapped round a small Savoy at my neighbour's. Two – I want to be chauffeur-driven each way; British Rail having gone completely mad in my opinion, all vertical blinds and chilli con carne – and the driver must be blemish-free – because I'm not coming all the way from Cheadle glued to somebody's carbuncles. Three – I must have a decent dressing-room, and not that cubby-hole next to the chocolate machine. How you're expected to gather your thoughts up to the thud of a falling Bounty I do not know. There's a bit of a dubious silence, and the producer says she'll have to ask upstairs – I thought that's leadership for you – where were you when they bombed Plymouth?

Anyway – we reached a compromise – I got what I wanted and they didn't. I've quite a nice dressing room, I have it Box and Cox with the late-night Vicar. And the chauffeur's called Kent. Kent! I said to him, 'That's not a name, it's a cricket team.'

Anyway – I must go. If we beat the traffic, Mr Culverhouse is
taking me for a prawn salad at The Happy Rickshaw.
Chinese, but we ask for the other menu. *(Getting up)* Morag!
Tuh, there's no laying hands on her now she's engaged . . .

Margery and Joan: Two

Joan	Fascinating as ever, Philippa, and I for one had never really realized how enjoyable and, I may say, hilarious welding could be. Now it's over to Margery for this week's topic of national importance.

Strolls over.

	Hello, Margery, what's this week's topic of national importance?
Margery	Hello, Joan. Well, we like to pride ourselves on this programme that we cover areas of concern ignored or even overlooked by the media.
Joan	So what scandal or hitherto unrecognized social problem are we tackling today, Margery?
Margery	Unemployment, Joan.
Joan	Go on Margery, this is fascinating.
Margery	Now I'm not a statistician, Joan.
Joan	And you don't look like one, Margery, quite a bonus.
Margery	But I researched into this pretty thoroughly on my way to the studios this morning, in the mini-cab.
Joan	Because you don't drive, do you Margery?
Margery	No, and so I'm very interested in something we'll be looking at later, which is a specially adapted diesel-powered waterproof armchair.
Joan	But back to the dreary side of life for a moment, Margery. Unemployment – I've never heard of it. What is it?
Margery	I'll deal with that in a moment Joan, but let me tell you this – it affects an awful lot of people.
Joan	How many people, Margery?
Margery	Quite a few, Joan.
Joan	Are we talking about fifty-five-year-old-men in flat caps and bicycle clips, Margery?
Margery	No, we're talking about unemployment. *(Looking round)* Has

	something been changed? Marion?
Joan	So if people are unemployed, and basically that means – what?
Margery	It means they haven't got a job – Joan.
Joan	Really? As bad as that? Phew. So – I'm unemployed, I haven't got a job, what can I do?
Margery	Well of course, there are always lots of jobs advertised in your local paper, and on display at the Job Centre, that's the nice place in the High Street with the orange paint, or if you prefer to work from home – perhaps you have a valuable Afghan hound who can't be left, or cleaning staff you don't trust, then it's worth considering setting yourself up as an investment broker, or writing a best-selling novel.
Joan	So basically there's plenty of work about if we're prepared to scout around for it?
Margery	Absolutely, Joan.

They stroll over to another part of the set.

Joan	And what will you be looking at next week, Margery?
Margery	Well, you won't be seeing me next week, because I'll be covered in an operating gown – but you will be seeing my gall bladder which Joan will be removing live in the studio by means of a revolutionary new process so simple it can be performed by a nursing sister, or in an emergency, a qualified librarian.
Joan	And I'm particularly looking forward to that, because not only have I never seen a gall bladder, I'm absolutely clueless as to its whereabouts, so I could be getting in quite a pickle.

Lights dim, music in. Joan sits in the armchair and whizzes about. Margery walks off the set.

Margery	I'm sorry, I'm going to talk to Marion about this, I'm not happy . . .

Salesman

*Living room. Salesman with large samples case, a few
encyclopaedias scattered about, a reluctant woman leafing through
one.*

Man So all in all, these encyclopaedias are a marvellous
investment.

Woman But I don't think we'd ever –

Man I'm not saying you're going to read them every day of the
week – but whenever you wanted to refer to them – they'd be
there.

Woman That's what bothers me – it's that basically they'd be lying
about gathering dust – it's hard enough to keep the house
clean as it is.

Man *(whipping out 'Dustbuster'-type thing from the case)* In that case,
may I show you this marvellous little gadget? Runs on
re-chargeable batteries, you can do stairs, corners, soft
furnishings, cleavages ha ha *(lunges at her – she fends him off)*.

Woman No, I'm very happy with my own vacuum cleaner, thank you.

Man *(whizzing it about)* Dog hairs, nails, it's a remarkable little
machine, it really is.

Woman No, stop please. No, the house is only difficult to clean
because we're so near the main road, and we get a lot of dust
in through the windows.

Man *(putting away 'Dustbuster' and getting out double-glazing samples)*
So you're not double-glazed? It's a marvellous investment,
I'm not saying it's cheap, but with what you save in fuel bills,
you'll have made it back in eighty or ninety years, no danger.

Woman Yes, but how much money are we –

Man What are you – four bed two recep? At a rough guess and
using our own trained installation engineers, five thousand
eight hundred and seventy-two pounds fifty pence, give or
take.

Woman That's awfully expensive.

Man	They bring their own tea-bags.
Woman	We can't really –
Man	Or you could install it yourself – I say 'you' – obviously one wouldn't envisage a woman hopping around on scaffolding – don't want someone looking up and catching sight of your panty-bits. But your husband could do it –
Woman	He couldn't really, he has a heart condition.
Man	Has he? That must be a worry to you.
Woman	Well, yes.
Man	*(putting away double-glazing and bringing out insurance leaflets and tables of figures)* Is he insured? If he's, what, forty-five, let's see, if he pays seven, ten, say twelve-pound premium, that's not a lot if you consider the price of fags, if he staggers on till two thousand and thirty-eight, make him ninety-seven-ish, he could pick up somewhere in the region of fifty-eight thousand pounds. And if he kicks the bucket prior to that you get the mortgage paid off, a nice lump sum, a mock crocodile handbag and a slo-cooker.
Woman	He is fully insured, thank you.
Man	Well, how about yourself, women's lib and all that?
Woman	No, I haven't got any –
Man	We've a nice ladies' package going, if you don't smoke and come within the recommended doctor's whatsits. Height?
Woman	Five foot four.
Man	Weight?
Woman	Well, I don't really see that – er –
Man	You ladies! Tut tut tut. A bid of a sweetie gobbler, say no more. It is very easy to let those pounds pile on.
Woman	It certainly is.
Man	But getting them off? Another story. *(He whips out can of diet formula from case.)* You would not believe the fabulous success we're having with this unique liquid diet. You can't get it in the shops – 300 calories a day, all the essential vitamins and minerals you need, plus natural vegetable fibre so no lavatory hang-ups. And you never get bored because it's in a flavour *(He shows her the can)* See? Flavour.
Woman	Well, to be honest – I find this modern-day emphasis on physical appearance rather trivial and pointless – I feel there must be more to life than the everyday here and now . . .
Man	I agree *(putting diet away, bringing out illuminated model of*

	temple and prayer book). That's why I'm so thrilled to be associated with the Holy Temple of the Inner Light plc.
Woman	What is it?
Man	You've heard of the Mormons.
Woman	Oh, yes.
Man	It's a little bit like that, not so many wives, not so many Osmonds.
Woman	It's a religion?
Man	It's whatever it means to you, Mrs King. It's a faith, it's a discipline, it's a way of being. It brings together elements from all the great religions of the world, Buddhism, Judaism, Hindu, the teachings of the Dalai Lama, Mohammed, transubstantiation, reincarnation, druids, naiads, lay-lines – we fuse all these strands into a kind of global mysticism – do you follow me?
Woman	I'm not very well up on comparative religion, I'm appallingly ignorant generally, I just don't know what you're talking about.
Man	In that case, why don't you buy the bloody encyclopaedias!

Reports Local

Serious man at news desk.

Man   And here in our area rioting and unrest continues in the town centre. Earlier today we had reports of windows being smashed and cars overturned. Our report Sally Hardcastle is down there now with a film crew to bring us this report.

Pause – He listens to his earpiece.

I'm sorry – the film crew are still having their lunch – there's been some delay with the moussaka at The Grill and Griddle. Sally Hardcastle is phoning in this report from the scene of the troubles.

Flash up old school photo with Sally's face circled. He picks up his phone.

What's the situation now, Sally?

Sound of pips.

Hello? What's the situation now?

Sally   *(Voice Over)* Hello? Is that the television studios?

Man   Yes, go ahead, Sally.

Sally   Could you put me through to Studio Three, please, I've got a report for Desmond Hambley.

Man   This is Desmond, you're on the air – go ahead.

Sally   Oh hello, Desmond, I didn't recognize your voice – I didn't think we've spoken on the phone before.

Man   What's the news on the riot, Sally?

Sally   I've spoken to your wife, haven't I, about that buggy? *(Pips)* Hang on.

Man   Are you in the middle of the danger area? It sounds pretty noisy.

Sally	No, I'm in Lewis's. I'm in a booth on the second floor, near the Travel Agents'. The noise you can hear is coming from the cafeteria.

A picture comes up of Sally on the phone, a couple of people waiting behind her.

Man	Ah, we have your picture now.
Sally	Yes, John's turned up, but Dennis is still waiting for his pudding. No, we came away from the rioting because it was so noisy.
Man	Is the situation deteriorating?
Sally	Well, as I said, we came away because it was looking a bit nasty. I was worried about my Renault ...
Man	Are the police planning to move in?
Sally	Well, I haven't really seen any police – lunch took ages, I had to send my chicken back, it was practically pink, then I looked round the sales, so ...
Man	Have there been any casualties?
Sally	Look, I don't know, I can't really talk now – there's a lady been waiting for ages, and I haven't got any more change – look, I'll pop back to the studios later, shall I? We'll probably have to make a detour because of this awful riot, have you heard about it? Anyway, look, Sally Hardcastle, for Local News, Lewis's, second floor, near the Travel Agents'. Bye!

End on Man's face.

Dr Who

A typical episode; in colour but from no particular period. The doctor and his leggy blonde assistant Fiona (who is wearing a kilt) are running down the usual baco-foil tunnel. Music.

Doctor Hurry, Fiona!
Fiona I can't, Doctor, my stockings are rubbing together.
Doctor In here!

He presses a button on his lapel, which activates the silver-painted up-and-under garage door. They go through the door and stop as they come face-to-face with Crayola at his nerve centre.

Crayola Well, well!
Fiona Who is it, Doctor? I'm not very bright and I haven't got my glasses on.
Doctor It is my old enemy Crayola. Hulloa, Crayola.

Crayola, who has had his back turned to them facing his lousy control panel of blinking lights, turns round. He is the wrinkly sort with the crinkly voice, lots of wires attached everywhere. Hands coming out of some ridiculous part of his body, which is on a caterpillar wheeled trolley. Ears on his chest, mouth on his knee etc.

Crayola Doctor. It's been a long time.
Doctor Aeons.
Crayola As long as that? You don't look a day over five million; how do you do it?
Doctor Table tennis. *(Crayola laughs.)* We don't have much time. I'll keep him talking, you creep round behind him – disconnect his bladdermite tubing and neutralize his thermalobes.
Fiona But Doctor, we haven't got the ming-mongs!
Doctor In that case, I'll creep round behind him and you show him your operation scar.
Crayola *(suddenly ceasing to laugh)* I think not, Doctor.

Fiona	Doctor, look out!

Through the up-and-under door come the regulation three guards, two men (one black) and one woman – clingfilm wrapped round their heads, huge ears, bin-liner boiler suits, pointing hairdryers at the doctor.

Crayola	Game, set and match I think, Doctor.
Doctor	Run for it, Fiona!

They do so; the guards point their hairdryers at him, he freezes and goes negative.

Fiona	You've killed him!
Crayola	Not at all, my dear. We've merely converted his megaplumfinity into negative kreetathones.
Fiona	But what does that mean?

The guards look at each other and shrug.

Guard	Search me, dear.

Margery and Joan: Three

Joan	And we'll be having more childcare hints from Philippa next week, when she'll be telling us why raw steak and angostura bitters don't make a good meal for your new-born baby. Now it's over to Margery, who's been looking into the ancient and fascinating Japanese art of Bonsai. Hello Margery, you've been looking into the ancient and fascinating Japanese art of Bonsai, haven't you?
Margery	Hello, Joan. That's right. With summer fast approaching, we all need to know how to tan our bodies quickly, and more importantly, safely.

Joan is stunned. Silence.

Well, I'm glad you asked me that, Joan – because as you can see, there is a bewildering array of tanning products on the market. I'll just show a few . . .

She holds up products to the wrong camera, so we see them sideways on in long shot. By the time the cameras cut she is holding them out to a different camera so we get a close-up of her sleeves.

Joan	*(blankly)* What happened to Bonsai?
Margery	Scrapped.
Joan	Oh. *(Recovering)* So if I want to get a nice brown tan without burning, how do I go about it, Margery?
Margery	The golden rule, Joan – is – build up gradually. The first two weeks of your holiday, stay in your room with a hat and a pullover. And if you've got an old maxi-coat left over from the early seventies – wear that too.
Joan	And if I'm sixteen or seventeen, and have never seen a maxi-coat?
Margery	If you're sixteen or seventeen, my advice is stay at home and get those qualifications. So to sum up – first two weeks in

your room, followed by three or four weeks in a full-length dressing-gown – opening the lapels for a minute or two every other day. Never forget, you can still get a nasty sunburn even at night.

Joan And what about diarrhoea, Margery?

Margery I'm still having it every twenty minutes, Joan.

Joan But you've also been looking at the very latest in household gadgets, haven't you Margery?

Suntan table replaced by another with gadgets on.

Or perhaps you haven't, what do I know.

Margery Yes I have Joan, and a jolly interesting crop they are too. Now I don't use public transport myself, Joan, but a survey out this month shows that a surprisingly awful lot of people do.

Joan And that can lead to problems, can't it, Margery?

Margery That's right, Joan. And one of the worst problems is that at peak periods it's not always possible for a husband and wife to sit together.

Joan So if hubby's down at one end of the bus, with a hair or fluff on the back of his jacket, wifey can't always get near enough to do anything about it.

Margery Or she couldn't. Until this little gizmo came out. *(Picks up telescopic pincer thing:)* She can quietly get this out of her tote-bag, disengage the safety popper, and hey bingo, that offending hair is safely in the ashtray.

Joan Of course one thing about being in a crowd of people is that we can't always be sure of personal daintiness.

Margery That's right, Joan. Now I don't mind jamming a hand into my armpit and sniffing it in public, but some people do; and for them, these musical dress-shields are going to be a real boon. *(Produces ordinary dress-shield with tiny battery and wiring.)*

Joan How do they work, Margery?

Margery Well, I'm pretty whiffy today, so this should show you. Just pop it under my arm here, wait a moment – and if there's any pong at all, this happens. *(It plays a computerized version of 'Eidelweiss'.)* And a lovely melody to boot.

Joan And finally and very quickly, Margery?

Margery Finally and very quickly, Joan – redundancy.

Joan What about it, Margery?

Margery It's upsetting, it's traumatic, but above all, its embarrassing.
Joan So how do we keep it a secret, and stop people recognizing us in the queue at the social security?
Margery Not easy Joan – at least it wasn't – until this little hoo-hah popped up on general release.

She stands up and picks up a kind of shortened Punch and Judy booth.

Light, portable, you can wear this in the dole queue and friends and neighbours will pass you by, none the wiser.

She puts it on over her head, it comes down to waist level.

And when your number's called and you reach the window – *(rolls up a little blind in front of her face)* hey poncho – you can be seen and heard in perfect privacy.

Lights and music.

You'd probably need a bigger size, Joan.
Joan Thanks a buffalo. At least I'm not sniffing my fingers all the day long.

Craft Shop

Arty, hand-woven global village-type gift shop. Arty, hand-woven lady owner watches browsing girl.

Owner	Can I help, or are you just browsing?
Girl	I'm just looking for a present for somebody.
Owner	I see you're looking at the jerseys – they're hand-knitted from the unravelled climbing socks of Lakeland fell walkers.
Girl	Really.
Owner	Yes, if you look closely at the yarn you'll spot the occasional toenail or blister.
Girl	What are these?
Owner	Ukrainian prayer shawls, woven by the mothers of Russian dissidents while in a state of euphoria, which doesn't happen very often, which is why we've only got three.
Girl	How much is the chess set?
Owner	Well, I'm afraid its nine hundred and fifty pounds, but you see it is intricately carved from Lancashire cotton bobbins by disadvantaged Aborigines so –
Girl	Bit expensive.
Owner	We have lots of cheap items – our silk scarves there, two pounds each, all individually dyed using a mixture of beetroot juice, wild grasses and native saliva.
Girl	I can pay a bit more than that . . .
Owner	Perfume? *(Girl takes a whiff of a tester and backs off, blinking.)* That's an aphrodisiac scent, containing rare herbal essences and secretions from the sex glands of the Tibetan mountain rabbit – and we also do that in a drawer-liner.
Girl	It's a house-warming present.
Owner	Oh – how about these Bangladeshi washing stones – I believe you spread the clothes on one, and bang them with the other. I understand it gets them marvellously clean, though it's probably not tremendously good for the buttons.
Girl	Mmmm.

Owner Stationery? Cards, paper, envelopes – all hand-printed by goats.

Girl These are nice – what are they?

Owner Ah – now they're a set of primitive patterning cogs – they're actually for decorating the breasts of Malaysian sacrificial virgins, but I've found them very handy for pastry.

Girl No, it's all right, thanks – I'll leave it. I really wanted something a bit out of the ordinary.

Kitty: Two

She rushes on with bags and parcels, with her coat on.

Kitty   Now I'm keeping this on because I've got a mad dash to get
back to Cheadle. The Rummy Club Sound of Music opens
tonight. I'm prompter – and our Mother Superior's on tablets
so every other rehearsal it's been 'Climb Every What is it?'

Anyway – reincarnation! The producer set me off on it. She
had one of those sessions where you lie back and turn into
Florence Nightingale. She reckons she's had three previous
incarnations: I think one was a Roman soldier, I forget the
other two. Looking at her now, I'd plump for a Sumo wrestler
and a bull mastiff. But I'm quite interested in the
supernatural. My mother and I once paid out for a seance in
Widnes. We wanted to contact my father because we were
going camping and we couldn't lay hands on the mallet. This
medium – she couldn't have made contact with the other side
of a bedside table. She just kept saying she could tell we'd
suffered a grievous loss. I said, 'Yes, two pounds each to
come in, and our bus fares to Widnes.' But I quite fancied
regressing to my earlier lives, so I got Mr Culverhouse to
hypnotize me. So I'm lying down – he hasn't got the right sort
of watch so he's dangling a rubberized plug – and he counts
me back to 1901. 'Who are you', he says. Well everything's
dark, but I sense I'm wearing a corset, so that rules out
Edward the Seventh. Then suddenly, bang, bang, bang,
there's Helen Murchison at the front door assaulting my
knocker as per; so it's away with the hypnosis and out with the
mixed biscuits.

She'd come round on her way back from giving blood, and
why they want it beats me, because the way she eats, it must
be 'A' rhesus nougat. She'd come to tell me her daughter was

finally getting married after four years of living in sin just outside Nantwich. I said 'What's his name?' She said, 'He's called Nick, and he's very high up in sewage.' I thought, that's lucky. She said, 'It is a church wedding, but under the circumstances the bride's opted for knee-length shrimp.' She tried to impress Mr Culverhouse with her elaborate finger buffet, but he sees the world for what it is after fifty years in cocoa. She said if I wanted to give a present, they'd made out a little list. Little! It made the Domesday Book look like a raffle ticket. Videos, washing machines – the only thing under a fiver was a wall-mounted Brillo grip. So they're getting this. *(She produces an* awful *catering-size coffee tin covered in wallpaper and ric-rac braid to make a bin.)* I made it! You can't get them in the shops. I think what makes it is the ric-rac braiding. I was going to patent it, but I believe there's a lot of hanging around. Oh, and then she drops another bombshell. She chomps down the last of the Bourbons and says, 'Kitty – I'm leaving Bill – we're not compatible.' They never were – he loves opera, and she can't follow the plot of the Teddy Bears' Picnic. She only married him because he was pally with a man who made chocolate misshapes.

Now I must dash – it's curtain-up at seven and these motorways – they're forever coning you off – I blame the engineers. You can see them on the hard shoulder, larking about with their theodolites. *(Gathers her bits together.)* If anybody's been sitting on my wimples I'll play merry Hamlet . . .

Wine Bar

Very 'feminine' and 'nice' girl and slightly older man drinking after work in a wine bar.

Man   Cheers.

Girl   Cheers *(drinks)*. Mmm, quite nice and fruity.

Man   They know me here.

Girl   Really? Because some white wines – they can sort of make you scrunch your bottom up, can't they? But this is quite cordial, isn't it?

Man   Do you think you're going to enjoy working for the company?

Girl   Oh, yes. It's a very choice powder-room, ever such unusual washbasins, quite opaque.

Man   That's a very attractive dress, if I may say so.

Girl   Oh, do you like it? I think it makes me look a bit extinct, do you know what I mean? I like the fabric, though, it's quite commercialized.

Man   Do you have a boyfriend, or . . . ?

Girl   No, I don't really like steady relationships – they make me feel a bit Rice Krispie-ish, do you know what I mean?

Man   Because I'd very much like to take you out one evening, if I may.

Girl   I don't think so.

Man   Because I'm married?

Girl   I don't really like going out with people from work – it all gets sort of conjugated.

Man   Nobody has to know.

Girl   It always does get out, though. Offices are really ostentatious for gossip, aren't they?

Man   Well, it wouldn't matter, would it?

Girl   Well, it's against company policy, isn't it? People going out with their secretaries. There might be a big sort of moussaka about it.

Man   Yes, but what would be the worst that could happen?

Girl   Well, the worst that could happen would be that Head Office found out and I had to fire you, Colin. Cheers.

Margery and Joan: Four

Joan   *(in neck brace and knee-length plaster)* And as Philippa climbs
out of that piranha tank, I'm sure she won't mind if I let you
into a little secret – she's actually into the fourth week of a
very serious nervous breakdown! Now it's over to Margery,
who's been finding out what's available holiday-wise for those
of us who aren't going abroad this summer. Hello Margery,
what's available holiday-wise for those of us who aren't going
abroad this summer?

Margery Hello, Joan. Well believe it or not, but not every
holiday-maker will be flying to Marbella or Alicante with a
suitcase full of velour leisure shorts singing 'Y Viva España'.

Joan   And why is that, Margery?

Margery Possibly because they don't know the words to the second
verse, Joan.

Joan   So a lot of people will be looking for a reasonably priced
package in this country?

Margery That's right, Joan.

Joan   OK – so I'm single, I don't have very much money, I can't
afford to go abroad, I don't make friends easily, what can I
do?

Margery Look, we had all this out in the wine bar . . . *(Realises her
mistake.)* Well, there's lots of alternatives available, Joan, the
cheapest being a two-week conservation holiday in the West
Midlands dragging old bedsteads out of the Grand Union
Canal and living on pulses.

Joan   And what will I need to take with me?

Margery Well, if they haven't been soaked – a can of air-freshener.

Joan   And if I'm a book-lover and would like nothing better than to
meet my favourite authors?

Margery Then hie yourself along to the Swan Hotel, Warwick, where
you can mingle with popular novelists and have the chance to
examine such literary treasures as the original manuscript of
Wuthering Heights, James Herriot's collection of rubber

gloves, and most exciting of all – Jeffrey Archer's very first bank statement.

Joan   But you've also been looking at Singles Holidays, haven't you, Margery?

Margery   That's right, Joan. Because for every outgoing popular physically attractive swinger like me, there's an emotionally repressed lumpy old pongo like Joan. See how we got on.

Cut to film

A coach bowling along a cliff road.

Joan   *(Voice Over)* Margery and I are heading for the three-star Cliff Top Hotel – where single people of all sexes are hoping for sun, fun and a little bit of mountaineering.

Front of Hotel. Coach. Joan on the steps of the coach. Extras collecting luggage at back. Margery seen through the coach window heaving into a sick bag.

Joan   *(to camera)* Well, a bumpy five-hour drive on badly tarmacked B roads wouldn't suit everybody. *(Margery appears behind Joan, wiping her mouth.)* But we're both raring to pick up our bags and get going.

Walks to rear of coach. Margery picks up the last case.

Driver   *(as rehearsed)* The blue samsonite, please.
(closing the boot) Nope, that's the lot – sorry.

Twin-bedded room. Margery holding up racy evening clothes against herself and chucking them on the bed.

Joan   *(on other bed)* Well, I've been told my case will be here in the morning, so till then, Margery and I will be sharing the same toothbrush.

Margery   *(to herself)* That's what you think.

Joan   *(checking timetable)* Well, it's six o'clock, so I'm heading for the TV lounge, for the first event of Singles Week – a Twist 'n'

Jive session with the Pauline Mowbray Skiffle Experience. Coming, Margery?

Margery No thanks. I'm going to the bar.

Bar. Joan leaning up at the bar. Everyone very jolly. Waiter serves Joan a cocktail and moves out of shot.

Joan Well, after a few of the hotel's speciality cocktails, the ice is well and truly broken. Everyone's having a marvellous time! Over to you, Margery. Cheers!

Another part of the bar. Camera finds Margery performing a drunken dance with a reluctant businessman who's trying to get away.

Margery You don't need to phone your wife! Come on – forty-two and no bra, not bad, eh?

Back to Joan, immersed in her cocktail.

Joan And I might try that later in the week! Now it's off to bed, because believe you me, tomorrow's going to be a very full day!

Poolside. Joan in towelling robe and extremely elaborate swimming cap.

Joan Well, I've been shopping, I've visited the local museum and I'm just recovering from a vigorous session of poolside aerobics, and I imagine that Margery's been pretty busy as well. *(Waves up at a balcony)* Yoo-hoo! Margery!

Margery on a balcony wrapped in a sheet, having been 'at it' all night and just woken up. All messy hair and smudged eye-shadow.

Margery *(can't think or speak)* Hello, Joan. Yes – er – I've been pretty busy. *(Yawns.)* You know . . .

The businessman in towel stomps out on the balcony from the room, grabs a pair of underpants and goes back in, mumbling.

Man   Can't find your pants.
Margery What? *(Yawns.)*

Cliff face. Joan is half-way up the cliff dangling on a rope held by Margery, who has reached the top. Both are in full climbing gear. Margery still not with it.

Joan   Well, this is the highlight of the holiday as far as I'm concerned, a two-day course in simple mountaineering. It's a marvellous way for single people to get to know each other, because in a life-and-death situation like this, you're totally dependent on your climbing partner *(tugs the rope)*. Margery, I'm coming up!
Margery *(yawning)* OK.
Joan   *(starting to climb)* If Margery was to let her concentration lapse for just one second, I could literally –

She falls out of shot.

Back to the studio. Joan in neck brace as before.

Margery Well, that's it – and happy holidays!
Joan   Bye!

Music. Lights fade.

Margery When are they taking the pins out?
Joan   They're not.
Margery Bad luck.

Acorn
Antiques

Episode One

Scene One. A tiny set, very artificial looking. An antique shop. Through the back door is a kitchen, with the end of a draining board and then a gap where the flattage has run out. Outside the shop window is a crooked photo of a street. All the actors in this serial are over made-up (women) or speak ironically (men). Babs is blonde, sitting by a blank wall-plan. She's on the phone, holding it well away from her face for the camera. Music.

Babs   Acorn Antiques, can I help you? No, I'm afraid he's out buying antiques, who is it calling?

Mrs Overall, the daily help, comes in with coffee. Babs waves and smiles, then frowns abruptly.

Rowena? From Kuwait? Hello? Hello?

She puts the phone down.

Darn. Oh sorry, Mrs Overall.

Mrs Overall Here's your coffee, Miss Babs. Now what's wrong?

Babs   Oh nothing, just rather a mysterious phone call from the Far East.

Mrs Overall Yes, well, sometimes that's God's way of saying think on and look sharp.

Babs   You're right. Gosh. I am awful. Here I am blabbing away about my own troubles and I never asked you about your husband's car crash.

Mrs Overall Oh he's dead, Miss Babs. In fact I was going to ask you if I could have a couple of hours off on Thursday for the funeral.

Babs   Of course. Just pop back at five for the hoovering. What happened?

Mrs Overall His heart stopped beating.

Babs	Oh, no.
Mrs Overall	Yes, well, sometimes that's God's way of telling you you're dead. Not to worry, Bingo tonight. Mr Kenneth not down yet?
Babs	Er, no.
Mrs Overall	That's not like him, he's not having a nervous breakdown, is he?
Babs	To tell you the truth, Mrs Overall, we had a huge row last night, he put the triplets in the Wolsely and I haven't seen him since.
Mrs Overall	Men! Oh well, better get on and dust a few antiques.

Babs sips coffee and pulls a face.

Babs	Well, they say things go in threes.
Mrs Overall	Why, whatever's happened?
Babs	You forgot my sweeteners. Ho ho ho.
Mrs Overall	Ho ho ho.

They laugh.
Music.

Scene Two. Babs on the phone.

Babs	Yes, just bring your antiques in. Bye.

Enter an enigmatic man (Clifford).

Clifford	Babs?
Babs	Bored with Zurich, or did Zurich get bored with you?
Clifford	You always did ask a good question.
Babs	But did I ever get a good answer?
Clifford	You look well. Answering the phone in a family antiques business seems to suit you.
Babs	Thank you, kind sir.
Clifford	Babs, can't we . . . ?

Babs We? Who's we, Clifford? There might have been a we before you left me by the handbags in a well-known store . . .

Pause.

Clifford Don't say any more. I love you, Babs.
Babs I've changed, Clifford. I have triplets now.

He lunges at her over the desk.

Clifford Darn your triplets!

He kisses her, the desk cracks ominously. They corpse silently while kissing.
Music.
Credits.
We cut back to close-up of Clifford.

There's something I haven't told you. I go bell-ringing on Wednesday nights.

Episode Two

Scene One. Babs as before on the telephone.

Babs As I say, it certainly sounds like a genuine Picasso, Martin, but I would have to see it to be sure. Bye.

She looks at the phone and puts it down, smiling. Enter Berta, a Babs look-alike, but brunette where Babs is blonde.

Berta! You look marvellous! So you're out of intensive care!

Berta	I told Doctor Spencer I had to get back and help you out in the shop, so he cured me. So here I am. Ha Ha Ha.

They laugh.

Babs	Coffee, or are you still on your diet?
Berta	Oh, diet be blowed! Ha ha.
Babs	Mrs Overall!

She enters immediately.

Mrs Overall	Well, if it isn't Miss Berta!
Berta	Hello, Mrs O. How's widowhood treating you?
Mrs Overall	Mustn't grumble. I sometimes think being widowed is God's way of telling you to come off the pill.
Berta	Still the same Mrs O!
Mrs Overall	Well, this coffee won't get made on its own.

They all pause, realising a line has been missed.

Babs	Oh yes, two coffees, thank you.
Berta	No milk for me.
Mrs Overall	Well, this coffee won't get made on its own.

Exit Mrs Overall.

Babs	And a plate of your delicious home-made gingerbread, please. Bet you didn't get that in intensive care.
Berta	Oh, I don't know. Money talks, even in hospital, Babs. And though of course it was a dreadful shame Daddy being shot like that in Dhaka, being a millionairess does have its compensations.

Enter Mrs Overall with a tray full of scummy coffee and biscuits.

Mrs Overall	Here we are. It's awfully quiet in here. Anybody would

	think you were talking about million-pound legacies or something.
Babs	Good heavens, no.
Berta	Oh, come on, Babs. Mrs O's practically one of the family. Daddy's gone and got himself shot in Dhaka, Mrs O.
Mrs Overall	Oh, and he'd only just got over that chill on his kidneys. Well, you know what I think?
Berta	What?
Mrs Overall	I think you better have some milk in your coffee after all! Ha ha.
Berta	I think I had! Ha ha.

They laugh.

Scene Two. Babs and Berta poring over blank papers at the desk.

Berta	Yes, that's much better. If we deliver these antiques on Friday morning, we can take delivery of these antiques in the afternoon.

Babs nods, having no dialogue but waiting for someone to enter. Enter Derek, the handyman.

Derek	Excuse me, Miss Babs and Miss Berta, could I have a word?
Babs	Well, if it's to ask me for another job for your untrustworthy cousin Jacob, then the answer's no. His last little escapade cost me thirty-two pounds in French polish. Not to mention apologising to every Asian grocer between here and Manchesterford.
Derek	No, it's not that – it's your father, Miss Berta, he's been seen in the Post Office.
Berta	But my father's dead!

Music.
Credits.
Back to close-up of Derek.

Derek	He was buying a TV licence stamp and a padded envelope.

Episode Three

Scene One. Trixie is on the phone. She is very flighty and tarty.

Trixie	No, I'm sorry, Miss Babs has taken the triplets to see 'Get Carter', they won't be back till this afternoon. No, you won't recognise my voice, this is my first day in the antique shop, I've just been moved up from antique packing. Sorry? Trixie. Trixie Trouble, some people call me. Bye . . .

Mrs Overall enters disapprovingly with a cocktail and some biscuits.

Mrs Overall	Here's your cocktail, and don't blame me if you run out of stomach lining.
Trixie	I won't. Anyway, I only have to snap my fingers and somebody I know will come running with a dozen stomach linings.
Mrs Overall	I suppose you mean Mr Kenneth?
Trixie	He's already bought me a leotard and a wet-look wig.
Mrs Overall	And what did you have to do in return?
Trixie	You'd better ask the receptionist at the Formica Motel.
Mrs Overall	Disgusting. And him an ex-Territorial with triplets.
Trixie	That's a matter of conjecture. I found out quite a few things at the Formica Motel; one, that your precious Miss Babs checked in there nine months to the day before the triplets were born.
Mrs Overall	Who with?

Enter Derek. Trixie files her nails pointedly.

Derek	It's very quiet in here, I hope you weren't talking about me.

Scene Two. Babs at the desk with Derek.

Babs	Right, so we'll have those antiques packed up immediately and sent down to the station. Plenty of Sellotape, we don't want any more accidents.
Derek	Yes, Miss Babs.
Babs	*(over-casually)* How's your girlfriend these days, Derek? What was her name, Marie-Thérèse Francine Dubois?
Derek	Yes, Miss. She's – back in the convent, Miss.
Babs	Oh, no! After all that trouble you went to, to find her a pleated skirt. Did she leave a note?
Derek	She left a novel, but I don't think it's very commercial.

They speak together.

	Miss Babs!
Babs	Derek!
Derek	I still think about you, Miss Babs. When I'm watching the show-jumping or grilling a tomato.

She puts out a hand and snatches it back as Trixie enters. They all crowd into one shot.

Trixie	Oh, sorry. Hope I'm not interrupting anything.
Babs	Of course not, Trixie. We were just discussing the best way of packing a Spode tea service.
Trixie	Yes, well, we can't afford to have anything broken, can we?
Babs	What do you mean?
Trixie	Like your marriage to Mr Kenneth?

She pulls out some photos from her bag.

Trixie It's amazing what you can find in a waterproof packet tied to a lavatory ballcock if you look hard enough.

She tosses them down on the table. Reaction.
Music.
Credits.

Seems like I'm not the only one round here with a birthmark shaped like a moped – Mummy . . .

Episode Four

Scene One. Trixie and Mrs Overall at the desk.

Mrs Overall Well it's a long time since I've seen a diamond engagement ring as expensive as that. Not since Miss Babs got married.

Trixie Why, this is her ring, Mrs O! Don't forget we just found out Miss Babs is my mother!

Mrs Overall Why, of course. But doesn't that mean you're engaged to your own brother?

Trixie Well, yes, but Mummy spoke to the vicar and he's prepared to make an exception.

Mrs Overall That's a relief. Well, I'd better go and take away Miss Babs's coffee cup. It's a new brand, the last lot tasted a little bit odd apparently.

Enter Babs.

Babs Hello, Mrs O. I thought I'd bring my own coffee cup down today. You know, it still tastes a little bit odd.

Trixie What sort of little bit odd?

Babs Oh, I don't know, almost as if someone was trying to kill me . . .

Trixie	Oh Mum, you are an old silly billy – ho ho.

She stops laughing when she notices Babs and Mrs Overall look serious.

Babs	Well, you see, I am the majority shareholder in Acorn Antiques, since Berta's amnesia. If I were to die that would certainly suit Cousin Jerez very well.
Mrs Overall	But he's a notorious gambler and playboy. And anyway, he's in Marbella.

Enter Cousin Jerez with a peculiar accent.

Jerez	Correction, *was* in Marbella. Planes are very quick nowadays, or perhaps here in your world of antiques you did not know this.
Mrs Overall	I'll make some sherry, Miss Babs. *(Exits.)*

Babs corpses slightly at this mistake.

Jerez	And who is this charming young señorita?
Babs	She's my daughter, and she's engaged.
Jerez	Not too engaged to come out dancing this evening, I hope?
Trixie	I, I . . .
Babs	Aren't you and Bobby going crown green bowling this evening?
Trixie	No, he's ricked his wrist. Yes, I'd love to come out dancing.
Jerez	That's settled, then.
Trixie	Can I borrow your long-line bra, Mummy?
Babs	It's in my sideboard.
Jerez	Do you have any dance dresses that fasten with velcro?
Trixie	Yes, a blue one.
Jerez	Wear it.

Reaction from Babs.

Scene Two. The lounge. A sofa and a standard lamp. Babs and Jerez are having coffee.

Jerez   That was a delicious five-course meal, thank you. I'd forgotten how good you were with quails.

Babs   I may feed you, Cousin Jerez, but I don't like you. Let's cut the pleasantries, shall we? Just why do you want to buy my shares? You don't like antiques and you never have done.

Jerez   True. But I do like motorway service stations.

Babs   What do you mean?

Jerez   Look out of the window.

Babs   There are some council workmen putting a sign up. I can't quite . . . 'New motorway to be built here, starting the 25th'. That's tomorrow! Why haven't I had a letter?

Jerez whistles a few notes.

Why are you whistling like that? I know that tune, it's the one our postman always whistles. Oh I see, it wasn't a postman at all, it was you!

Enter Mrs Overall.

Mrs Overall   Can I clear away now, Miss Babs? The triplets are a bit fractious and I promised I'd pop up and read them a bit of Simone de Beauvoir.

Babs   Yes, do clear away, Mrs O. In fact, you may as well clear away the whole darn shop!

Music.
Credits.

Jerez   Could you fetch my briefcase, Mrs Overall? I'd like to show Miss Babs my theodolite.

Episode Five

Scene One. Derek puffing and panting, having just moved something. Enter Mrs Overall with tea.

Mrs Overall Here's your beef tea, Derek. You've never shifted that 1869 Bechstein all by yourself?

Derek Well, I didn't like to bother Mr Kenneth. He was having his breakfast.

Mrs Overall What was it Muesli? What was it, muesli?

Derek I think so, Mrs O.

Mrs Overall Yes well, I think muesli is God's way of making shredded wheat look exciting.

Derek winces.

It's your heart, isn't it, Derek? You strained it, didn't you, lifting that oil tanker off Miss Berta's handbag?

Derek Well, I knew she was right fond of it. Do you think those revolutionary new tablets will cure her amnesia?

Mrs Overall Well they might, if she could ever remember to take them.

Pause. Enter Trixie in a wedding dress.

Trixie Honestly, I could kill those triplets!

Mrs Overall shakes her head. Trixie realizes it's not her entrance and retreats, bumping into Babs.

Babs Hello Derek, Mrs O. Honestly, I just don't see how we can get this wedding ready in a month. Trixie hasn't even chosen her dress yet.

Derek What's happened about the new motorway, Miss Babs?

Babs Oh, I phoned up the Town Hall and they've agreed to re-route it and knock some poor people's houses down instead.

Mrs Overall	Oh, I am pleased. This calls for some tonic wine and a sponge finger.
Babs	Yes, Mrs O. I should jolly well think it does.

They all laugh. Derek winces and holds his chest.

	I say Derek, your heart's strong enough to put the marquee up all by yourself, isn't it?
Derek	If it's for an Acorn Antiques wedding, Miss Babs, I'll put it up even if it kills me.

Mrs Overall and Babs look apprehensive.

Scene Two. The lounge. Berta and Babs on the sofa. Trixie rushes in as before, in a clean wedding dress.

Trixie	Honestly, I could kill those triplets!
Babs	Calm down, Trixie, whatever's the matter?
Trixie	They've put jammy fingerprints all over the front – all over it at the back.
Babs	We'll get Mrs O to sponge it off.

Mrs Overall enters as she is being called for.

	Mrs O!
Mrs Overall	What on earth's wrong with the front of your frock? Looks like jam.
Trixie	On the back, yes.
Mrs Overall	*(out of character)* What?
Trixie	There is jam on the back. The triplets didn't put any on the front.

Mrs Overall freezes, completely lost.

	Shall I come along with you and you'll find something to sponge it with?
Mrs Overall	Come along with me and I'll find something to sponge it with.

After a short pause, they leave the room.

Babs   Trixie's going to look gorgeous this afternoon, isn't she, Berta?

Berta   I don't know any Trixies.

Laughs slightly at this odd remark.

I don't know anybody. I live in a world of strangers.

Enter Clifford.

Babs   Clifford! What are you doing here? I thought I made my feelings quite clear last November in the British Home Stores.

Clifford   But I'm here to see Berta.

Babs   Berta? But you hardly know her.

Clifford   You may well be right, Babs, but the fact remains, whether she can remember it or not, Berta and I were married by the Bishop of Manchesterford the Tuesday before last.

Music.
Credits.

Babs   So that's why there was confetti on her body-warmer!

Episode Six

Scene One. Clifford, face unmarked, is mopping his nose with a bloodstained hanky. Berta and Babs stand by, faces blank. They receive some cue and begin acting.

Babs   Well, Clifford, you came in at exactly the right moment.

	Trust me to forget Cousin Jerez was an expert knife-thrower.
Clifford	He won't be building any more motorways round here in a hurry.
Babs	What's in your letter, Berta?
Berta	It's from the Bishop of Manchesterford. No, I can't have an annulment, and yes, I did leave my gardening gloves in the vestry.

Short pause. Enter Mrs Overall.

	Hear that, Mrs O?
Berta	Look Mrs O, no amnesia!
Mrs Overall	Oh, I am pleased.
Berta	And do you know what was the first thing I remembered, what it was?
Mrs Overall	No, I don't, Miss Berta.
Berta	I remembered that I'm absolutely mad about your delicious home-made gingerbread!

They all laugh.

Mrs Overall	Coming right up, Miss Berta.
Clifford	Could Berta and Babs fetch it themselves, Mrs O? I'd, er, like a word.
Babs	Why, of course we could. As Mrs O would say, fetching your own gingerbread is God's way of letting you have an extra piece!

Babs and Berta exit laughing. As Clifford speaks Babs knocks into something off the set.

(Babs	What blithering nuisance left that here?)
(Voice	Ssh!)
Clifford	There's been a new development over Berta's father's will. A new one has been found, dated the day he died . . .
Mrs Overall	And who's the sole beneficiary this time?

Clifford	That's the problem. It's a little redhead he met in the blackout in 1943. They had one night of passion and he never saw her again.
Mrs Overall	Or he thought he never saw her again!
Clifford	What do you mean, Mrs O?
Mrs Overall	Oh, I'm grey now, Mr Clifford, fairly grey indeed, but right up to 1947 my hair was red – as red as a London bus!

Music.

Scene Two. The lounge. A celebration. Mrs Overall, Trixie, Derek, Babs, Berta and Clifford, all drinking water out of champagne glasses.

Berta	I can't believe Mrs O is my mother!
Mrs Overall	Well, I am. The doctor said he'd never seen a finer pair of twins.
Berta	Twins? But –
Mrs Overall	A lovely big boy.
Berta	But where is he now?
Mrs Overall	I had to give him away – we hadn't room for the two cots.
Babs	Oh well, he probably would have turned into a hulking great brute anyway.

She stares at Derek thoughtfully.

Trixie	Oh I spoke to our family doctor, Doctor Wimley, today.
Babs	And?
Trixie	Apparently, being spiteful and having lots of extra-marital affairs could bring back my jaundice, so I'm going to be really nice from now on.
Clifford	So we can't call you Trixie Trouble any more.
Trixie	No, in fact its Sister Trixie – I've taken holy orders. Bobby's running me up to the convent in the Wolseley. Bye!

Exit Trixie. The phone rings.

Babs   Hello? I thought you'd committed suicide. OK, see you later. That was my so-called husband, not dead at all. He says put the triplets in their body-warmers – he's taking us all to Manchesterford Zoo, if you please!

Mrs Overall   It was just a cry for help, Miss Babs. Otherwise why try to slash your wrists with an electric razor?

Babs   I'd better go and find that king-size thermos. Looking at animals can be thirsty work.

Berta   Oh, we'll go and look for it, Babs.

Clifford   Yes, Berta and I have lots to talk about.

Mrs Overall   Well, if it's to be another christening, I'll need plenty of notice, or we won't have nearly enough delicious home-made gingerbread.

Berta   We will!

Clifford and Berta leave, laughing.

Babs   She may find my thermos, but will she ever find her twin brother?

Mrs Overall   All I know is, he's called Derek and he's a handyman in an antiques shop.

Babs   Derek? That's your name, isn't it, Derek?

Derek   Well, yes, Miss Babs.

Babs   And this is an antiques shop and you are a handyman!

Derek   I must be Miss Berta's twin brother then, Miss Babs.

Babs   Yes, run along and tell her, Derek!

Exit Derek.

Babs   Phew – it's been an . . . Sorry, Mrs O, both talking at the same time there.

Mrs Overall   I was just saying, someone had better answer that phone.

Phone begins to ring.

Babs	Oh blow, I suppose I'd better answer it.
Mrs Overall	You answer it and I'll bring you a nice hot cup of coffee.
Babs	You don't have to.

Phone stops ringing.

After all, you are the sole proprietor of Acorn Antiques now. Hello?

Mrs Overall leaves.

The 'Mona Lisa'? Yes, I certainly have heard of it. Yes do, we're open till five. Bye.

Mrs Overall comes back in with coffee.

Looks like we won't have to go out of business after all. I've just been offered Leonardo da Lisa's 'Mona Vinci' at a very reasonable price.

Mrs Overall	And Miss Berta's found your thermos, and apparently it's not a thermos at all, it's a very valuable Georgian silver wine cooler!
Babs	Well, they say things go in threes.
Mrs Overall	Why, whatever's the third thing?
Babs	You remembered my sweeteners! Ho ho.

They laugh.
Music.
Credits.

Mrs Overall	Oh Miss Babs, I'm awfully sorry, I think I've given you the wrong coffee – that one's full of poison guaranteed to cause agonizing death within minutes!

Reaction from Babs

Episode Seven

---

*Film. Ext. Day. Village High Street. Small van labelled
'Acorn Antiques' pulls up in front of a shop bearing no
resemblance to the one in the studio. The shop has been hastily
and badly re-named 'Acorn Antiques', but the real name of the
shop can be seen underneath. Miss Babs gets out of the van,
holding an antique, goes over on her ankle as she steps down,
and goes into the shop. Small group of interested onlookers
nearby stare at the camera throughout.*

---

*Scene One. Shop as before. Babs selling an antique to our extras
as before. She hands over a large paper bag (printed with 'Acorn
Antiques') and some change.*

Babs   And fifty-three change. Bye!

Extras leave. Phone rings.

Acorn Antiques, can I help you? Gainsborough's Blue
Boy? Yes, I think we have it in mauve, I'll just check.

Flips over blank bits of paper.

Yes, we do; shall I pop it under the counter for you? Not
at all, bye!

Puts phone down. Enter Mrs Overall with tray of coffee.

Mrs Overall Here's your coffee, Miss Babs.
Babs   Thanks Mrs O, no poison this time I hope.
Mrs Overall Yes, I'm sorry about that – attempting to murder you was
     just a silly way of trying to draw attention to myself. I

shan't need to do it again now you've bought me this
lovely blouse.

*Babs smiles absently and then sighs. Mrs Overall misses the
cue, Babs sighs again, more obviously.*

Mrs Overall Why, whatever's the matter, Miss Babs? Have you got an
incurable disease, or is it just the sterilized milk?
Babs I wish it were.
Mrs Overall Then what on earth –
Babs I won't beat about the bush, Mrs O. Ever since
Mr Kenneth left to become a follower of that weird
religious sect, Acorn Antiques has been losing money.
And this letter you were just asking me about is to Dorcas
and Hincaster.
Mrs Overall The Manchesterford estate agents?
Babs Yes. Pop it into the pillar box on the corner immediately,
Mrs O – Acorn Antiques is going up for sale!

Mrs Overall goes out of the door.

Music.

---

*Cut to film. Ext. Day. Street. Mrs Overall, now miraculously
attired in coat and hat, comes out of the shop, walks to the post
box, takes from the pocket of her coat an entirely
different-looking letter, stares at it meaningfully and puts it
back in her pocket. All this is watched by gawpers in distance.*

---

*Scene Two. Living room. Babs and Clifford. He is snuggling
up to Babs on the settee. She is unresponsive.*

Clifford What's wrong, Babs? Last night you were so warm and
passionate . . .

Babs	Last night was yesterday, Clifford. I was happy, we had champagne, we danced . . .
Clifford	You danced – magnificently . . .
Babs	Oh, anyone can do the can-can.
Clifford	Not in a snack bar.

As suddenly as he can, Clifford goes down on one knee.

Babs!

A beat late, Mrs Overall enters.

Mrs Overall	There's a visitor, Miss Babs. *(Mumbles absently)* Oh Mrs O.
Babs	Oh, Mrs O, can't you see we're busy?

Cliffords gets up, annoyed.

Mrs Overall	But this is important.
Clifford	*This* is important.
Mrs Overall	*(as herself)* Yes, 'this is important', I said that, didn't I?
Babs	Clifford was about to ask me a very important question, Mrs O.
Mrs Overall	In that case, I'll wait outside.

Mrs Overall goes out.

Clifford	Babs – will you marry me?
Babs	Of course, Clifford, but do you know what you're taking on?
Clifford	A loveable scatterbrain with the nicest lipstick in Manchesterford.
Babs	Lipstick – and debts.
Clifford	Debts?
Babs	Quite frankly, Clifford, I'm flat, flat broke.
Clifford	But you gave me oysters.
Babs	Instant mashed potato and a heck of a lot of nail varnish.

But money doesn't matter, Clifford. *(Turns round and sees he's gone – or nearly gone)* Clifford? Clifford?

Enter Mrs Overall.

Mrs Overall Oh Miss Babs, you've never been jilted again.

Babs I think I jolly well have, Mrs O.

Mrs Overall Men! If they're not doing that they're becoming world heavyweight boxers.

Babs Oh – who was the visitor?

Mrs Overall It was your wicked cousin Jerez, Miss Babs, completely reformed and doing a sandwich course in computer studies at Fuengirola Poly. He dropped in to see if you wanted twenty-five thousand pounds to boost your flagging antiques business.

Babs Twenty-f– I could fill the place with antiques for that, and fit a new cistern in the downstairs cloakroom into the bargain! Well, where is Cousin Jerez, Mrs O – bring him in!

Music.
Credits (list of credits to end with antiques adviser – Rosamund Crull).

Mrs Overall Oh, he couldn't wait, Miss Babs. I told him you were having a proposal done and he caught the next plane back to Marbella!

Episode Eight

Scene One. The shop. Babs, Jerez and Mrs Overall laughing on cue.

Babs But what I can't understand is why Dorcas and Hincaster –

Mrs Overall	The Manchesterford estate agents, yes?
Babs	Why they never put Acorn Antiques on the property market.
Mrs Overall	Because I never posted the letter.
Babs	So they never got the letter at all.
Mrs Overall	No – because I never posted it.
Jerez	Well, that is too complicated for a simple Spaniard like me, but as they say, All's Well *(The other two are supposed to join in with the second half of this, but aren't sure when to come in)* That Ends Well!
Babs	That ends well.
Mrs Overall	All's well that ends well. Well, this calls for a cup of delicious home-made coffee.
Jerez	Home-made coffee? I'm afraid I do not –
Mrs Overall	Well, we have been economizing and this is Acorn Antiques – so what do you think I've been making the coffee out of?
Babs	I give in.
Mrs Overall	Antiques!

Exit Mrs Overall, laughing. Stops laughing abruptly, and clears throat.

Babs	But seriously, Cousin Jerez – it was marvellous of you to lend me the money – are you sure you don't want anything in return?
Jerez	I would like, how do you say in the English – to marry you.
Babs	Well, that's not quite the correct jargon, but I do get your drift. I'm sorry, Jerez, it's not possible.

Jerez whips round and bangs his face on a camera.

Jerez	Ow. What are you sayin' to me?
Babs	When I married Mr Kenneth I gave birth to three children, all born on the same day, all triplets – two of them had dangerously straight hair and had to be rushed immediately to the hairdressers, nurses worked day and

night with curling tongs and heated rollers – and if that's what marriage entails, then quite frankly Cousin Jerez, the answer's no, no –

Mrs Overall opens the door and closes it again.

The answer's no, no, no!

Music.

Cut to film. The shop. Jerez comes out, slams the door, hails a taxi. There is no sound. Clifford collides with him, catapulting from behind the camera.

Scene two. The shop. The door is now open. Enter Mrs Overall with coffee.

Mrs Overall   Whatever was that terrible bang?

Babs   Cousin Jerez slamming the door. The Spaniards may have enormous onions, but their manners leave a lot to be desired.

Mrs Overall   And their football's deteriorated since the World Cup, if you ask me. *(Pause.)* So no fat cheque.

Babs   In other words, Mrs O, we're right back to square – ·

Enter Clifford.

Clifford   One?

Babs   Clifford! But –

Clifford   Our friend Jerez seemed in rather a hurry. *(Takes out a piece of paper labelled 'Jerez – cheque'.)* Certainly he never noticed I'd taken this from his overcoat pocket.

(Jerez wasn't wearing an overcoat, at least not in the film.)

Babs   The cheque! Quick, Mrs O, it's three twenty-five, take it

to the local branch of the nearest bank and cash it immediately!

Mrs Overall I certainly will, Miss Babs. *(Setting off)* And on my way back, I'll buy us some ginger bourbons and a lovely new cistern for the downstairs cloakroom.

Babs You do that.

Clifford Hey! Don't forget the cheque *(throws a paper dart)*. Catch!

It goes nowhere near her. We hear an urgent voice off saying 'Leave it, just go.' Exit Mrs Overall.

Thought any more about marrying me?

Music.
Credits.

Babs I can never marry Clifford – I have a terrible disease. I'm allergic to men's pyjamas. One whiff of a pyjama jacket – even a pocket of a pyjama jacket – and I could literally drop – down – dead!

Episode Nine

Scene One. Shop. Babs on the phone. Extras as usual.

Babs Hello – Acorn Antiques, can I help you? I'm sorry – you'll have to speak up – we're having extensive alterations and drastic refurbishments.

Sound of half-hearted laughing.

No, we're sticking with mauve. Look – I'll have to go, Mrs Overall's standing over me with a cup of coffee. Bye!

Babs puts phone down. Mrs Overall catapults in with coffee.

Mrs Overall	I've been standing here so long this coffee's practically congealified!
Babs	Oh Mrs O, nobody would think you had a degree in linguistics and advanced semantics.
Mrs Overall	Well, I had to do something while I was recovering from that transplant.
Babs	Yes, we were grateful to you for donating all that bone marrow to Miss Berta.
Mrs Overall	I hope she got it all right.
Babs	I'm afraid some of it had leaked out of the Jiffy bag.
Mrs Overall	Men!

Slight hiatus.

Babs	Yes, the doctors are very pleased with her.
Mrs Overall	I heard she may never play the gramophone again.
Babs	Oh, that sounds like the postman. That looks like an important letter.

Props boy tries to stuff large envelope through the letter box – it won't go – he pushes it through the side of the door.

I'll get it, Mrs O – oh, you're too quick for me – I can never lift a finger when you're around.

Mrs Overall sets off very slowly for the door.

Mrs Overall	*(pronouncing it correctly)* It's your decree nisi, Miss Babs.
Babs	*(pronouncing it the same way)* 'Nisi', Mrs O.
Mrs Overall	'Nisi'. I always get that word wrong.
Babs	I can't bear to look – have I got custody of the triplets?
Mrs Overall	I'm afraid not, Miss Babs, but you have won a weekend for two in the Peak District and a deep fat fryer.
Babs	Do you think those triplets were really mine, Mrs O? After all, I did only go into hospital to have my ears pierced.
Mrs Overall	Well, look at it this way – you can't break an omelette

without beating eggs. Eating eggs.

Babs sighs ruefully.

Music.

Film. Ext. day. Hospital. Berta comes out, sees a crawling mini-cab, hails it and gets in.

Int. Back of cab. Berta is actually saying something like 'I'll just pretend to be saying something'.

Berta   *(dubbed on later)* Acorn Antiques, please.

Scene Two. Dining Room. A dining table with chairs along one side only, to leave room for the cameras at the other side of the table. Babs, Clifford and Trixie sit facing the camera. Trixie dressed as a nun, loads of eye make-up etc. On cue, they all put down their spoons as if they've just finished their pudding.

Trixie   Oh Mummy, that was a truly delicious Prune Melba.
Babs   High praise indeed from a Mother Superior!
Trixie   Oh Mummy, you know I've been expelled from the convent. I'm only wearing this old habit because I forgot to collect my dry cleaning.
Clifford   Yes, why did you get expelled?
Trixie   *(off-hand)* Oh, I just broke a few things.
Clifford   Like what?
Trixie   Oh, just a few vows.
Babs   Listen!

Sound of black cab.

Clifford   *(very slowly)* It sounds like –

Babs	*(jumping in)* I think you're right.
Clifford	*(determined to finish his line)* A taxi.
Babs	Derek can't be back from the clinic this early.

Enter Berta with a carry-cot, tilted at a dangerous angle.

	Berta!
Berta	You may as well know, I've discharged myself.
Babs	Come and sit down, you're just in time for coffee. Clifford, run and fetch Mrs O.

Berta sits down.

She's in the scullery stuffing an aubergine. Trixie – show him the way.

Clifford leaves very slowly, Trixie can't get past him.

Now, I couldn't help noticing – what's in the carry-cot?

Berta   See for yourself.

Cut to library film of a baby in a different carry-cot.

Babs   A baby! Where did that come from? And while we're on the subject – where's your eighty per cent lambswool eau-de-nil donkey jacket?

Berta   I, I . . .

Mrs Overall appears in shot without having come through the door.

Mrs Overall Miss Berta! You've never gone and done one of your silly, silly swaps!

Music.
Credits.

Berta	But that's enough about me, what's all this building work I saw as I came in?
Babs	I should have sent you a telemessage –
Mrs Overall	The fact is, Miss Berta, Acorn Antiques is re-opening as a health club and leisure centre.

Reaction from Berta. Screen goes blank.

Mrs Overall	*(Voice Over)* With sun beds! *(In own voice)* Why, why, why do I always forget those darn sun beds, anybody know?

Episode Ten

Scene One. The shop. Extras as before but now dressed in towelling dressing gowns with 'AA' on the back, and flippers. Babs is in her usual gear, with a sweatband round her wig.

Babs	Enjoy your swim – just leave your antiques in the cubicle – they'll be perfectly safe.

Extras nod and smile without speaking. Enter Berta from another door in top half of suit, tracksuit pants and court shoes.

	Berta! Feel better for your run?
Berta	I certainly do. After all, running does keep you fit and could be a considerable contributory factory in reducing heart disease. Where's Mrs O? It was only the thought of her macaroons that kept me going.
Babs	*(pressing buttons on new intercom)* Mrs Overall, coffee for two in reception, please. Now *(leaves button pressed down, strange female voice comes from it)*
Voice	– went all the way to Nottingham, all the way back.

Babs switches it off.

Babs	Now – there's something I've been meaning to –

Enter Derek and Trixie in judo gear. Trixie with lots of jewellery and high heels.

Babs	Ah! Derek and Trixie, how did you get on in the international judo competition?
Derek	We came third, Miss Babs. Tibet was first, then Manchesterford.
Babs	Well done. Now get along to Maintenance, Derek, please. A parcel's just arrived and we haven't a clue if it's a Henry Moore or part of the central heating.
Derek	Right away, Miss Babs *(doesn't move).*
Babs	*(supposedly stopping him in the doorway)* Oh, Derek –
Derek	Yes, Miss Babs?
Babs	Oh, nothing, it doesn't matter.
Trixie	Mummy?
Babs	Yes, darling?
Trixie	Oh, nothing, it doesn't matter.
Berta	Mrs O is being a long time with those macaroons. I hope –
Babs	What?
Berta	Oh, nothing – it doesn't matter.

Enter Mrs Overall.

Babs	Mrs O, you have been a long time, I hope there's nothing wrong.
Mrs Overall	Why should there be anything wrong, Miss Babs?
Babs	No reason, it's just –
Mrs Overall	Except of course that –
Babs	That?
Berta	Go on.
Trixie	Yes?
Mrs Overall	Except that – oh, it's nothing, it doesn't matter.

Reaction from other three. Music.

Film. Usual street. Babs walking along, reaches a doctor's house, looks up at the name plate, checks it on the piece of paper she's carrying (cut in close-up of piece of paper held by hairy male hand), checks the name plate again, steels herself and goes in.

Scene Two. Sitting room. Babs, Berta (still with sweatbands) and Clifford (in tennis gear with tan make-up stopping just below the chin). Enter Mrs Overall in leotard and tights, and carrying tray.

Mrs Overall	Here we are. A nice tray of decaffeinated coffee with low-fate milk and sugar-free sugar.
Babs	Goodness, how healthy.
Mrs Overall	Oh, I enjoyed myself.
Babs	And how was the aerobics class?
Mrs Overall	Oh, I enjoyed myself. The correct footwear, a supportive brassière to prevent chafing and plenty of individual attention from a qualified instructor.
Babs	It sounds ideal *(suddenly looks worried)*.
Mrs Overall	It was only the exercises I didn't take to.
Clifford	Babs? You look pensive.
Babs	No I'm not, I was just thinking.
Berta	*(getting up with difficulty, wedged in the sofa)* Well, I think I'll go for a ten-mile bicycle ride.
Babs	Well, don't forget your florescent clothing and protective headgear.
Berta	I won't.
Babs	And Berta –
Berta	Ah – ha?
Babs	Oh, nothing – it doesn't matter.

Exit Berta.

Look, you two, this isn't easy to say . . .

Mrs Overall I knew it – the mysterious man with the bins seen lurking by the binoculars – it's Trixie's twin cousin, isn't it, he won't rest until Acorn Antiques Leisure Centre and Sunbed Centre has been closed down.

Music.
Credits.

Babs *(The table is now covered in milk dripping everywhere.)* No, it's not that. I went to see our family doctor, Dr Wimley, today.
Mrs Overall Oh, Miss Babs, what did he say?
Clifford Yes, for heck's sake Babs, what did the doctor say?
Babs He said he was sorry about the noise but there were men outside digging up the pavement.

Episode Eleven

Scene One. Shop. Extras as before (no dressing gowns). Babs staring at letter. Enter Berta from the house.

Berta Is that the bill from the wholesalers?
Babs Yes, and its rather puzzling.
Berta Why, what does it say?
Babs See for yourself.

Babs breathes huge sigh and blows it off the table.

Berta *(trying to appear to read it and still stay in shot)* That's ridiculous. They've charged us for seven Laughing Cavaliers!
Babs It must be a misprint, I'm sure we only ordered four.

Enter Mrs Overall.

Mrs Overall I know it's only a quarter to, but I've just this minute whipped my coconut buns out of the microwave. Miss Berta?

Berta Well, you know me and coconut.

Mrs Overall Not to worry. We got it all out of the carpet last time. How's the baby, Miss Berta? Still breastfeeding?

Berta Well, I know I should be passing on my immunities, but with a bra-slip and a jersey two-piece it's just not on.

Babs Clifford should have been here by now.

Clifford can be seen through the window of the shop, laughing animatedly, talking to a stage-hand.

Mrs Overall He's been looking very strange these past few days. I hope he hasn't done anything silly.

Babs Anything silly?

Berta Like what?

Mrs Overall Like putting on a false nose and learning the banjulele.

Berta No, it's all right, I can hear his car.

Babs Yes, thank heavens he has such a distinctive horn.

Clifford stubs out his fag on the set, and acting ponderously as before, comes into the shop.

Clifford! What's wrong, you're as white as a sheet! *(He's as brown as ever.)*

Clifford I have something to tell you, Babs.

Berta Shall I go?

Clifford No, stay. And please come back, Mrs O. *(She hasn't moved but does so on his line.)* What I have to say concerns everybody.

Sits down heavily on a small ornate table, the leg crunches and he slips sideways a few inches.

Film. Street. Derek pacing up and down outside the shop door. He comes to a decision and walks away.

Scene Two. Sitting Room. Mrs Overall standing. Clifford sitting.

Mrs Overall   Come on, Mr Clifford – while Miss Babs and Miss Berta
are sellotaping that bit back onto Michelangelo's 'David',
why don't you tell me all about it?

Clifford   The fact is, Mrs O, my life seems completely grey, bleak
and pointless.

Mrs Overall   Yes well, sometimes that's God's way of getting you to
enjoy 'Gardener's World'.

*Clifford stands up suddenly, catching the boom operator
unawares, hits his head on it, and collapses in pain, moaning.
Mrs Overall is oblivious to all this.*

Mrs Overall   You see, you're smiling, things can't be all that bad, out
with it!

Clifford   *(in pain)* Bloody Norah. Oh, blimey.

Mrs Overall   Oh, you're not! Mr Clifford, what shocking news!

Enter Babs and Berta.

Well, I finally winkled it out of him, Miss Babs, and it
took some winkling.

Babs   Don't say any more, Mrs O. The baby alarm was on in
the antiques packing department, and Berta and I heard
the whole darn thing!

Music.
Credits.

*Enter Derek in street clothes, nearly the same as in the film.
Clifford has left the set.*

Babs   Yes, come in Derek, we all know your sordid little secret.
Why don't you and Clifford have a session right here and
now?

Derek	That's what I came to tell your Mr Clifford. The accordion and the banjulele – they've disappeared into thin air!

Reaction from Clifford's chair.

Episode Twelve

Scene One. The sitting room. Berta ironing a shirt. Clifford, Trixie and Derek are all jammed on the sofa.

Berta	So you and Derek weren't having an affair after all?
Trixie	Oh, no. He was just lying on top of me to get the creases out of my negligée.
Berta	I knew there must be a perfectly reasonable explanation.
Trixie	*(struggling up from the sofa)* Anyway, I have to get back to the convent.
Berta	The convent? Why?
Trixie	I forgot my teapot.
Derek	I'll give you a lift.
Trixie	Well, all right, but don't crash through a grocer's window this time. Those tinned pears really hurt me. Bye!

Exit Derek and Trixie.

Berta	Bye! *(having completely mangled the shirt).*
Berta	There, that looks a bit better.
Clifford	Perfect. Berta – I've been meaning to –
Berta	Just unplug the iron for me, could you?
Clifford	A pleasure *(he bends to do so).*
Berta	Only don't touch it with your bare hands because . . .
Clifford	Argggh!
Berta	Because . . . it's faulty . . .

Enter Mrs Overall with a tray.

Mrs Overall Whatever was that heartrending scream, Miss Berta? I
thought somebody was being electrocuted.
Berta Look!
Mrs Overall Oh, my good golliwog!

She drops the tray on Clifford's foot.

Clifford Ow!
Berta Is he – dead?
Mrs Overall Well, put it this way, Miss Berta, I needn't have bothered
rinsing out the extra mug.
Berta No, Clifford will never touch your macaroons again!

Enter Babs.

Babs What was that terrible noise? It sounded like a tray of
coffee being dropped on someone who's just been
electrocuted.
Mrs Overall
Berta *(nearly together)* Look!
Babs He's dead. *(Bursts into tears.)*
Mrs Overall Crying won't bring him back, Miss Babs.
Babs *(cheering up)* No, that's true.
Mrs Overall Why don't we all have a mug of my delicious home-made
sherry and a couple of sausage dumplings?
Babs Yes, Mrs O, why don't we?

They all laugh. Music.

---

*Film. Street. Derek and Trixie bring out from the back of the
Acorn Antiques van a large cardboard carton labelled 'Venus de
Milo. Fragile. This way up. Use no Hooks' etc. They take it
into the shop.*

Scene Two. The shop. Extras leaving as usual, Babs on the phone.

Babs *(waving goodbye to extras)* Ah oui, bien sûr, j'aime beaucoup le World Cup, aussi. Naturellement. Au revoir.

Babs puts the phone down. Derek and Trixie come in with carton, now upside down. Next dialogue at high speed.

Derek We've brought the 'Venus de Milo', Miss Babs.
Trixie And we want to say goodbye.
Babs Goodbye? But why?
Derek We're going away.
Babs Away? Where?
Trixie Together.
Babs Together? When?
Derek We're going overland to Morocco.
Babs You're going overland to Morocco? Why?

Enter Berta from street.

Berta What's wrong, Babs?
Babs It's Derek and Trixie; they're going away, travelling overland to Morocco, together.
Berta Derek and Trixie are overland travelling away to Morocco, together. But why?
Trixie Everyone says you can get really nice jumpsuits. Bye!

Trixie and Derek leave.

Babs Right – back to business – these antiques.

Babs draws Berta away to one side as the focus of the scene changes to Mrs Overall, who enters stealthily from the street and tiptoes past them. We are not supposed to hear their

dialogue but the mike is in the wrong place.

Babs	I'll just go blah blah blah blah.
Berta	And I'll nod back blah blah blah blah . . .
Babs	Give the blithering old nuisance time to get to the table. Chippendale.
Berta	Mahogany.
Babs	Da da de dum. Right. Mrs O! We never heard you come in. What happened to the body?
Mrs Overall	Mr Clifford? He's gone nice and stiff, so I've propped him up by the ironing board.
Babs	How lovely.
Mrs Overall	Well he was that tall, there was no room to hoover.
Berta	Mmm, what's that delicious smell?
Mrs Overall	That must be my macaroons. I've had them on a low light since Wednesday.
Berta	I'll get them.

Exit Berta.

Mrs Overall	Slice them finely, or someone might choke to death . . . I don't think she heard me. *(Pulls face to indicate sudden worry.)*
Babs	What's wrong, Mrs O?
Mrs Overall	The tea-leaves in my cup this morning, something's wrong somewhere.
Babs	Why?
Mrs Overall	It was a cup of Horlicks.
Babs	It's strange to think of Clifford lying in the sitting room, all alone.

Clifford seen in outdoor clothes crossing the back of the set with a bag, waving goodbye to someone unseen, miming 'Let's have a drink', etc.

Mrs Overall	Not to worry. When Mr Overall (no relation) was dying, he said, 'Well, Boadicea, I shall never have to play

	another game of Travel Scrabble.'
Babs	Why did he call you Boadicea?
Mrs Overall	He was barmy, Miss Babs.

Berta comes in with the tray.

Berta	Your macaroons smell delicious.
Babs	Yes, Mrs O, you sample the first one.
Mrs Overall	Well, I will, but just in case anything should happen when I bite into it *(music)* I just want to say what I feel for Acorn Antiques and the folk who work there. I'm only a simple woman, I haven't any 'O' levels or life-saving certificates, I've never been abroad or fully participated in a Summit Conference, but I have feelings . . .

Babs and Berta gradually stop acting and get bored.

. . . and what I feel for Acorn Antiques and you Miss Babs and you Miss Berta *(turns macaroon over, it has a few scribbled lines pasted on it)* is nothing more or less than plain simple *(squints at macaroon)* cove – love.

She bites into it, chokes to death, and carefully lowers herself to the floor, avoiding the furniture and pulling down her skirt.

Babs	She's choking on her own macaroon. Quick, get Dr Wimley, the family doctor!
Berta	I can't, he's being blackmailed in the Sudan.
Babs	Oh, darn. Well, quite frankly Berta, as far as Mrs O is concerned, it's far too late.

Abrupt change from mood music to theme music.
Credits.
Cut back to Babs and Berta in tears crouched uncomfortably by Mrs Overall.

Babs	Mrs Overall – that macaroon you just choked on – I'm going to send the recipe to the *Weekly News*.

Mrs Overall   Oh, I am pleased.

She dies. Pause.

(In own voice) Are we off? I thought that went quite well,
didn't you?
Voice Off   Still on air!

She dies again reluctantly.

THE END

THE MAKING OF
Acorn Antiques

The Making of Acorn Antiques

*Int. Office. Day. Opening sequence of 'Acorn Antiques' –
entirely as usual. Camera pulls back – we are watching a TV
screen in the 'Acorn Antiques' production office. Paul Heiney is
sitting on a desk watching it. He switches it off with his remote
control and swivels to camera.*

Paul   How many people tune in to hear that oh-so-familiar
music every evening? About fifty-four. But what goes on
behind the scenes? What *don't* the public see? *(He runs the
sentence through again in his head, then carries on.)*

Walks over to a door marked 'Script Conference In Progress'

Let's find out what exactly does or doesn't go into the
making of 'Acorn Antiques'.

CAPTION 'THE MAKING OF "ACORN ANTIQUES"'

Paul taps on the door.

Marion   *(out of vision)* Get out!

---

*Conference room. Day. Marion Clune, at the head of the table,
is checking through that week's scripts, talking into a phone
jammed into her neck and checking a wallplan behind her, all
at the same time. Round the table are Simon, the weedy
director, and a few writers including Roberts and Watkins.*

Paul   *(out of vision)* It's seven o'clock on Monday morning and
Marion Clune, 'Acorn Antiques'' much feared executive
producer, is knocking the week's scripts into shape.

Marion   *(tossing the scripts back like homework)* Blake, Thursday's
not bad, Roberts, Monday's script – not totally bananas

about the AIDS story – would Mrs Overall really know what a condom is?

Simon *(eagerly)* She could call it a 'Comdon'.

Marion *(seriously)* Yes, that's very funny, we'll use it. No, this AIDS idea has been an itsy bit overplayed – let's box a wee bit dangerous – I'm talking off the top of my hairdo now – let's really go for it – earwax – I've never seen it tackled – it's an issue, it's health – suppose Berta gets earwax – no – she finds a syringe.

Roberts Could I just throw something in here, Marion?

Marion Feel free, mucho libre –

Roberts I think perhaps AIDS has more potential, dramatically, than earwax.

Marion *(not even looking up)* Right, you're fired. Don't talk to the press if you like having kneecaps *(tossing another script back as Roberts leaves, stunned)*. Tuesday's script, very good Watkins – funny way to spell 'Acorn'. Friday's . . .

Ext. Church hall. Day.

Paul And those very scripts end up here, where the actors and director sweat to produce the magic that *is* 'Acorn Antiques'.

He goes inside.

Church hall. The floor is marked up. A few odd pieces of furniture. Thermoses in a corner where Albert and Michaela are sitting. Far away from them sits Mrs Overall in lovely tailored slacks. Clifford sits alone, embroidering a tray cloth. In the middle of rehearsing stand Babs in jaunty casuals and unfamiliar hairdo and Derek resplendent in an off-the-shoulder overcoat and toupé. Simon watches intently, making squares of his fingers to represent the camera lens.

Babs *(mumbling to herself)* Put the phone down. Down it goes, turn to Derek . . . Simon? Yes?

Derek And I'll look sort of questioningly at you.

Babs *(off-hand)* Will you? So turn to Derek. 'That was the Immigration Authority, Derek.'

He gasps.

	Are you going to do that, because I'll leave a gap.
Derek	No, it was my tooth again.
Babs	Poor you. 'Immigration Authority, Derek. It's not good news, I'm afraid.'
Derek	Miss Babs?
Babs	Can't we cut that 'Miss Babs'? It's Bab Bab Bab every two minutes. Anyone mind? Simon? No? OK. 'Good news, I'm afraid. You're being repatriated, you've to catch the first train to Kirkcudbright tomorrow morning.'
Derek	It's Kirkcudbright.
Babs	I know that – Babs wouldn't. Simon? Agreed?
Derek	Then I'll look – because he's quite stunned by this news, isn't he?
Babs	No idea.
Derek	Then I'll turn and go *(starts to do it very slowly and dramatically)*.
Babs	*(walking off the set)* The camera's on me there anyway, isn't it? Simon? Yes? Tea break? Simon? Yes? Black coffee please, Albert!

Calls from everyone else for tea and coffee.
Berta dashes in.

Berta	Hello!

They all gather round concernedly, cries of 'Darling!' 'How is everything?', etc.

Mrs Overall	Oh darling, how did you get on?
Babs	Oh yes darling, any luck?
Berta	Not bad *(waves carrier bag)*. No éclairs, but a lot of those nice long doughnuts.

Cries of 'well done', 'how marvellous', etc.

Same. Paul, Mrs Overall and Kenny sitting a little way off from the others.

Paul	Are you like the part you play? Are you in fact Mrs Overall?
Mrs Overall	I think Bo and I are rather alike, Paul, yes . . .
Paul	Bo?
Mrs Overall	Boadicea. We're both rather gutsy ladies, very determined, strong moral sense, we've both had rather difficult lives, a certain amount of personal loss . . . *(She loses her thread as she dwells on this.)*
Derek	They're both very warm and very giving.
Mrs Overall	*(patting his hand)* Bless you for that, my darling. And of course I'm rather younger and I hope rather more attractive!

They all laugh.

Paul	*(laughing)* So the famous lumpy tights and, er, varicose veins are just something that goes on with the make-up?
Mrs Overall	*(after nasty silence)* Have you got the crossword, Kenny my darling?

Same. Clifford and Paul

Paul	Are you all one big happy family? Do you all get on well?
Clifford	*(thinks)* I should say, on the whole, no.

Same. Mrs Overall, Derek and Paul.

Paul	There's been rather a lot made in the Press of a feud between you and certain younger members of the cast – any truth in that?
Mrs Overall	*(shrugging enigmatically)* Dear Paul, I'm a huge, huge star – this is the price I pay. Look how the Press treated poor Yorky.
Derek	Fergie.
Mrs Overall	Fergie.

Ext. The location shop front and street. Day.

Marion and Simon in earnest conversation as the camera is being set up for a shot of Mrs Overall leaving the shop with a letter. Paul is hanging around, not liking to interrupt.

Paul (*out of vision*) Thursday is set aside for outside filming, and here on the 'Acorn Antiques' lot a tricky shot is being discussed.

Marion So Mrs Overall comes out, takes out the letter, posts it, goes back in. Bueno. Let's shoot it.

Simon Except we haven't got the letter box.

Paul Ah – so –

Marion (*furious*) Mickey! Here! Now! (*The props boy Mickey runs up.*)

Mickey Yes, Miss Clune?

Marion (*slapping him on each side of the head in turn*) You don't – chew – gum. (*Holding hand out*) Take it out. Give it to me. You're fired. What say, Simon?

Simon (*agitated*) No letter box, she can't post the letter.

Marion No problem. Nila problemo. Slip in a line 'Oh Miss Babs the letter box has been stolen by international terrorists, what a palaver . . .'

Mrs Overall with a fur coat over her costume, supported by Derek, totters up.

Simon What, and pick that up in another story later?

Marion No (*concerned*). How are they, Bo?

Mrs Overall They're fine, I'm fine. Kenny – if you could hover with my Veganin?

Kenny (*taking her coat*) I'll be here.

Paul Is there some sort of problem –

Marion (*back to business*) Small change, Bo – the letter box has been stolen –

Mrs Overall So I come out –

Marion Come out –

Mrs Overall Walk walk walk to the pillar box –

Marion Blimey oh fiddledebob – no pillar box.

Mrs Overall React react react.

Marion That's it.

Simon Oh fantastic, it's here!

Man in anorak dumps down pillar box.

Marion	Right – back to plan A – there is now a pillar box.
Mrs Overall	Oh, there is a pillar box. First there's no pillar box, then one appears. What next, no pavement, no shop? *(She notices Paul and the film crew.)* Sorry, do you mind – this is rather a tricky manoeuvre – rather fussing to be filming as one's working.
Paul	OK. Cut it.

Make-up room. Babs and Berta larding it on. Clifford being made up by girl, Derek hanging round chatting to him.

Paul	*(out of vision)* It's Friday, just time for a quick make-up check before the cameras finally roll.
Girl	I thought perhaps as Mr Clifford has been in prison for a year, he perhaps would be quite pasty, so I thought I'd use this instead of the Cool Copper.
Clifford	No, I'll stick with the usual, I think.
Paul	So where will I find Mrs Overall?
Babs	In her dressing room, I expect.
Derek	*(out of vision)* I said 'Excuse me – I had leather shorts before George Formby had a ukulele' –
Paul	So you've all got a dressing room to relax in, have you?
Berta	No, not all of us.

Mrs Overall's cosy dressing room. The room is full of flowers, cards, photos of Russell Grant, Derek and Mrs Overall's mother, stuffed toys etc.

Paul	And these are all presents?
Mrs Overall	People are so so so kind. I'm just a jobbing actress, who scraped to put herself through the RADA and yet somehow I've captured the hearts of the nation – it's almost frightening.
Paul	*(sniffing at fancy jar)* And what's this?
Mrs Overall	It's a haemorrhoid preparation to be brutally frank, Paul *(winces as she takes it from him).*

Studio, the usual set. Albert and Michaela position themselves by their antique. Babs, Berta and Clifford sort themselves out by the desk.

Paul *(out of vision)* This is it. This is the moment when all that hard work pays off. As the actors stand by on the studio floor . . .

Int. Gallery. Day. Marion, Simon and batty PA.

Paul *(out of vision)* . . . Marion and Simon get ready to record episode 1,573 of 'Acorn Antiques'.

Marion *(into mike)* OK, running up recording. You've done a marvellous week's work – relax, enjoy it, but above all – don't touch the antiques – I want them back in my lounge in one piece. Stand by.

Simon Cue titles.

Opening sequence comes up on monitors.

Side of set. Mrs Overall with Paul, waiting to enter with tray.

Paul How are you feeling?

Mrs Overall I won't talk, Paul my darling, I just have to gather myself in, focus . . . 'be' . . .

Gallery (as before).

Simon Cue Albert and Michaela.

PA Coming to 2. No . . . 3. No, it *was* 2. Now coming to 3. Oh . . .

Simon And in on Babs!

Babs *(on monitor)* I've had a most peculiar letter . . .

Marion Good and close camera 2. Love those nostrils.

Side of set (as before).

Mrs Overall *(in full flow)* And Princess Margaret is so like me, give,

give, give *(hands Paul the tray)*. Do you mind, I did promise the specialist – well –

Gallery (as before).

Berta	*(on monitor)* I don't know about you Clifford, but I could jolly well do with a nice cup of tea and a chocolate bhaji.
Babs	So could jolly well I.
Marion	*(over Babs's line)* Nice nod to the Asians there.
PA	Coming to 3. Oh, what page are we on now?
Simon	Stand by, Mrs Overall, steady on the doorway 3.

Side of set (as before).

Mrs Overall I said – for you Lord Delfont –

Assistant Floor Manager runs up frantically waving.

I'm talking Sally – for you, Lord Delfont it will be a pleasure and an honour.

Gallery (as before). Monitor: Babs, Clifford and Berta wait silently.

Simon	Where is she? Cue her!
Marion	She'll be there, be calm, be calm. *(Screaming)* COME ON!

Side of set (as before).

AFM	You're on!
Mrs Overall	I'm aware of that Sally, after thirty years in the business.

Goes on, leaving Paul with the tray.

Gallery (as before).

Simon	No tray! Where's the bloody tray?
Marion	We'll cope.

Simon	It's mentioned!
Marion	Mentioned?

Cut to close-up of monitor.

Babs	Mrs Overall, we could smell your bhajis a mile away!
Berta	And do I spy a new tray?

Silence.

Marion	She'll get us out of it, come on Bo. Improvise!

Back to monitor.

Mrs Overall	Yes, I just had to bring it in and show you. Take it, isn't it light?
Babs	*(miming)* Mmm, and such a lovely shade of mauve. Look, Clifford!
Clifford	It's magnificent.
Simon	*(overlapping Babs's line)* Shall we cut? Go back?
Marion	No, we professionals notice these things, but Joe Public never clocks a darn thing.

She sits happily watching the monitor as Paul appears in the doorway with the tray.

Still Barmy

Spaghetti

Lunchtime in a small Italian restaurant. Philippa and Faith drinking wine.

Philippa Cheers.

Faith Cheers. How's things?

Philippa Oh, its been a terrible week. Monday I thought I was having an early menopause.

Faith And were you?

Philippa No, the dog had been beggaring about with the thermostat.

Faith I didn't know you had a dog.

Philippa It's my mother's. She's in Marbella for the winter. Twelve pounds a week all in.

Faith That's very cheap.

Philippa She's sharing a room with two dustmen.

Faith Does she like Spain?

Philippa She likes the majesty and grandeur of the landscape, but she's not keen on the bacon.

Faith What sort of dog is it?

Philippa Oh, performing. Rolls round the kitchen on a beach ball *(is interrupted by arrival of cheeky Italian waiter who serves two pasta dishes)*. Thank you.

Waiter Pasta – bit fattening, hey? Something to grab hold of . . . nice one *(They half-smile, he leaves.)*

Philippa They're all like that here. Jamming their groins into your tortellini. Then on Tuesday, Nick left home.

Faith What, for good?

Philippa He's taken the toolshed.

Faith I thought you were so well-suited.

Philippa We were – especially physically. Every time I gave him the old come hither, he came hither.

Faith You were quite experimental, weren't you?

Philippa Oh yes, outdoors; three in a bed –

Faith With the man next door?

Philippa I don't recommend it. They got on to politics and I ended up watching 'Take the High Road' with the sound off.

Waiter in.

Waiter Parmesan?
Philippa Thank you.
Faith Thank you.
Waiter Yum, yum, very nice, very cheesy.

Makes kissing noises and leaves.

Philippa We should have gone to the Snacketeria. One thing about self-service is no one tries to arouse your sexuality. No, Nick, apparently, is in love with someone else.
Faith How long's that been going on?
Philippa Must be yonks, because he told me 'their tune' was 'Chirpy Chirpy Cheep Cheep'.
Faith Who is it?
Philippa You know I mentioned a very small neighbour of mine – buys children's clothes and spends the VAT on tequila?
Faith Mmm.
Philippa It's her. I wondered why he'd had that cat-flap widened.

Waiter in with huge pepper mill.

Waiter Pepper, ladies? Make you nice and hot.
Both Thank you.
Waiter Nice big one, eh? I know what you ladies like *(leaves)*.
Philippa Thank heavens the sausage was off. So I'm totally disillusioned. No more sex, I'm going to become a nun.
Faith I thought you had to be able to play billiards.
Philippa Oh no, that's all changed. I'm joining a convent in Smethwick on Friday. I have to take one small suitcase and a jigsaw.
Faith What's the habit like?
Philippa Hot pants.
Faith They're very outdated.
Philippa Well, you have to make some sacrifices.
Faith Won't you miss the physical side of life?
Philippa No, Faith, because I'm basically a very cerebral and spiritual

person – I don't go round panting for bodily intimacy like a misguided poodle.

Waiter nuzzles up to Philippa.

Waiter   You like to come and be very naughty with me in the staff washroom? Lots of sexy fun with nice big Italian boy?

Philippa *(hesitating slightly)* Oh, go on then. Faith?

Faith   Just a black coffee, thank you.

Medical School

An interview room. Two men and a woman behind a table. Paralytically nervous girl in suit sitting down. All the interviewers are completely non-committal throughout.

First man Sit down, er, Sarah.

Sarah Thank you.

First man It's only an interview, we're not going to eat you.

Sarah Ha ha ha.

First man I see you're taking Biology, Physics, Chemistry and English, all good A levels for medical school. How do you think you're going to do?

Sarah Well, I might get an A for physics, I might get an A, two Bs and a C for biology or I might get a B for physics, what I get very much depends . . .

First man Thank you.

Second man I see you're doing the Duke of Edinburgh's Award Scheme – do you think that's character-building?

Sarah Yes, I think it builds character, it is character building, yes, it is a character building thing, yes.

Second man In what way does it build character, do you think?

Sarah In what way – I think in the way that – just the way you'd expect, really.

Second man Thank you.

First man Sarah – do you think there's any link between environment and disease?

Sarah Do you mean *the* environment?

First man Living conditions – do you think living conditions can affect health?

Sarah Yes, I think they probably can.

First man In what way?

Sarah If you shared a bedroom with someone who had measles then you might get measles, or if you were very rich and had very thick carpets you might trip and break your

	ankle, it would affect you in that way.
First man	What about if you were very poor?
Sarah	If you were very poor, then you wouldn't have that kind of carpet.
First man	Do you think poor housing would have an adverse effect on health?
Sarah	Yes, I think it would have an adverse effect on health because, because it would affect people's health adversely.
First man	Thank you.
Woman	Sarah – do you think there's a gap between the media's portrayal of doctors and doctors in real life?
Sarah	Yes I think there is a gap because the doctor in East Enders has bushy eyebrows and it might make people think that if you're a doctor you have to have bushy eyebrows and you might not have bushy eyebrows but you might want to be a doctor, and that's not really fair . . .
Woman	Thank you.
First man	What do you think about the National Health Service?
Sarah	In what way, 'think'?
First man	Do you think it's crumbling, or doing very well, or . . .
Sarah	I think that probably that parts of it are crumbling, and parts of it are doing very well, I think you have to look at both sides.
First man	Go on.
Sarah	Of course some people say well oh let's close casualty departments and spend the money on nuclear weapons but I think you have to sit back and say if there is a nuclear war then we'll need casualty departments.
Second man	You don't think in a nuclear war we'll all be annihilated?
Sarah	No.
Woman	What qualities do you think you'll bring to the medical profession? *(Pause.)* Are you particularly warm, or compassionate?
Sarah	I'm quite tidy.
Woman	Thank you.
First man	What was the last book you read, Sarah?
Sarah	*Othello*. It's a book by William Shakespeare of the Royal Shakespeare Company. I've got the book, and I've got it on little cards as well.

First man	What do you think is the main theme of *Othello*?
Sarah	I don't think it's got one, really. It's just various people talking, and sometimes they do things in brackets.
First man	And do you think Othello was ill –
Sarah	*(quickly)* No.
First man	To act in the way he did – was he suffering from anything, when he discovered Desdemona's handkerchief?
Sarah	I think he might have been suffering from a cold.
First man	Right Sarah, thank you very much indeed.

Sarah goes out. They write.

	I thought she was jolly good, didn't you?
Woman	Excellent.
Second man	Very astute.
First man	Unconditional offer?
Woman	Absolutely.
Second man	Definitely.

He didn't: One

Bus stop. Kelly-Marie Tunstall and her pal.

Kelly So he walked over, right, big 'I am' and he had tattoos up his arms right, an anchor here and a microwave here.

Pal He didn't.

Kelly	He did. He said do you want a drink or do you want a kick up the bum with an open-toed sandal. I said get you Eamonn Andrews.
Pal	You didn't.
Kelly	I did. I said I'll have a pint of babycham, some pork scratchings and a yellow cherry and if I'm not here when you get back I'll be in t' toilet putting hide and heal on my love bites.
Pal	You didn't.
Kelly	I did. So I come out of toilets, right, and he says hey scallop face your skirt's all caught up in your knickers at back, I said I pity you do you know why, he says why, I says 'cos it happens to be the latest fashion, I read it in a book, he says what book, I said Vogue that's what book, he said oh likely likely when do you read Vogue, I said when I'm in the hospital having exploratory surgery that's when. So he said oh.
Pal	He didn't.
Kelly	He did. And he sits there, right, picking the quiz off his beer-mat, and he says what were they exploring for, I said well it wasn't the Left Bank of the blinking Limpopo.
Pal	You didn't.
Kelly	I did. I said if you must know Magnus Magnusson I was rushed in last Wednesday when I swallowed the upholstery attachment of an Electrolux 567. He said how did you do that, I said I were hoovering a pelmet with my mouth open. Like that.
Pal	You weren't.
Kelly	I was. He said was it a long operation, I said it was a bit longer than normal because while they were stitching me I said could they put a new zip in my drainpipes.
Pal	You didn't.
Kelly	I did. Anyway, he stands up and he says do you want to come for a Chinese or do you want a clip round the ear with a wrestler's braces? I said I'll come for a Chinese because I've had a clip round the ear with a wrestler's braces and there's nowt to it.
Pal	You didn't.
Kelly	I did. He fell about laughing. Like this. I could see all cheese and onion crisps in his fillings.
Pal	You couldn't.

Kelly   I could. So we sit down and he says right I'm bloke I'm
          ordering, I says haven't you ever heard of Women's Lib he
          says no, I said oh. Anyway, we get t'end of meal, right, he's
          having a crack at burping and I'm chasing a lychee round a
          saucer, he says can I walk you home?

Pal   He didn't.

Kelly   He did. I said what's brought this on, bird bath? I said you
          needn't get any funny ideas because my mum and dad'll be
          up, I don't fancy you, and the surgeon says I can't joggle
          about for a fortnight.

Pal   He didn't.

Kelly   Who?

Pal   Surgeon.

Kelly   He did. So I said you can walk me home, but you're not
          pressing me up against the doorbell. So he puts down his
          banana fritter, he says Kelly-Marie Tunstall, just because I
          have tattoos and a hairy navel button does not mean I do not
          have the instincts of an English gentleman. Please believe me
          when I say I will be happy to escort you to your abode of
          residence, asking nothing in return but the chance of seeing
          you again.

Pal   He didn't.

Kelly   No, he didn't. He caught his bus and I had to pay for my own
          lychees.

Tattoo Parlour

Small shop, a few sample designs on the wall, and electric equipment. Two young slightly drunk sailors come in, ring the bell for service and stand shoving each other and laughing. Enter nice cosy woman.

Woman Can I help you, boys?

Eric Isn't there a feller?

Woman Mr Armstrong's having a lie down, I'm afraid. I'd rather not wake him. He's just done flags of all nations on a twelve-stone Wren.

Eric Shall we go, Paul?

Woman I'm a qualified tattooist as well as my husband. That's how we met. I had the shop next door, and he used to pop over if I needed an extra hand with a tricky buttock.

Paul There's another shop up the road, isn't there?

Woman Harry Abraham's? You should be all right there, they do have marvellous antibiotics these days, don't they?

Paul How do you mean?

Woman Apart from which he bolts his food.

Eric Eh?

Woman One hiccup halfway through the execution of a naked woman, and you're going through life with a bicep full of hermaphrodite.

Eric OK, well we'll stay here then, shall we?

Woman Lovely, right. Have a seat. What designs had you in mind?

Eric Don't know – we only came in because we couldn't get into 'Bambi'.

Paul What about a name? My girlfriend's name.

Woman What is her name, dear?

Paul Pat.

Woman Not much to get your teeth into there. Hardly worth plugging the needle in for. I should leave that till you meet a girl who'll pay for a good bit of scrolling.

Eric	My girl at home's called Suzannah Margaret Mary.
Woman	Is it a steady relationship?
Paul	Not really.
Woman	You see, by the time I was up to the double 'n' you could have split up. Then you're either scouting round for another Suzannah Margaret Mary, or you find a girl with another name altogether who's broadminded, illiterate or never reads in bed. No, if you're stuck on having a name, boys, have something that can't cause embarrassment in later life, like 'Mother' or 'Miriam Stoppard'.
Eric	No . . .
Paul	What about an anchor and 'HMS Indestructible'? On my arm.
Woman	Yes, but what happens when you leave the Navy? It's going to look very incongruous if you go into the antiques business and have to roll your sleeves up to manoeuvre a Chesterfield.
Paul	I never thought of that.
Woman	This is what I'm here for – we don't want you to roll in here drunk and wake up the next morning covered in inappropriate remarks.
Eric	Hey – daggers! A pointed dagger, and it's dripping blood – like in three drops.
Woman	Not very cheerful, a dagger. If you're set on dripping, how about a leaky teapot?
Eric	No . . .
Paul	Hey – a panther! No, a cheetah – pouncing – right across my back – like that! *(Points to picture.)*
Woman	Stand up. Mmm. You've not really got the breadth of back for a fully successful cheetah. Have to be something a bit smaller. How about a Chihuahua?
Paul	Chihuahuas don't pounce.
Woman	They do if you tread on them.
Eric	*(ripping his shirt off and posing)* I've got a big back – I could have a cheetah.
Woman	Yes, but you see, dear, by the time I'd woven its paws in and out of your acne, it wouldn't be pouncing so much as waving.
Paul	*(laughing)* Tell her what you said to me on the way in.
Eric	What?
Paul	You know!
Eric	I didn't know it were a woman then, did I?

Woman	Oh, I've seen it all before dear – think of me as an usherette.
Paul	He said he wanted a Ferrari on his – thingy.
Woman	Well I'm happy to do that, though you must understand in moments of excitement it will distort. And if you're posted to a cold climate it may tend to look more like a Reliant Robin. *(They sit dejected.)* Look, why not have one of our set pieces? *(Demonstrating on one of them:)* The Parthenon across here, rambling roses to the elbow, two naked women either side of the spinal column, Caucasian or Oriental depending on what ink there is in the stockroom, a map of the London underground down each leg, finishing across here with an illustrated recipe for Baked Alaska.
Paul	That's sounds great, doesn't it, Eric? How much is that?
Woman	Eight colours and a no-fade warranty – 350 pounds.
Eric	We can't afford it.
Woman	Never mind boys, how much money have you got?

They sift through their pockets.

Paul	We spent a lot on booze, didn't we?
Eric	*(sheepishly)* About four quid.
Woman	And you want a tattoo for that?
Eric	Yes.
Woman	OK, Boys. *(Slapping a transfer on the back of his hand)* Lick that.

Partly Political Broadcast

Caption: 'Jean and Barbara'.

Barbara   Just to say if Jean and I are elected, we're obviously going to do our best to serve the constituency. I'm going to serve it Monday through Wednesday.

Jean   And I'll do Thursday through Saturday.

Barbara   And we'll do alternative Sundays, because I like to worship on that day.

Jean   And I like to have a good go at the kitchen cupboards.

Barbara   We both know this area pretty well, don't we.

Jean   Yes, in fact we can remember when the Old Malthouse Arts Centre used to be a Bingo Hall.

Barbara   That's right, and, and the Co-op used to do coffee and a little bun-ny-type snack for forty pence, do you remember?

Jean   Yes, because that's where you knocked into that stand of ovenproof tableware with your wonky buggy.

Barbara   And we said pity it wasn't buggy-proof! *(Laughs.)* Anyway. We're both quite political, aren't we?

Jean   Reasonably political. I was originally Liberal, and still think David Steel has a lot of credibility, popping up to the Borders every weekend to chop logs.

Barbara   And I was a Conservative, but looking back I think I was swayed by their rhetoric. And of course their garden parties had the best bran tubs.

Jean   You had those secateurs for years, didn't you?

Barbara   But we've both broken away, haven't we? Rather like Shirley Williams, whom we both admire, on the whole.

Jean   We feel she needs a little updating, eyeshadow-wise, but –

Barbara   And we've formed a new political party.

Jean   It's just called the Jean and Barbara Political Party.

Barbara   It's got its own colour.

Jean	The mainstream parties seem to have left the field clear as far as pastels are concerned.
Barbara	So we plumped for taupe.
Jean	Mushroom.
Barbara	Can we just say we've always been very active in local politics, haven't we?
Jean	Oh yes, I wrote to the papers and said now the dustmen didn't have to hump the actual bins, should we still tip?
Barbara	And we both boycotted a restaurant once where there was a strike.
Jean	That's right. The waiters were holding placards up outside asking you not to go in.
Barbara	So we didn't.
Jean	We never went in anyway.
Barbara	No, but we were still making a firm political stance. In fact we popped back after we'd done our shopping and boycotted it again, didn't we?
Jean	But we definitely know what people in this area want, don't we? Have you got our manifesto, Ba?
Barbara	*(rooting in handbag)* No, I think I used it to jam my quarterlight.
Jean	Well, anyway. It was – libraries. More Large Print novels, especially Jackie Collins.
Barbara	That's for my grandad. He likes smut and he can't focus.
Jean	More ramps. Ramp access – very very important for the wheelchair-bound.
Barbara	And for the able-bodied, it's a lovely tone-up for the calves and thighs *(slapping them)*.
Jean	Proper sugar bowls on each table at The Swiss Cottage, not packets by the till.
Barbara	Free dental treatment for old and sundry alike.
Jean	Especially the woman on the pastry counter at Lewis's because she's just upsetting, I won't go in.
Barbara	We want an increase in Family Income Supplement; we want a more frequent bus service.
Jean	And we want a much bigger hut at the Sauna Centre, it's nose to nipple in there.
Barbara	Mixed Wednesdays you have to beat them with twigs to get them to come out! But seriously . . .
Jean	Yes. *(Pause.)* Well, that's about it. I'd better go, Ba, I'm

doing something out of a book with sweetbreads.

They gather up their things.

Barbara	Anyway, so vote for us if you feel like it next Thursday.
Jean	Only if you're out anyway.
Barbara	Oh yes, don't go specially.

They put coats on etc.

Jean	Lennons' sale previews Thursday.
Barbara	You could gen up on the reductions and then vote . . .
Voice Over	That was a partly political broadcast on behalf of Jean and Barbara.
Barbara	*(Voice Over)* Oh call me Ba, everyone else does!

Continuity

Susie	*(behind her is a map of Britain with flashing lights)* And Employment Update. Job losses – three thousand in Paisley and eight hundred in Sunderland with the closure of GK Metalworks. Job gains – good news in Hove is that Mrs Mason of the Sea Breeze Restaurant is taking on somebody to peel the potatoes.

Mr Right

Film. A tidy dull suburban street of semis and front gardens. A small neat woman, Pam, with a shopping trolley, waving to an occasional front window as she passes. She lets herself into one of the houses.

Pam *(Voice Over)* I believe there's one man in this world that's meant for me, and I'm looking for him quite assiduously, and I'd really quite like him not to be Mexican, just because of the sombrero, it would give us all sorts of problems with the serving-hatch.

The hall of Pam's house, as she takes off her coat, calls hello to her mother, and takes the shopping trolley into the kitchen.

Pam *(Voice Over)* I've got everything else, suede coat, two-speed hammer drill, and all I need now is Mr Right.

TITLE 'MR RIGHT'

Pam's kitchen. Pam is at the kitchen table, apparently peeling potatoes.

Corin *(Voice Over)* Pamela Twill is forty-seven. She's never been married, she's never been engaged, she's never been to a Spinners concert with anyone called Roger.

Corin *(In camera. To Pam)* Has anyone ever proposed, Pam?

Pam Oh yes, lots of people. A lot of widowers, a deckchair attendant, an anaesthetist, someone who made lampshades out of thermal underwear . . .

Corin But you've never said yes.

Pam I've never said yes. I'm looking for Mr Right, Corin. I've met Mr Wrong, I've met several Mr Reasonably OKs, and I've

	spent a very long afternoon in a bus shelter with Mr Halitosis but –
Corin	Do you think you're too choosy, pernickety?
Pam	No.
Corin	What are you doing with those potatoes?
Pam	Well, before I put them on to boil, I'm just carving them into the faces of minor celebrities, Corin. I've done Cliff Michelmore, here, and Anona Wynn, and I'm just having a crack at Jeremy Beadle.
Corin	And do you do this every time you have boiled potatoes?
Pam	Oh yes, though I wouldn't normally do Jeremy Beadle, because of his perm, but –

Pam's lounge. Pam and her mother, an over-made-up drunken, chainsmoking old tart in a wheelchair. Pam has a coffee, mother has all the makings for a gin and tonic on the tray of her chair.

Mother	You'll never get a man dressed like that anyway, Pam.
Pam	I don't want a man dressed like this. *(Winks at Corin.)*
Mother	When I was your age I wore my blouses so tight my bosoms applied for a transfer. Any more gin?
Pam	In the pantry.

Mother wheels menacingly towards the camera.

Mother	Get out of my bloody way!
Corin	Has your mother always been in a wheelchair?
Pam	Oh, no. She was a very active nymphomaniac for many years, and eventually of course, something snapped . . .
Corin	Is that partly why you've never married – you feel you can't leave her?
Pam	I can't stick her, never mind leave her. No, I'm only – she's still quite insatiable, even now. I mean it's not nice, is it, someone kerb-crawling in an invalid car?
Mother	*(Off)* Well, whereabouts, you sexless dodo?
Pam	Next to the weedkiller! *(Winks at Corin.)* Some hopes!

Pam's office. Three desks. Pam, Margaret and Poll. All very similar, hanging up coats, gloves etc., putting on office cardi's and settling down at their desks.

Pam	*(Voice Over)* I share an office with Margaret and Poll. We dovetail pretty neatly together in the frantic hustle of a typical high-pressure, big-business situation.
Poll	*(reading from newspaper)* Right. Pam – Aquarius. This is a good day for buying a beige headscarf, but make sure it goes into the tumble dryer because you have been caught like that before. Margaret – Aries – your haemorrhoids should be on the wane . . .

Fade out Poll, fade up Corin.

Corin	*(Voice Over)* But today brings a break for Pam from office routine, for, in her ceaseless search for the man of her dreams, she has made an appointment with a computer dating agency.
Poll	*(still reading)* and be particularly wary of salesmen offering low-priced tweezers and denture tablets. Right . . .

Dating agency. Walls covered in wedding photos. Dim girl nervously feeding Pam's details into a computer.

Girl	So what is it – meeting a man with a view to marriage?
Pam	Yes.
Girl	Some of our ladies just want someone to repoint the brickwork. Any particular colour of man?
Pam	No, I don't think so. I'm not nuts on freckles.
Girl	No freckles. What type of personality?
Pam	What type have you?
Girl	Outgoing, homeloving, miserable. You'll find there's quite a big choice at the miserable end of the market.
Pam	Dull, I think. Dull-ish.
Girl	Does he have to be able to –
Pam	Sorry?
Girl	Oosiswhat inter-thingy. Do you wish the marriage to be constipated?
Pam	I –
Girl	Are you looking for physical fill-fullment?
Pam	Yes.
Girl	It's just that some of our gentlemen can't manage that type of activity. They tend to be the miserable ones . . . It's now

searching, and with any luck should come up with the name of your computer date just about now. Ooh, I'm new – it's flashing a recipe for flaky pastry. Mrs Lomax!

Town hall clock (or similar landmark). Pam waiting in her best clothes.

Corin *(Voice Over)* Pam is waiting for her first glimpse of her computer date, Donald Renshaw.

Donald, a perfectly normal-looking fifty-ish businessman, approaches Pam, shakes hands and leads her away.

Corin *(Voice Over)* On paper he's perfect; will Mr Renshaw turn out to be Mr Right?

Restaurant. Pam and Donald being seated at a table. Waiter pulls out Pam's chair as she is sitting down, she falls under the table. He helps her up and gives them both a menu.

Donald Soup of the day, please.
Waiter Yes sir, which one?
Donald Thursday.
Pam *(pointing to item on menu)* Sorry, what are these?
Waiter Grilled mushrooms with garlic, white wine and chopped parsley.
Pam Do you think I could have them without the garlic?
Waiter No garlic.
Pam And no white wine.
Waiter No wine.
Pam And I won't have the mushrooms.
Waiter How would you like the parsley?
Pam Just how it comes, thank you *(waiter leaves)*, but not too chopped.

Time lapse.

Corin *(Voice Over)* Half-way through the main course. How are they getting on?

Pam   No, I think you're right. I think that tablecloth is a slightly different colour.

Donald   Slightly more of an off-white.

Pam   That's right. Sort of white with a hint of beige, as they say.

They fall silent.

Time lapse.

Corin   *(Voice Over)* We're nearing the end of the pudding; has romance flourished over the meringue glacé?

Pam   I think one just has this idea, doesn't one, that in a restaurant like this, all the tablecloths will be the same colour, but –

Donald   It's remarkable how many shades of tablecloth there are just in this one room.

Pam   One room – I agree. As I say – but – er . . .

They fall silent.

Ladies' powder-room. Pam enters, and immediately backs away.

Pam   Oh I'm sorry, I – oh, we're filming.

Corin   Well, to me, Donald seems dull, obsessive, repetitive, humourless and crass. Would you agree?

Pam   Oh definitely – I'm hooked – that's my man!

Doctor's waiting room. Pam sits reading Brides *Magazine.*

Corin   *(Voice Over)* With Pam's marriage to Donald only a week away, she feels the time is right for a little chat with the doctor.

The surgery door opens. A man is ushered out by the doctor, frothing at the mouth, bouncing against the walls like a mad moth etc.

Doctor   As I say, Jim, some people do get a very slight reaction with that one – enjoy your holiday anyway. Miss Twill?

Pam steps over the man who is now staggering to the door on all fours.

Surgery.

Pam   – so I just wanted a little chat before the wedding night, Doctor.

Doctor   Very sensible. What about?

Pam   Well, I've never had physical fill-fullment, and I thought I'd just pop in and get the gen, Doctor.

Doctor   Very wise. Well it's quite simple. The woman has an egg in her waterworks, and this comes to an arrangement with the man's plumbing, and Bob's your uncle. *(Standing up)* Any problems, just pop back and see me.

Pam   Thank you, Doctor.

Pam's back garden. Through the window we can see Donald and mother. Pam and Colin in deckchairs.

Corin   *(Voice Over)* And the final obstacle. Will Pam's mother and Donald get on, or will she turn against him and ban next Thursday's wedding?

Corin   They seem to be getting on quite well.

Pam   Mmmm.

Corin   How do you envisage married life?

Pam   Rather like single, I suppose. I think in my mind's eye I can see a bigger teapot.

Corin   And the intimate side of things?

Pam   Well, I must admit it'll be the first time I've seen a man's pyjama case.

A burst of laughter from inside the house. Ripping noise from Corin's deckchair and he sinks half-way through it. Pam looks at him.

Church. Corin waiting on the steps.

Corin   *(to camera)* Well, it's the big day. Pam asked us not to film the ceremony itself, and with a sensitivity rare amongst documentary film-makers, we've agreed.

Organ music heard from church.

Here they come! Any minute now we'll get our first glimpse of Mr and Mrs Donald Renshaw.

Donald comes out of the church pushing mother in her chair, in a mad wedding dress. Pam, in a neat suit, throws confetti over them.

Corin   Sorry – Donald – you haven't married Pam's mother?
Mother Yes, he bloody has! He knows a bit of a swinger when he sees one. Now put your foot down and get me to the bubbly!

Donald wheels mother away. Pam sweeps up the confetti.

Corin   Pam – this is awful – how do you feel?
Pam   Little bit disappointed, obviously.
Corin   Don't you feel bitter?
Pam   Not really.
Corin   To be their bridesmaid, so generous, and to throw confetti . . .
Pam   It's poisoned.
Corin   Sorry?
Pam   The confetti. They won't get far.

Pam winks at Corin.

He Didn't: Two

Kelly	So I get to work, right – and I'm just sitting on t'photocopier having a crack at my earwax and in walks Mr Fisher.
Pal	He didn't.
Kelly	He did. Right grumpy. Reeking of Rennies. He says Kelly-Marie Tunstall do you know what time it is? I said yeah I do ta very much.
Pal	You didn't.
Kelly	I did. So he gets right mad and he starts shaking, I love it

	when he does that 'cos all his dandruff drops into his top pocket. He said it's ten-fifteen and I want an explanation. I said all right five minutes ago it was ten past ten, that do yer?
Pal	You didn't.
Kelly	I did. He said I'm waiting, so I parked my chewy on my bra strap and I said – well – I was just posting this coupon for me mam, right – competition – I drink toilet cleaner because . . . okey dokey and this right rabid dog came bounding across the road and bit me right in the pedal-pushers.
Pal	It didn't.
Kelly	It did. So there's somewhat of a commotion, right, and this man came up and he said you know what you've got I said what he said hydrophobia, I said that's that morbid fear of a Cross Channel Ferry and he laughed. Like this. I could see his uvula.
Pal	You couldn't.
Kelly	I could. It were just like the adverts. And he said hydrophobia means you can never ever imbibe water – I said I'm not bothered I only drink Pony – he said no it's right incredibly dangerous and you have to have an operation right now!
Pal	He didn't.
Kelly	He did. And he said and fortunately I'm qualified to do it, though I'm actually a tree surgeon and I've only ever done it on a sycamore. Well, he hadn't got any anaesthetic so I had a right big whiff of *Rive Gauche* and next thing I knew I was on the ten o'clock bus completely cured.
Pal	You weren't.
Kelly	I was. But Mr Fisher's gone a bit puce, right. I said you want to study the heart disease statistics in the British Medical Journal, you do. He said Kelly-Marie Tunstall you have been repeatedly warned for persistent lateness and coming to work in a nightie, I've a good mind to fire you on the spot.
Pal	He didn't.
Kelly	He did. I said you can fire away, but I'm not leaving otherwise I'll tell everyone what happened on Christmas Eve when you drank two pints of correcting fluid and sexually harassed me with an outsize party squeaker.
Pal	He didn't.
Kelly	No he didn't – he nibbled my Twiglets and passed out – but it shut him up.

We're Half Asleep

Logo and signature tune 'We're Half Asleep!'. Bleak little studio. Girl presenter, fiddling with her hair, realizes she's on air but isn't too bothered.

Girl   Oh, right. OK. Well, a lot of you have been to zoos I suppose, and seen a lot of ezotic, sorry, exoktic, God I can't talk this morning, exotic animals. Right? But have you ever thought of keeping one in your back garden? Well, someone who has, or does rather, has thought of it, does do it, whatever, is er Louise erm Louise, God I've been getting this name wrong all morning – Louise Kazinski.

She strolls over to po-faced thirteen-year-old.

Hello, Louise.
Louise   Hello.
Girl   It is Kazinski – I got that right, didn't I?
Louise   Not really.
Girl   So, what have you brought along to show us?
Louise   What?
Girl   Weren't you bringing something, or something?
Louise   No, you can't travel them about really.
Girl   What's that?
Louise   Alligators.
Girl   Oh right, got you. Alligators. Dummee. No, you see *(to camera)* someone had scribbled over my running-order thing and there was a word beginning with 'a' and I thought it said animals but it said alligators so there we go. Right, Louise, alligators – how many have you got?
Louise   Ten, at the moment.
Girl   Ten, gosh, it must be quite a problem finding room for them all, what do you do, keep them in the bath?
Louise   No, we've built an artificial environment –

Girl	Really, gosh, that must be quite difficult. And how many have you got?
Louise	Ten – I –
Girl	Gosh, that's quite a lot. And are they little tiny ones, they're presumably not the great big ones?
Louise	Well, up to five feet long.
Girl	Gosh, that's quite big. They must take up quite a lot of space, where on earth do you keep them all?
Louise	My father's built a kind of art –
Girl	Dad's sorted something out has he, that's good. Fathers do have their uses, though not if they glug away at the old gin bottle like mine does, anyway, shouldn't have said that really, never mind, er – right, so – how big actually are they, actually?
Louise	Well, in the wild they can grow up to ten feet, but they don't grow that much in captivity.
Girl	Ten feet, gosh, that's quite a lot of feet isn't it, and how many have you got of those?
Louise	Well, ten, but like I said – our ones –
Girl	*(interrupting)* Yes, well, ten times ten, says she doing her maths bit, one hundred feet, just about isn't it, quite a lot of crocodile.
Louise	Yes.
Girl	Really? Well, thanks very much for coming along Louise – I'm sure we've all learnt a lot of new things we didn't already know. One thing I must ask you – how many alligators have you actually got?
Louise	Ten.
Girl	Gosh, as many as that.

Lights fade but not sound.

Right, that's it – we just have to look as if we're talking now, it just makes a better picture. So where do you find room for them all anyway, in the bath?

The Trolley

Restaurant – lunchtime – businessmen. Two completely straight businessmen, waiting for pudding.

Alan	Well, those figures sound very promising, Tim – how's Plymouth looking?
Tim	*(waggling hand)* Plymouth? Either way, Alan, either way – it's on hold – I feel personally Plymouth could be another Exeter.
Alan	Really? That's interesting.
Tim	We're very much keeping an ear to the ground with Plymouth.
Alan	I think what the regional boys tend to forget –

He breaks off as extremely dim waitress arrives with sweet trolley.

	Tim?
Tim	Alan?
Alan	Just coffee thank you – yeah, the regional boys –
Tim	Yes, just coffee for me too please – regional boys?
Alan	Is that we have to consider the Isle of Wight as well.

They notice the waitress is still there with the trolley.

	Two coffees, yes?
Waitress	Coffees what?
Alan	What?
Waitress	Have you seen it?
Alan	*(completely lost but trying not to lose face)* Erm –
Waitress	Have you seen it on the trolley?
Alan	Just two coffees, no sweet.
Waitress	Just two coffees no sweet?
Alan	That's it. What was I – the Isle of Wight –

Waitress	Have you seen it on the trolley?
Alan	*(no idea what she's talking about)* No, yes, thank you.
Waitress	Is it a sorbet?
Alan	Just the coffees, thank you. Now, er, Plymouth –
Waitress	Can you point at it?
Alan	No, we don't want anything on the trolley.
Waitress	Oh, anything on the trolley.
Alan	No, just take the trolley away dear, thank you, and we'll just have coffee, thank you.

She wheels it away.

Tim	*(to cover a sticky moment)* I must give you the print-out from Expo – it came out pretty much as you predicted –

The waitress wheels the trolley back.

Alan	Yes, so I believe . . .
Waitress	They're good castors, aren't they? I been right over to cutlery.
Alan	We don't want a pudding, we have a lot to discuss –
Waitress	You don't want a pudding.
Alan	Right.
Waitress	But you're having a sweet.
Tim	Er love – we're just having the old 'café', coffee.
Alan	I'll handle this Tim, thanks very much.
Waitress	Coffee.
Alan	Coffee.
Waitress	Is it on the trolley?
Alan	I asked you to take the trolley away.
Waitress	I did do.
Alan	Then you brought it back.
Waitress	Then I brought it back.
Alan	Now – take it away –
Waitress	Take it away what?
Alan	The trolley.
Waitress	The trolley. Take it away, the trolley.
Alan	And don't bring it back.
Waitress	What? The trolley!

She wheels it away

Tim	That sorted that out anyway, Alan.
Alan	Yes, well, just don't butt in next time OK, promotion's not automatic, you know.

Pause.

	Yes, there, er, Expo figures – Colin phoned them through to the top floor –
Tim	Now I didn't know that.
Alan	Oh yes, that's fairly automatic since the shake-up –

She wheels it back in.

Waitress	What did you say after take the trolley away?
Alan	Get me the bill.
Waitress	Get me the bill. No, it wasn't that.
Alan	I want the bill.
Waitress	Can you point at it?
Alan	Listen to me.

The Waitress listens intently.

	Are you listening to me?
Waitress	I was just then – have I to carry on?
Alan	I am not going to stand up and make a scene. Please fetch, to this table, now, the headwaiter, the man in the dark jacket pouring the wine. Just bring him here, please.
Waitress	Can you mind my trolley?
Alan	Yes.

She goes. They sit in tense silence. The head waiter arrives, suave Italian.

Head waiter	Is everything all right for you, sir? I trust the meal was to your liking, and how can I be of assistance?
Alan	I would like the bloody bill, please.
Head waiter	The bloody bill. *(In waitress's voice, with her expression)* Is it on the trolley?

He didn't: Three

Kelly   Anyway, so. I'm stretched out in my new swimming costume, right – cut up here, cut down here, keyhole *(indicating leg, chest and midriff)* and I'm boiling hot and the light's burning my eyes and my mam comes up and says Kelly-Marie Tunstall will you switch that cooker off and get off that ironing board.

Pal   She didn't.

Kelly   She did. And we're having our tea, right, pommes lyonnaise
and spam nuggets – and she said you'd better know – I'm
running away with a nuclear physicist and if you look behind
the clock you'll find fifteen quid and a bag of oven chips.

Pal   She didn't.

Kelly   She did. She said when your dad comes in tell him not to try
and find me 'cos I'm changing my name, cutting my hair and
laughing on the other side of my face.

Pal   She didn't.

Kelly   She did. And she laughed. Like this. I said I hope that's not
hereditary 'cos it hurts your eyeballs. She said well actually
you're adopted – you were left on my doorstep wrapped in the
business section of the *Sunday Times.*

Pal   You weren't.

Kelly   I was. And it's right embarrassing when you're fourteen. She
said your real father is a right prominent rhythm guitarist and
your mother does the ironing for University Challenge.

Pal   She doesn't.

Kelly   She does. Then I got this letter, right, all typed – loads of
spelling – it said Kelly-Marie Tunstall your father has been
killed whilst falling under a bus, and you might be in for one
million pounds and half-shares in a stationary caravan at
Cleveleys.

Pal   It didn't.

Kelly   It did. So I went to see the solicitor, right, all dressed up –
black bondage outfit, tan accessories, and he said
Kelly-Marie Tunstall, I'm going to give you a cheque for one
million pounds, and all you have to do is give up Babycham,
learn the oboe, and have one thigh tattooed with a crude
caricature of Rupert Murdoch.

Pal   He didn't.

Kelly   He did! *(Shows tattoed thigh.)* So I had that done, learnt the
oboe and then I phoned up and told him to stuff it. What's the
point of having a million pounds if you can't get legless on
Babycham? Eh?

Lady Police Serial

Juliet and Wilberforce, the desk sergeant, chatting at the front desk. They both have their hats on.

Juliet	Wilberforce.
Wilberforce	Ma'am?
Juliet	Do you mind if I ask you something?
Wilberforce	I don't, no.
Juliet	Do you know how to make a cup of tea?
Wilberforce	No, I don't, ma'am.
Juliet	No, neither do I. *(Bangs on desk.)* And I should know! Wilberforce – I've just had a call from Harry Potter.
Wilberforce	Harry Potter the safebreaker? Little feller? Black 'tache, hangs round The Mop and Bucket, easily led but unexpectedly generous?
Juliet	That's him. Do you know him?
Wilberforce	No. What did he want, ma'am?
Juliet	I don't know, we were cut off before he could tell me. He might have been murdered – I'll pop round on my way home. What happened about the brick that went missing from the building site, Wilberforce?
Wilberforce	It's been found, ma'am. It's chipped along one corner, but they think it's going to be all right.
Juliet	That's good. Our Asian friends – are they still being racially harrassed?
Wilberforce	No. Those National Front skinheads have completely changed their tune, thanks to you. In fact, they're throwing a party for the entire Asian community tomorrow.
Juliet	Right. I thought that new ping-pong table would do the trick. I might go to the party, Wilberforce – I've got a serge sari – where is it being held?
Wilberforce	Kitchener Street, ma'am – five streets away from the old playground where someone who did some shoplifting's

	mother was found wandering in a confused state – do you know it?
Juliet	Yes, I do. It backs on to the Cut where old Barney the tramp drowned himself because his dog had been run over by a Bedford van – I forget the registration number.
Wilberforce	We all had a whip-round, ma'am, as you suggested, and bought him a new puppy.
Juliet	Did it work?
Wilberforce	Yes, the old tramp's alive again now. In fact, he's thinking of doing social sciences at the Open University.

Message comes through on the radio.

Voice   Oscar Delta Tango Charlie Farnsbarns to base, over.

Juliet grabs the mike.

Juliet   I'll deal with this, Wilberforce. You go and check on Garstang's Television and Video Rental shop in the High

	Street. I passed there this morning and some of those televisions looked like they were about to be stolen.
Wilberforce	Right away, ma'am. *(Leaves.)* I've just got to get some after-dinner mints and change my library books.
Juliet	Good lad.
Wilberforce	*(stopping in doorway)* Where is the High Street, ma'am?
Juliet	Not sure, Wilberforce. Ask when you get there.

He leaves. She speaks into mike.

	Oscar Delta Tango Charlie Farnsbarns, come in please – this is Bippetty Boppetty Eggwhisk Goulash Pantiegirdle, over.
Voice	There's an incident taking place on the moors, ma'am.
Juliet	Got that. Anything else I should know?
Voice	It's quite windy.
Juliet	Will I need a poncho?
Voice	You might need a sheepskin coat.
Juliet	I'm on my way. Don't do anything stupid, Constable.

Voice   Like what, ma'am?

Juliet   Hot air ballooning. It can be very dangerous given bad
weather conditions like those you've described. I'll be
with you as soon as I've had a good cry, because I'm only
a woman and from time to time the pressure gets to me,
tough as I am. Over and out. Wah!

Self-service

Department store, upmarket self-service counter. Extremely long slow queue. A couple of girls serving behind. Our two nice ladies are at the end of the queue by the trays. Enid has a beret and no hair visible.

Enid	*(taking a tray)* Do you know, I've scoured this store from top to bottom, can I find a side-winding thermal body belt, can I buffalo.
Wyn	What did you want one for?
Enid	*(handing her tray over the counter)* Excuse me – I think you'll find there's spam on that. *(Taking another tray)* That gippy kidney.
Wyn	Flared up?
Enid	I'll say – it's like being continually poked – can you imagine that? *(Wyn can't.)* Dr Brewster says if I don't keep it lagged for the winter I could be spending a penny every twenty minutes come March.
Wyn	Can't they operate?
Enid	I haven't time to go in. I'm on the phone day and night about that carpet. What's the soup, dear?
Girl	Country vegetable.
Enid	What country – Taiwan?
Wyn	Have they not sent it? Your carpet. *(Rootles round the counter.)* There's croutons.
Enid	With my molars? Filthy French habit. Oh they sent it – I sent it back. I said, 'Do I look like a woman who would grace her lobby with a bordered Axminster?' I've told them time beyond number I'm the wall-to-wall elephant.
Wyn	Is that steak?
Enid	I would doubt it. Probably some poor beast that came a cropper at Beechers Brook. Er, dear – is this fish boned?
Girl	No.
Enid	I should check your insurance. Then I had a huge to-do

	and hoohah at the hairdressers.
Wyn	What about these Dublin prawns?
Enid	Never touch prawns. Do you know, they hang round sewage outlet pipes treading water with their mouths open – they love it!
Wyn	Still going to Maison Renée?
Enid	Chez Maurice was putting out feelers . . .
Wyn	Oh no, he reeks of neutralizer.
Enid	And he's forever dabbing at his cold sores with *Old Spice* –
Wyn	Aren't prawns an aphrodisiac?
Enid	I wouldn't put it past them. Well, I'm at Renée's – waiting to be shampooed – flicking through a *Woman's Weekly* – lovely piece on Alma Cogan. *(They've now reached veg, and the queue's stopped.)* Sorry – what's the hold-up here, dear?
Girl	We're waiting for fresh cauli . . .
Enid	Fresh! You might as well wait for Maurice Chevalier. So I'm called into the cubicle – it's all separate at Renée's – not like these terrible modern places where you find yourself sharing a perm trolley with two footballers – *(annoyed at the delay)* this is ridiculous *(pushing past the veg waiters)*. Can I thrust by – I'm a diabetic.

They are now at the sweet section.

	So in comes Renée.
Wyn	She must be getting on.
Enid	Well, this is the trouble. If she leans too far forward with a sponge roller she topples out of her walking frame – and you really have to shout up – I don't particularly want the whole world knowing I'm not a natural conker.
Wyn	Is that trifle?
Enid	It may have been in a previous existence. *(Elaborately casually looking away)* Don't have the gateaux – I just saw her scratching her armpit with the cake slice. And Renée's very set in her ways, style-wise – I don't mind – I'm a great admirer of Phyllis Calvert.
Wyn	So why hence the hoohah?
Enid	Well, I decided to go a shade mad because we've the Smoked Meat Purveyors Buffet 'n' Mingle at the weekend.

Irate voice from a woman a couple of people further down the queue.

Woman   Could we get by please; we're not having a sweet.

Woman and friend push by our two.

Enid   Very wise, with those hips. So I said, 'Skip the conker, Renée – I'll have burnished beech-nut and to heck with it.'
Wyn   So?
Enid   Well, you know she's colour blind and they've only a gas mantle round the back?
Wyn   Colour blind?
Enid   Can't tell red from blue. Once tottered into a brothel thinking it was a police station.

They reach Tea, Coffee and the Till.

Second girl   Tea, Coffee?
Enid   No.
Wyn   She didn't.
Enid   Oh, it was all right – one of the girls came out and helped her pump her tyres up.
Second girl   Sorry, are you still waiting for something?
Enid   Yes, a small mineral water and an orange squash, please.
Second girl   Water and squash back down the end by the trays. *(To next customer)* Tea, Coffee?

Enid and Wyn leave their trays behind and push past everybody back to the starting point. They pick up two trays and rejoin the queue.

Enid   You've a look of Eva Braun, did you know? Well – what Renée mixed up in the back – burnished beech-nut it was not – more like varicose violet – I could have wept.

Engrossed, they move off again – past the water and squash – people behind them as before.

Wyn	Did you have to pay?
Enid	Well, she knocked off my bourbons but – *(they move along)*. Then in comes Maxine, waving her whitlow . . .
Wyn	Is she the bodybuilder?
Enid	No that's Lois *(start to fade)*. No, Maxine's the one I told you about – excuse me – grey eggs – is that an Arab custom?

Cast List

All the sketches in this volume were first performed in *Victoria Wood As Seen on TV* (2nd series), shown on BBC2 in November, 1986, with the exception of the first six episodes of 'Acorn Antiques', which were performed in the first series, shown on BBC2 in January, 1985, and those marked with a *, first performed in a special programme on BBC television in autumn 1987.

Nora	*Nora*	Victoria Wood
No Gossip	*1st Lady*	Victoria Wood
	2nd Lady	Julie Walters
Margery and Joan	*Margery*	Julie Walters
	Joan	Victoria Wood
Men Talking	*1st Man*	Michael Nightingale
	2nd Man	Eric Richards
	3rd Man	Graham Seed
Today in Hospital	*Corin*	Duncan Preston
	Cleaner	Peter Martin
	Receptionist	Heather Baskerville
	Elaine	Victoria Wood
	Conrad	Andrew Livingston
	Doctor	Benjamin Whitrow
	Mrs Jones	Myrtle Devonish
	1st Student	Nicholas Barnes
	2nd Student	Ravindar Valia
	3rd Student	Richard Brenner
	Noreen	Kathryn Apanowicz
	Della	Beverly Martin
	Kevin	Philip Lowrie
	Drunken Man	Clive Panto
Kitty	*Kitty*	Patricia Routledge
Salesman	*Man*	Duncan Preston
	Woman	Celia Imrie
Reports Local	*Man*	Duncan Preston

	Woman	Celia Imrie
Dr Who*	*Doctor*	Jim Broadbent
	Fiona	Georgia Allen
	Crayola	Duncan Preston
	Guard	Johnny Worthy
Craft Shop	*Owner*	Rosalind March
	Girl	Celia Imrie
Wine Bar	*Man*	Ronnie Letham
	Girl	Carolyn Pickles
Acorn Antiques	*Babs*	Celia Imrie
	Mrs Overall	Julie Walters
	Clifford	Duncan Preston
	Bertha	Victoria Wood
	Trixie	Rosie Collins
	Derek	Kenny Ireland
	Jerez	Peter Ellis
	Extras	Albert & Michaela Welch
The Making of	*Marion Clune*	Maggie Steed
Acorn Antiques*	*Simon*	Sam Kelly
	Roberts	Nicholas Barnes
	Mickey	Bryan Burdon
	Make-up Girl	Jane Hardy
	PA	Deborah Grant
	Assistant Floor Manager	Colin Simmonds
Spaghetti	*Philippa*	Julie Walters
	Faith	Victoria Wood
	Waiter	Gerard Kelly
Medical School	*1st Man*	Terence Longdon
	2nd Man	Duncan Preston
	Sarah	Victoria Wood
	Woman	Celia Imrie
He Didn't	*Kelly*	Victoria Wood
	Pal	Mary Jo Randle
Tattoo Parlour	*Woman*	Victoria Wood
	Eric	Michael Gunn
	Paul	Gerard Kelly
Partly Political Broadcast	*Barbara*	Julie Walters
	Jean	Victoria Wood
Susie (Continuity)*	*Susie*	Susie Blake

Mr Right	*Pam*	Anne Reid
	Corin	Duncan Preston
	Mother	Dora Bryan
	Poll	Meg Johnson
	Girl	Victoria Wood
	Donald	Michael Nightingale
	Waiter	David Adams
	Doctor	John Nettleton
We're Half Asleep	*Girl*	Celia Imrie
	Louise	Nadine Wilson
The Trolley	*Alan*	Graham Seed
	Tim	Duncan Preston
	Waitress	Victoria Wood
	Head Waiter	Chris Sanders
Lady Police Serial	*Juliet*	Victoria Wood
	Wilberforce	Duncan Preston
	Voice	Stephen Hancock
Self-service*	*Enid*	Julie Walters
	Wyn	Victoria Wood
	1st Girl	Sue Wallace
	Woman	Celia Imrie
	2nd Girl	Lill Roughley

now and then and sang hesitant, clever, nervous, gentle dithyrambs about how we were beginning to feel towards one another. Actually we did not have the feelings we said we had until we spoke them — at least I didn't; to phrase them was to invent them and own them. We whipped our strangeness and newness into a froth that resembled love, and we dared not play too long with it, talk too much of it, or it would flatten and fizzle away. So we moved back and forth from chairs to water, from talk to silence, and considering my unshakable edginess with Brenda, and the high walls of ego that rose, buttresses and all, between her and her knowledge of herself, we managed pretty well.

At about four o'clock, at the bottom of the pool, Brenda suddenly wrenched away from me and shot up to the surface. I shot up after her.

"What's the matter?" I said.

First she whipped the hair off her forehead. Then she pointed a hand down towards the base of the pool. "My brother," she said, coughing some water free inside her.

And suddenly, like a crew-cut Proteus rising from the sea, Ron Patimkin emerged from the lower depths we'd just inhabited and his immensity was before us.

"Hey, Bren," he said, and pushed a palm flat into the water so that a small hurricane beat up against Brenda and me.

"What are you so happy about?" she said.

"The Yankees took two."

"Are we going to have Mickey Mantle for dinner?" she said. "When the Yankees win," she said to me, treading so easily she seemed to have turned the chlorine to marble beneath her, "we set an extra place for Mickey Mantle."

"You want to race?" Ron asked.

"No, Ronald. Go race alone."

Nobody had as yet said a word about me. I treaded unobtrusively as I could, as a third party, unintroduced, will step back and say nothing, awaiting the amenities. I was tired, however, from the afternoon's sport, and wished to hell brother and sister would not tease and chat much longer. Fortunately Brenda introduced me. "Ronald, this is Neil Klugman. This is my brother, Ronald Patimkin."

Of all things there in the fifteen feet water, Ron reached out his hand to shake. I returned the shake, not quite as monumentally as he apparently expected; my chin slipped an inch into the water and all at once I was exhausted.

"Want to race?" Ron asked me good-naturedly.

"Go ahead, Neil, race with him. I want to call home and tell them you're coming to dinner."

"Am I? I'll have to call my aunt. You didn't say anything. My clothes —"

"We dine *au naturel*."

"What?" Ronald said.

"Swim, baby," Brenda said to him and it ached me some when she kissed him on the face.

I begged out of the race, saying I had to make a phone call myself, and once upon the tiled blue border of the pool, looked back to see Ron taking the length in sleek, immense strokes. He gave one the feeling that after swimming the length of the pool a half dozen times he would have earned the right to drink its contents; I imagined he had, like my Uncle Max, a colossal thirst and a gigantic bladder.

Aunt Gladys did not seem relieved when I told her she'd have only three feedings to prepare that night. "Fancy-shmancy" was all she said to me on the phone.

We did not eat in the kitchen; rather, the six of us —
Brenda, myself, Ron, Mr. and Mrs. Patimkin, and
Brenda's little sister, Julie — sat around the dining room
table, while the maid, Carlota, a Navaho-faced Negro who
had little holes in her ears but no earrings, served us the
meal. I was seated next to Brenda, who was dressed in
what was *au naturel* for her: Bermudas, the close ones,
white polo shirt, tennis sneakers and white socks. Across
from me was Julie, ten, round-faced, bright, who before
dinner, while the other little girls on the street had been
playing with jacks and boys and each other, had been on
the back lawn putting golf balls with her father. Mr.
Patimkin reminded me of my father, except that when he
spoke he did not surround each syllable with a wheeze. He
was tall, strong, ungrammatical, and a ferocious eater.
When he attacked his salad — after drenching it in bottled
French dressing — the veins swelled under the heavy skin
of his forearm. He ate three helpings of salad, Ron had
four, Brenda and Julie had two, and only Mrs. Patimkin
and I had one each. I did not like Mrs. Patimkin, though
she was certainly the handsomest of all of us at the table.
She was disastrously polite to me, and with her purple eyes,
her dark hair, and large, persuasive frame, she gave me the
feeling of some captive beauty, some wild princess, who has
been tamed and made the servant to the king's daughter —
who was Brenda.

Outside, through the wide picture window, I could see
the back lawn with its twin oak trees. I say oaks, though
fancifully, one might call them sporting-goods trees. Beneath their branches, like fruit dropped from their limbs,
were two irons, a golf ball, a tennis can, a baseball bat,
basketball, a first-baseman's glove, and what was appar-

ently a riding crop. Further back, near the scrubs that bounded the Patimkin property and in front of the small basketball court, a square red blanket, with a white O stitched in the center, looked to be on fire against the green grass. A breeze must have blown outside, for the net on the basket moved; inside we ate in the steady coolness of air by Westinghouse. It was a pleasure, except that eating among those Brobdingnags, I felt for quite a while as though four inches had been clipped from my shoulders, three inches from my height, and for good measure, someone had removed my ribs and my chest had settled meekly in towards my back.

There was not much dinner conversation; eating was heavy and methodical and serious, and it would be just as well to record all that was said in one swoop, rather than indicate the sentences lost in the passing of food, the words gurgled into mouthfuls, the syntax chopped and forgotten in heapings, spillings, and gorgings.

To Ron: When's Harriet calling?

Ron: Five o'clock.

Julie: It *was* five o'clock.

Ron: Their time.

Julie: Why is it that it's earlier in Milwaukee? Suppose you took a plane back and forth all day. You'd never get older.

Brenda: That's right, sweetheart.

Mrs. P.: What do you give the child misinformation for? Is that why she goes to school?

Brenda: I don't know why she goes to school.

Mr. P. (*lovingly*): College girl.

Ron: Where's Carlota? Carlota!

Mrs. P.: Carlota, give Ronald more.

CARLOTA (*calling*): More what?

RON: Everything.

MR. P.: Me too.

MRS. P.: They'll have to *roll* you on the links.

MR. P. (*pulling his shirt up and slapping his black, curved belly*): What are you talking about? Look at that?

RON (*yanking his T-shirt up*): Look at *this*.

BRENDA: (*to me*) Would you care to bare your middle?

ME (the choir boy again): No.

MRS. P.: That's right, Neil.

ME: Yes. Thank you.

CARLOTA (*over my shoulder, like an unsummoned spirit*): Would *you* like more?

ME: No.

MR. P.: He eats like a bird.

JULIE: Certain birds eat a lot.

BRENDA: Which ones?

MRS. P.: Let's not talk about animals at the dinner table. Brenda, why do you encourage her?

RON: Where's Carlota, I gotta play tonight.

MR. P.: Tape your wrist, don't forget.

MRS. P.: Where do you live, Bill?

BRENDA: Neil.

MRS. P.: Didn't I say Neil?

JULIE: You said "Where do you live, *Bill?*"

MRS. P.: I must have been thinking of something else.

RON: I hate tape. How the hell can I play in tape?

JULIE: Don't curse.

MRS. P.: That's right.

MR. P.: What is Mantle batting now?

JULIE: Three twenty-eight.

RON: Three twenty-five.

JULIE: Eight!

RON: Five, jerk! He got three for four in the second game.

JULIE: *Four* for four.

RON: That was an error, Minoso should have had it.

JULIE: *I* didn't think so.

BRENDA (*to me*): See?

MRS. P.: See what?

BRENDA: I was talking to Bill.

JULIE: Neil.

MR. P.: Shut up and eat.

MRS. P.: A little less talking, young lady.

JULIE: *I* didn't say anything.

BRENDA: She was talking to me, sweetie.

MR. P.: What's this *she* business. Is that how you call your mother? What's dessert?

The phone rings, and though we are awaiting dessert, the meal seems at a formal end, for Ron breaks for his room, Julie shouts "Harriet!" and Mr. Patimkin is not wholly successful in stifling a belch, though the failure even more than the effort ingratiates him to me. Mrs. Patimkin is directing Carlota not to mix the milk silverware and the meat silverware again, and Carlota is eating a peach while she listens; under the table I feel Brenda's fingers tease my calf. I am full.

We sat under the biggest of the oak trees while out on the basketball court Mr. Patimkin played five and two with Julie. In the driveway Ron was racing the motor of the Volkswagen. "Will somebody *please* move the Chrysler out from behind me?" he called angrily. "I'm late as it is."

"Excuse me," Brenda said, getting up.

"I think I'm behind the Chrysler," I said.

"Let's go," she said.

We backed the cars out so that Ron could hasten on to his game. Then we reparked them and went back to watching Mr. Patimkin and Julie.

"I like your sister," I said.

"So do I," she said. "I wonder what she'll turn out to be."

"Like you," I said.

"I don't know," she said. "Better probably." And then she added, "or maybe worse. How can you tell? My father's nice to her, but I'll give her another three years with my mother . . . Bill," she said, musingly.

"I didn't mind that," I said. "She's very beautiful, your mother."

"I can't even think of her as my mother. She hates me. Other girls, when they pack in September, at least their mothers help them. Not mine. She'll be busy sharpening pencils for Julie's pencil box while I'm carrying my trunk around upstairs. And it's so obvious why. It's practically a case study."

"Why?"

"She's jealous. It's so corny I'm ashamed to say it. Do you know my mother had the best back-hand in New Jersey? Really, she was the best tennis player in the state, man or woman. You ought to see the pictures of her when she was a girl. She was so healthy-looking. But not chubby or anything. She was soulful, truly. I love her in those pictures. Sometimes I say to her how beautiful the pictures are. I even asked to have one blown up so I could have it at school. 'We have other things to do with our money, young lady, than spend it on old photographs.'

Money! My father's up to here with it, but whenever I buy a coat you should hear her. 'You don't have to go to Bonwit's, young lady, Ohrbach's has the strongest fabrics of any of them.' Who *wants* a strong fabric! Finally I get what I want, but not till she's had a chance to aggravate me. Money is a waste for her. She doesn't even know how to enjoy it. She still thinks we live in Newark."

"But you get what you want," I said.

"Yes. Him," and she pointed out to Mr. Patimkin who had just swished his third straight set shot through the basket to the disgruntlement, apparently, of Julie, who stamped so hard at the ground that she raised a little dust storm around her perfect young legs.

"He's not too smart but he's sweet at least. He doesn't treat my brother the way she treats me. Thank God, for that. Oh, I'm tired of talking about them. Since my freshman year I think every conversation I've ever had has always wound up about my parents and how awful it is. It's universal. The only trouble is they don't know it."

From the way Julie and Mr. Patimkin were laughing now, out on the court, no problem could ever have seemed less universal; but, of course, it was universal for Brenda, more than that, cosmic — it made every cashmere sweater a battle with her mother, and her life, which, I was certain, consisted to a large part of cornering the market on fabrics that felt soft to the skin, took on the quality of a Hundred Years' War . . .

I did not intend to allow myself such unfaithful thoughts, to line up with Mrs. Patimkin while I sat beside Brenda, but I could not shake from my elephant's brain that she-still-thinks-we-live-in-Newark remark. I did not speak, however, fearful that my tone would shatter our post-dinner ease and intimacy. It had been so simple to be intimate with water pounding and securing all our pores, and later, with the sun heating them and drugging our senses, but now, in the shade and the open, cool and clothed on her own grounds, I did not want to voice a word that would lift the cover and reveal that hideous emotion I always felt for her, and is the underside of love. It will not always *stay* the underside — but I am skipping ahead.

Suddenly, little Julie was upon us. "Want to play?" she said to me. "Daddy's tired."

"C'mon," Mr. Patimkin called. "Finish for me."

I hesitated — I hadn't held a basketball since high school — but Julie was dragging at my hand, and Brenda said, "Go ahead."

Mr. Patimkin tossed the ball towards me while I wasn't looking and it bounced off my chest, leaving a round dust spot, like the shadow of a moon, on my shirt. I laughed, insanely.

"Can't you catch?" Julie said.

Like her sister, she seemed to have a knack for asking practical, infuriating questions.

"Yes."

"Your turn," she said. "Daddy's behind forty-seven to thirty-nine. Two hundred wins."

For an instant, as I placed my toes in the little groove that over the years had been nicked into a foul line, I had one of those instantaneous waking dreams that plague me from time to time, and send, my friends tell me, deadly cataracts over my eyes: the sun had sunk, crickets had come and gone, the leaves had blackened, and still Julie and I stood alone on the lawn, tossing the ball at the basket; "Five hundred wins," she called, and then when she beat me to five hundred she called, "Now *you* have to reach it," and I did, and the night lengthened, and she called, "*Eight* hundred wins," and we played on and then it was eleven hundred that won and we played on and it never was morning.

"Shoot," Mr. Patimkin said. "You're me."

That puzzled me, but I took my set shot and, of course, missed. With the Lord's blessing and a soft breeze, I made the lay-up.

"You have forty-one. I go," Julie said.

Mr. Patimkin sat on the grass at the far end of the court. He took his shirt off, and in his undershirt, and his whole day's growth of beard, looked like a trucker. Brenda's old nose fitted him well. There was a bump in it, all right; up at the bridge it seemed as though a small eight-sided diamond had been squeezed in under the skin. I knew Mr. Patimkin would never bother to have that stone cut from his face, and yet, with joy and pride, no doubt, had paid to have Brenda's diamond removed and dropped down some toilet in Fifth Avenue Hospital.

Julie missed her set shot, and I admit to a slight, gay, flutter of heart.

"Put a little spin on it," Mr. Patimkin told her.

"Can I take it again?" Julie asked me.

"Yes." What with paternal directions from the sidelines and my own grudging graciousness on the court, there did not seem much of a chance for me to catch up. And I wanted to, suddenly, I wanted to win, to run little Julie into the ground. Brenda was back on one elbow, under the tree, chewing on a leaf, watching. And up in the house, at the kitchen window, I could see that the curtain had swished back — the sun too low now to glare off electrical appliances — and Mrs. Patimkin was looking steadily out at the game. And then Carlota appeared on the back steps, eating a peach and holding a pail of garbage in her free hand. She stopped to watch too.

It was my turn again. I missed the set shot and laughingly turned to Julie and said, "Can I take it again?"

"No!"

So I learned how the game was played. Over the years Mr. Patimkin had taught his daughters that free throws were theirs for the asking; he could afford to. However, with the strange eyes of Short Hills upon me, matrons, servants, and providers, I somehow felt I couldn't. But I had to and I did.

"Thanks a lot, Neil," Julie said when the game was ended — at 100 — and the crickets had come.

"You're welcome."

Under the trees, Brenda smiled. "Did you let her win?"

"I think so," I said. "I'm not sure."

There was something in my voice that prompted Brenda to say, comfortingly, "Even Ron lets her win."

"It's all nice for Julie," I said.

3

The next morning I found a parking space on Washington Street directly across from the library. Since I was twenty minutes early I decided to stroll in the park rather than cross over to work; I didn't particularly care to join my colleagues, who I knew would be sipping early morning coffee in the binding room, smelling still of all the orange crush they'd drunk that weekend at Asbury Park. I sat on a bench and looked out towards Broad Street and the morning traffic. The Lackawanna commuter trains were rumbling in a few blocks to the north and I could hear them, I thought — the sunny green cars, old and clean, with windows that opened all the way. Some mornings, with time to kill before work, I would walk down to the tracks and watch the open windows roll in, on their sills the elbows of tropical suits and the edges of briefcases, the properties of businessmen arriving in town from Maplewood, the Oranges, and the suburbs beyond.

The park, bordered by Washington Street on the west and Broad on the east, was empty and shady and smelled of trees, night, and dog leavings; and there was a faint damp smell too, indicating that the huge rhino of a water cleaner had passed by already, soaking and whisking the downtown streets. Down Washington Street, behind me, was the Newark Museum — I could see it without even looking: two oriental vases in front like spittoons for a rajah, and next to it the little annex to which we had traveled on special buses as schoolchildren. The annex was a brick building, old and vine-covered, and always reminded me of New Jersey's link with the beginning of the country, with George Washington, who had trained his scrappy army — a little bronze tablet informed us children — in the very park where I now sat. At the far end of the park, beyond the Museum, was the bank building where I had gone to college. It had been converted some years before into an extension of Rutgers University; in fact, in what once had been the bank president's waiting room I had taken a course called Contemporary Moral Issues. Though it was summer now, and I was out of college three years, it was not hard for me to remember the other students, my friends, who had worked evenings in Bamberger's and

Kresge's and had used the commissions they'd earned pushing ladies' out-of-season shoes to pay their laboratory fees.
And then I looked out to Broad Street again. Jammed between a grimy-windowed bookstore and a cheesy luncheonette was the marquee of a tiny art theater — how many
years had passed since I'd stood beneath that marquee,
lying about the year of my birth so as to see Hedy Lamarr
swim naked in *Ecstasy*; and then, having slipped the ticket
taker an extra quarter, what disappointment I had felt at
the frugality of her Slavic charm . . . Sitting there in the
park, I felt a deep knowledge of Newark, an attachment
so rooted that it could not help but branch out into affection.

Suddenly it was nine o'clock and everything was scurrying. Wobbly-heeled girls revolved through the doors of
the telephone building across the way, traffic honked desperately, policeman barked, whistled, and waved motorists
to and fro. Over at St. Vincent's Church the huge dark
portals swung back and those bleary-eyes that had risen
early for Mass now blinked at the light. Then the wor-
shipers had stepped off the church steps and were racing
down the streets towards desks, filing cabinets, secretaries,
bosses, and — if the Lord had seen fit to remove a mite of
harshness from their lives — to the comfort of air-condi-
tioners pumping at their windows. I got up and crossed
over to the library, wondering if Brenda was awake yet.

The pale cement lions stood unconvincing guard on the
library steps, suffering their usual combination of elephan-
tiasis and arteriosclerosis, and I was prepared to pay them
as little attention as I had for the past eight months were
it not for a small colored boy who stood in front of one of
them. The lion had lost all of its toes the summer before

to a safari of juvenile delinquents, and now a new tor-
mentor stood before him, sagging a little in his knees, and
growling. He would growl, low and long, drop back,
wait, then growl again. Then he would straighten up, and,
shaking his head, he would say to the lion, "Man, you's
a coward . . . " Then, once again, he'd growl.

The day began the same as any other. From behind the
desk on the main floor, I watched the hot high-breasted
teen-age girls walk twitchingly up the wide flight of marble
stairs that led to the main reading room. The stairs were
an imitation of a staircase somewhere in Versailles, though
in their toreador pants and sweaters these young daughters
of Italian leatherworkers, Polish brewery hands, and Jewish
furriers were hardly duchesses. They were not Brenda
either, and any lust that sparked inside me through the
dreary day was academic and time-passing. I looked at
my watch occasionally, thought of Brenda, and waited for
lunch and then for after lunch, when I would take over the
Information Desk upstairs and John McKee, who was only
twenty-one but wore elastic bands around his sleeves, would
march starchily down the stairs to work assiduously at
stamping books in and out. John McRubberbands was in
his last year at Newark State Teachers College where he was
studying at the Dewey Decimal System in preparation for
his lifework. The library was not going to be my lifework, I
knew it. Yet, there had been some talk — from Mr. Scapello, an old eunuch who had learned somehow to disguise
his voice as a man's — that when I returned from my summer vacation I would be put in charge of the Reference
Room, a position that had been empty ever since that morning when Martha Winney had fallen off a high stool in the
Encyclopedia Room and shattered all those frail bones that

come together to form what in a woman half her age we would call the hips.

I had strange fellows at the library and, in truth, there were many hours when I never quite knew how I'd gotten there or why I stayed. But I did stay and after a while waited patiently for that day when I would go into the men's room on the main floor for a cigarette and, studying myself as I expelled smoke into the mirror, would see that at some moment during the morning I had gone pale, and that under my skin, as under McKee's and Scapello's and Miss Winney's, there was a thin cushion of air separating the blood from the flesh. Someone had pumped it there while I was stamping out a book, and so life from now on would be not a throwing off, as it was for Aunt Gladys, and not a gathering in, as it was for Brenda, but a bouncing off, a numbness. I began to fear this, and yet, in my muscleless devotion to my work, seemed edging towards it, silently, as Miss Winney used to edge up to the *Britannica*. Her stool was empty now and awaited me.

Just before lunch the lion tamer came wide-eyed into the library. He stood still for a moment, only his fingers moving, as though he were counting the number of marble stairs before him. Then he walked creepily about on the marble floor, snickering at the clink of his taps and the way his little noise swelled up to the vaulted ceiling. Otto, the guard at the door, told him to make less noise with his shoes, but that did not seem to bother the little boy. He clacked on his tiptoes, high, secretively, delighted at the opportunity Otto had given him to practice this posture. He tiptoed up to me.

"Hey," he said, "where's the heart section?"

"The what?" I said.

"The heart section. Ain't you got no heart section?"

He had the thickest sort of southern Negro dialect and the only word that came clear to me was the one that sounded like heart.

"How do you spell it?" I said.

"*Heart.* Man, pictures. Drawing books. Where you got them?"

"You mean art books? Reproductions?"

He took my polysyllabic word for it. "Yea, they's them."

"In a couple places," I told him. "Which artist are you interested in?"

The boy's eyes narrowed so that his whole face seemed black. He started backing away, as he had from the lion. "All of them . . . " he mumbled.

"That's okay," I said. "You go look at whichever ones you want. The next flight up. Follow the arrow to where it says Stack Three. You remember that? Stack Three. Ask somebody upstairs."

He did not move; he seemed to be taking my curiosity about his taste as a kind of poll-tax investigation. "Go ahead," I said, slashing my face with a smile, "right up there . . . "

And like a shot he was scuffling and tapping up towards the heart section.

After lunch I came back to the in-and-out desk and there was John McKee, waiting, in his pale blue slacks, his black shoes, his barber-cloth shirt with the elastic bands, and a great knit tie, green, wrapped into a Windsor knot, that was huge and jumped when he talked. His breath smelled of hair oil and his hair of breath and when he spoke, spittle cobwebbed the corners of his mouth. I did not like him and at times had the urge to yank back on his armbands and slingshoot him out past Otto and the lions into the street.

"Has a little Negro boy passed the desk? With a thick accent? He's been hiding in the art books all morning. You know what those boys *do* in there."

"I saw him come in, John."

"So did I. Has he gone *out* though."

"I haven't noticed. I guess so."

"Those are *very* expensive books."

"Don't be so nervous, John. People are supposed to touch them."

"There is touching," John said sententiously, "and there is touching. Someone should check on him. I was afraid to leave the desk here. You know the way they treat the housing projects we give them."

"*You* give them?"

"The city. Have you seen what they do at Seth Boyden? They threw *beer* bottles, those big ones, on the *lawn*. They're taking over the city."

"Just the Negro sections."

"It's easy to laugh, you don't live near them. I'm going to call Mr. Scapello's office to check the Art Section. Where did he ever find out about art?"

"You'll give Mr. Scapello an ulcer, so soon after his egg-and-pepper sandwich. I'll check, I have to go upstairs anyway."

"You know what they do in there," John warned me.

"Don't worry, Johnny, *they're* the ones who'll get warts on their dirty little hands."

"Ha ha. Those books happen to cost — "

So that Mr. Scapello would not descend upon the boy

with his chalky fingers, I walked up the three flights to Stack Three, past the receiving room where rheumy-eyed Jimmy Boylen, our fifty-one-year-old boy, unloaded books from a cart; past the reading room, where bums off Mulberry Street slept over *Popular Mechanics*; past the smoking corridor where damp-browed summer students from the law school relaxed, some smoking, others trying to rub the colored dye from their tort texts off their fingertips; and finally, past the periodical room, where a few ancient ladies who'd been motored down from Upper Montclair now huddled in their chairs, pince-nezing over yellowed, fraying society pages in old old copies of the Newark *News*. Up on Stack Three I found the boy. He was seated on the glass-brick floor holding an open book in his lap, a book, in fact, that was bigger than his lap and had to be propped up by his knees. By the light of the window behind him I could see the hundreds of spaces between the hundreds of tiny black corkscrews that were his hair. He was very black and shiny, and the flesh of his lips did not so much appear to be a different color as it looked to be unfinished and awaiting another coat. The lips were parted, the eyes wide, and even the ears seemed to have a heightened receptivity. He looked ecstatic — until he saw me, that is. For all he knew I was John McKee.

"That's okay," I said before he could even move, "I'm just passing through. You read."

"Ain't nothing *to* read. They's pictures."

"Fine." I fished around the lowest shelves a moment, playing at work.

"Hey, mister," the boy said after a minute, "where is this?"

"Where is what?"

"Where is these pictures? These people, man, they sure does look cool. They ain't no yelling or shouting here, you could just see it."

He lifted the book so I could see. It was an expensive large-sized edition of Gauguin reproductions. The page he had been looking at showed an 8½ × 11 print, in color, of three native women standing knee-high in a rose-colored stream. It *was* a silent picture, he was right.

"That's Tahiti. That's an island in the Pacific Ocean."

"That ain't no place you could go, is it? Like a ree-*sort?*"

"You could go there, I suppose. It's very far. People live there . . . "

"Hey, *look*, look here at this one." He flipped back to a page where a young brown-skinned maid was leaning forward on her knees, as though to dry her hair. "Man," the boy said, "that's the fuckin life." The euphoria of his diction would have earned him eternal banishment from the Newark Public Library and its branches had John or Mr. Scapello — or, God forbid, the hospitalized Miss Winney — come to investigate.

"Who took these pictures?" he asked me.

"Gauguin. He didn't take them, he painted them. Paul Gauguin. He was a Frenchman."

"Is he a white man or a colored man?"

"He's white."

"Man," the boy smiled, chuckled almost, "I knew that. He don't *take* pictures like no colored men would. He's a good picture taker . . . *Look, look*, look here at this one. Ain't that the fuckin *life?*"

I agreed it was and left.

Later I sent Jimmy Boylen hopping down the stairs to tell McKee that everything was all right. The rest of the day was uneventful. I sat at the Information Desk thinking about Brenda and reminding myself that that evening I would have to get gas before I started up to Short Hills, which I could see now, in my mind's eye, at dusk, rose-colored, like a Gauguin stream.

When I pulled up to the Patimkin house that night, everybody but Julie was waiting for me on the front porch: Mr. and Mrs., Ron, and Brenda, wearing a dress. I had not seen her in a dress before and for an instant she did not look like the same girl. But that was only half the surprise. So many of those Lincolnesque college girls turn out to be limbed for shorts alone. Not Brenda. She looked, in a dress, as though she'd gone through life so attired, as though she'd never worn shorts, or bathing suits, or pajamas, or anything but that pale linen dress. I walked rather bouncingly up the lawn, past the huge weeping willow, towards the waiting Patimkins, wishing all the while that I'd had my car washed. Before I'd even reached them, Ron stepped forward and shook my hand, vigorously, as though he hadn't seen me since the Diaspora. Mrs. Patimkin smiled and Mr. Patimkin grunted something and continued twitching his wrists before him, then raising an imaginary golf club and driving a ghost of a golf ball up and away towards the Orange Mountains, that are called Orange, I'm convinced, because in that various suburban light that's the *only* color they do not come dressed in.

"We'll be right back," Brenda said to me. "You have to sit with Julie. Carlota's off."

"Okay," I said.

"We're taking Ron to the airport."

"Okay."

"Julie doesn't want to go. She says Ron pushed her in the pool this afternoon. We've been waiting for you, so we don't miss Ron's plane. Okay?"

"*Okay.*"

Mr. and Mrs. Patimkin and Ron moved off, and I flashed Brenda just the hint of a glare. She reached out and took my hand a moment.

"How do you like me?" she said.

"You're great to baby-sit for. Am I allowed all the milk and cake I want?"

"Don't be angry, baby. We'll be right back." Then she waited a moment, and when I failed to deflate the pout from my mouth, she gave *me* a glare, no hints about it. "I *meant* how do you like me in a dress!" Then she ran off towards the Chrysler, trotting in her high heels like a colt.

When I walked into the house, I slammed the screen door behind me.

"Close the other door too," a little voice shouted. "The air-conditioning."

I closed the other door, obediently.

"Neil?" Julie called.

"Yes."

"Hi. Want to play five and two?"

"No."

"Why not?"

I did not answer.

"I'm in the television room," she called.

"Good."

"Are you supposed to stay with me?"

"Yes."

She appeared unexpectedly through the dining room. "Want to read a book report I wrote?"

"Not now."

"What do you want to do?" she said.

"Nothing, honey. Why don't you watch TV?"

"All right," she said disgustedly, and kicked her way back to the television room.

For a while I remained in the hall, bitten with the urge to slide quietly out of the house, into my car, and back to Newark, where I might even sit in the alley and break candy with my own. I felt like Carlota; no, not even as comfortable as that. At last I left the hall and began to stroll in and out of rooms on the first floor. Next to the living room was the study, a small knotty-pine room jammed with cater-cornered leather chairs and a complete set of *Information Please Almanacs*. On the wall hung three colored photo-paintings; they were the kind which, regardless of the subjects, be they vital or infirm, old or youthful, are characterized by bud-cheeks, wet lips, pearly teeth, and shiny, metallized hair. The subjects in this case were Ron, Brenda, and Julie at about ages fourteen, thirteen, and two. Brenda had long auburn hair, her diamond-studded nose, and no glasses; all combined to make her look a regal thirteen-year-old who'd just gotten smoke in her eyes. Ron was rounder and his hairline was lower, but that love of spherical objects and lined courts twinkled in his boyish eyes. Poor little Julie was lost in the photo-painter's Platonic idea of childhood; her tiny humanity was smothered somewhere back of gobs of pink and white.

There were other pictures about, smaller ones, taken with a Brownie Reflex before photo-paintings had become fashionable. There was a tiny picture of Brenda on a horse;

another of Ron in bar mitzvah suit, *yamalkah*, and *tallas*; and two pictures framed together — one of a beautiful, faded woman, who must have been, from the eyes, Mrs. Patimkin's mother, and the other of Mrs. Patimkin herself, her hair in a halo, her eyes joyous and not those of a slowly aging mother with a quick and lovely daughter.

I walked through the archway into the dining room and stood a moment looking out at the sporting goods tree. From the television room that winged off the dining room, I could hear Julie listening to *This Is Your Life*. The kitchen, which winged off the other side, was empty, and apparently, with Carlota off, the Patimkins had had dinner at the club. Mr. and Mrs. Patimkin's bedroom was in the middle of the house, down the hall, next to Julie's, and for a moment I wanted to see what size bed those giants slept in — I imagined it wide and deep as a swimming pool — but I postponed my investigation while Julie was in the house, and instead opened the door in the kitchen that led down to the basement.

The basement had a different kind of coolness from the house, and it had a smell, which was something the upstairs was totally without. It felt cavernous down there, but in a comforting way, like the simulated caves children make for themselves on rainy days, in hall closets, under blankets, or in between the legs of dining room tables. I flipped on the light at the foot of the stairs and was not surprised at the pine paneling, the bamboo furniture, the ping-pong table, and the mirrored bar that was stocked with every kind and size of glass, ice bucket, decanter, mixer, swizzle stick, shot glass, pretzel bowl — all the bacchanalian paraphernalia, plentiful, orderly, and untouched, as it can be only in the bar of a wealthy man who

never entertains drinking people, who himself does not
drink, who, in fact, gets a fishy look from his wife when
every several months he takes a shot of schnapps before
dinner. I went behind the bar where there was an aluminum sink that had not seen a dirty glass, I'm sure, since
Ron's bar mitzvah party, and would not see another, probably, until one of the Patimkin children was married or engaged. I would have poured myself a drink — just as a
wicked wage for being forced into servantry — but I was
uneasy about breaking the label on a bottle of whiskey.
You had to break a label to get a drink. On the shelf back
of the bar were two dozen bottles — twenty-three to be ex-
act — of Jack Daniels, each with a little booklet tied to its
collared neck informing patrons how patrician of them it
was to drink the stuff. And over the Jack Daniels were
more photos: there was a blown-up newspaper photo of
Ron palming a basketball in one hand like a raisin; under
the picture it said, "*Center*, Ronald Patimkin, Millburn
High School, 6'4", 217 pounds." And there was another
picture of Brenda on a horse, and next to that, a velvet
mounting board with ribbons and medals clipped to it:
Essex County Horse Show 1949, Union County Horse
Show 1950, Garden State Fair 1952, Morristown Horse
Show 1953, and so on — all for Brenda, for jumping and
running or galloping or whatever else young girls receive
ribbons for. In the entire house I hadn't seen one picture
of Mr. Patimkin.

The rest of the basement, back of the wide pine-paneled
room, was gray cement walls and linoleum floor and con-
tained innumerable electrical appliances, including a
freezer big enough to house a family of Eskimos. Beside
the freezer, incongruously, was a tall old refrigerator; its an-

cient presence was a reminder to me of the Patimkin roots in Newark. This same refrigerator had once stood in the kitchen of an apartment in some four-family house, probably in the same neighborhood where I had lived all my life, first with my parents and then, when the two of them went wheezing off to Arizona, with my aunt and uncle. After Pearl Harbor the refrigerator had made the move up to Short Hills; Patimkin Kitchen and Bathroom Sinks had gone to war: no new barracks was complete until it had a squad of Patimkin sinks lined up in its latrine.

I opened the door of the old refrigerator; it was not empty. No longer did it hold butter, eggs, herring in cream sauce, ginger ale, tuna fish salad, an occasional corsage — rather it was heaped with fruit, shelves swelled with it, every color, every texture, and hidden within, every kind of pit. There were greengage plums, black plums, red plums, apricots, nectarines, peaches, long horns of grapes, black, yellow, red, and cherries, cherries flowing out of boxes and staining everything scarlet. And there were melons — cantaloupes and honeydews — and on the top shelf, half of a huge watermelon, a thin sheet of wax paper clinging to its bare red face like a wet lip. Oh Patimkin! Fruit grew in their refrigerator and sporting goods dropped from their trees!

I grabbed a handful of cherries and then a nectarine, and I bit right down to its pit.

"You better wash that or you'll get diarrhea."

Julie was standing behind me in the pine-paneled room. She was wearing *her* Bermudas and *her* white polo shirt which was unlike Brenda's only in that it had a little dietary history of its own.

"What?" I said.

"They're not washed yet," Julie said, and in such a way that it seemed to place the refrigerator itself out-of-bounds, if only for me.

"That's all right," I said, and devoured the nectarine and put the pit in my pocket and stepped out of the refrigerator room, all in one second. I still didn't know what to do with the cherries. "I was just looking around," I said.

Julie didn't answer.

"Where's Ron going?" I asked, dropping the cherries into my pocket, among my keys and change.

"Milwaukee."

"For long?"

"To see Harriet. They're in love."

We looked at each other for longer than I could bear. "Harriet?" I asked.

"Yes."

Julie was looking at me as though she were trying to look behind me, and then I realized that I was standing with my hands out of sight. I brought them around to the front, and, I swear it, she did peek to see if they were empty.

We confronted one another again; she seemed to have a threat in her face.

Then she spoke. "Want to play ping-pong?"

"God, yes," I said, and made for the table with two long, bounding steps. "You can serve."

Julie smiled and we began to play.

I have no excuses to offer for what happened next. I began to win and I liked it.

"Can I take that one over?" Julie said. "I hurt my finger yesterday and it just hurt when I served."

"No."

I continued to win.

"That wasn't fair, Neil. My shoelace came untied. Can I take it — "

"No."

We played, I ferociously.

"Neil, you leaned over the table. That's illegal — "

"I didn't lean and it's not illegal."

I felt the cherries hopping among my nickels and pennies.

"Neil, you gypped me out of a point. You have nineteen and I have eleven — "

"Twenty and *ten*," I said. "Serve!"

She did and I smashed my return past her — it zoomed off the table and skittered into the refrigerator room.

"You're a cheater!" she screamed at me. "You cheat!" Her jaw was trembling as though she carried a weight on top of her pretty head. "*I hate you!*" And she threw her racket across the room and it clanged off the bar, just as, outside, I heard the Chrysler crushing gravel in the driveway.

"The game isn't over," I said to her.

"You cheat! And you were stealing fruit!" she said, and ran away before I had my chance to win.

Later that night, Brenda and I made love, our first time. We were sitting on the sofa in the television room and for some ten minutes had not spoken a word to each other. Julie had long since gone to a weepy bed, and though no one had said anything to me about her crying, I did not know if the child had mentioned my fistful of cherries, which, some time before, I had flushed down the toilet.

The television set was on and though the sound was off and the house quiet, the gray pictures still wiggled at the far end of the room. Brenda was quiet and her dress circled her legs, which were tucked back beneath her. We sat there for some while and did not speak. Then she went into the kitchen and when she came back she said that it sounded as though everyone was asleep. We sat a while longer, watching the soundless bodies on the screen eating a silent dinner in someone's silent restaurant. When I began to unbutton her dress she resisted me, and I like to think it was because she knew how lovely she looked in it. But she looked lovely, my Brenda, anyway, and we folded it carefully and held each other close and soon there we were, Brenda falling, slowly but with a smile, and me rising.

How can I describe loving Brenda? It was so sweet, as though I'd finally scored that twenty-first point.

When I got home I dialed Brenda's number, but not before my aunt heard and rose from her bed.

"Who are you calling at this hour? The doctor?"

"No."

"What kind phone calls, one o'clock at night?"

"Shhh!" I said.

"He tells *me* shhh. Phone calls one o'clock at night, we haven't got a big enough bill," and then she dragged herself back into the bed, where with a martyr's heart and bleary eyes she had resisted the downward tug of sleep until she'd heard my key in the door.

Brenda answered the phone.

"Neil?" she said.

"Yes," I whispered. "You didn't get out of bed, did you?"

"No," she said. "the phone is next to the bed."

"Good. How is it in bed?"

"Good. Are you in bed?"

"Yes," I lied, and tried to right myself by dragging the phone by its cord as close as I could to my bedroom.

"I'm in bed with you," she said.

"That's right," I said, "and I'm with you."

"I have the shades down, so it's dark and I don't see you."

"I don't see you either."

"That was so nice, Neil."

"Yes. Go to sleep, sweet, I'm here," and we hung up without goodbyes. In the morning, as planned, I called again, but I could hardly hear Brenda or myself for that matter, for Aunt Gladys and Uncle Max were going on a Workmen's Circle picnic in the afternoon, and there was some trouble about grape juice that had dripped all night from a jug in the refrigerator and by morning had leaked out onto the floor. Brenda was still in bed and so could play our game with some success, but I had to pull down all the shades of my senses to imagine myself beside her. I could only pray our nights and mornings would come, and soon enough they did.

4

Over the next week and a half there seemed to be only two people in my life: Brenda and the little colored kid who liked Gauguin. Every morning before the library opened, the boy was waiting; sometimes he seated himself on the lion's back, sometimes under his belly, sometimes he just stood around throwing pebbles at his mane. Then he would come inside, tap around the main floor until Otto stared him up on tiptoes, and finally headed up the long marble stairs that led to Tahiti. He did not always stay to lunch time, but one very hot day he was there when I arrived in the morning and went through the door behind me when I left at night. The next morning, it was, that he did not show up, and as though in his place, a very old man appeared, white, smelling of Life Savers, his nose and jowls showing erupted veins beneath them. "Could you tell me where I'd find the art section?"

"Stack Three," I said.

In a few minutes, he returned with a big brown-covered book in his hand. He placed it on my desk, withdrew his card from a long moneyless billfold and waited for me to stamp out the book.

"Do you want to take this book *out*?" I said.

He smiled.

I took his card and jammed the metal edge into the machine; but I did not stamp down. "Just a minute," I said. I took a clipboard from under the desk and flipped through a few pages, upon which were games of battleship and tick-tack-toe that I'd been playing through the week with myself. "I'm afraid there's a hold on this book."

"A what?"

"A hold. Someone's called up and asked that we hold it for them. Can I take your name and address and drop a card when it's free . . ."

And so I was able, not without flushing once or twice, to get the book back in the stacks. When the colored kid showed up later in the day, it was just where he'd left it the afternoon before.

As for Brenda, I saw her every evening and when there was not a night game that kept Mr. Patimkin awake and in the TV room, or a Hadassah card party that sent Mrs. Patimkin out of the house and brought her in at unpredictable hours, we made love before the silent screen. One muggy, low-skied night Brenda took me swimming at the club. We were the only ones in the pool, and all the chairs, the cabañas, the lights, the diving boards, the very water seemed to exist only for our pleasure. She wore a blue suit that looked purple in the lights and down beneath the water it flashed sometimes green, sometimes black. Late in the evening a breeze came up off the golf course and we wrapped ourselves in one huge towel, pulled two chaise longues together, and despite the bartender, who was doing considerable pacing back and forth by the bar window, which overlooked the pool, we rested side by side on the chairs. Finally the bar light itself flipped off, and then, in a snap, the lights around the pool went down and out. My heart must have beat faster, or something, for Brenda seemed to guess my sudden doubt — *we should go,* I thought.

She said: "That's okay."

It was very dark, the sky was low and starless, and it took a while for me to see, once again, the diving board a shade lighter than the night, and to distinguish the water from the chairs that surrounded the far side of the pool.

I pushed the straps of her bathing suit down but she said no and rolled an inch away from me, and for the first time in the two weeks I'd known her she asked me a question about me.

"Where are your parents?" she said.

"Tucson," I said. "Why?"

"My mother asked me."

I could see the life guard's chair now, white almost.

"Why are you still here? Why aren't you with them?" she asked.

"I'm not a child any more, Brenda," I said, more sharply than I'd intended. "I just can't go wherever my parents are."

"But then why do you stay with your aunt and uncle?"

"They're not my parents."

"They're better?"

"No. Worse. I don't *know* why I stay with them."

"Why?" she said.

"Why don't I know?"

"Why do you stay? You do know, don't you?"

"My job, I suppose. It's convenient from there, and it's cheap, and it pleases my parents. My aunt's all right really . . . Do I really have to explain to your mother why I live where I do?"

"It's not for my mother. I want to know. I wondered why you weren't with your parents, that's all."

"Are you cold?" I asked.

"No."

"Do you want to go home?"

"No, not unless you do. Don't you feel well, Neil?"

"I feel all right," and to let her know that I was still me, I held her to me, though that moment I was without desire.

"Neil?"

"What?"

"What about the library?"

"Who wants to know that?"

"My father," she laughed.

"And you?"

She did not answer a moment. "And me," she said finally.

"Well, what about it? Do I like it? It's okay. I sold shoes once and like the library better. After the Army they

tried me for a couple months at Uncle Aaron's real estate
company — Doris' father — and I like the library better
than that . . ."

"How did you get a job *there?*"

"I worked there for a little while when I was in college,
then when I quit Uncle Aaron's, oh, I don't know . . ."

"What did you take in college?"

"At Newark Colleges of Rutgers University I majored
in philosophy. I am twenty-three years old. I — "

"Why do you sound nasty again?"

"Do I?"

"Yes."

I didn't say I was sorry.

"Are you planning on making a career of the library?"

"Bren, I'm not planning anything. I haven't planned a
thing in three years. At least for the year I've been out of
the Army. In the Army I used to plan to go away week-
ends. I'm — I'm not a planner." After all the truth I'd
suddenly given her, I shouldn't have ruined it for myself
with that final lie. I added, "I'm a liver."

"I'm a pancreas," she said.

"I'm a — "

And she kissed the absurd game away; she wanted to be
serious.

"Do you love me, Neil?"

I did not answer.

"I'll sleep with you whether you do or not, so tell me the
truth."

"That was pretty crude."

"Don't be prissy," she said.

"No, I mean a crude thing to say about me."

"I don't understand," she said, and she didn't, and that

she didn't pained me; I allowed myself the minor subter-
fuge, however, of forgiving Brenda her obtuseness. "Do
you?" she said.

"No."

"I want you to."

"What about the library?"

"What about it?" she said.

Was it obtuseness again? I thought not — and it wasn't,
for Brenda said, "When you love me, there'll be nothing
to worry about."

"Then of course I'll love you." I smiled.

"I know you will," she said. "Why don't you go in the
water, and I'll wait for you and close my eyes, and when
you come back you'll surprise me with the wet. Go
ahead."

"You like games, don't you?"

"Go ahead. I'll close my eyes."

I walked down to the edge of the pool and dove in. The
water felt colder than it had earlier, and when I broke
through and was headed blindly down I felt a touch of
panic. At the top again, I started to swim the length of the
pool and then turned at the end and started back, but suddenly I was sure that when I left the water Brenda would
be gone. I'd be alone in this damn place. I started for the
side and pulled myself up and ran to the chairs and
Brenda was there and I kissed her.

"God," she shivered, "You didn't stay long."

"I know."

"My turn," she said, and then she was up and a second
later I heard a little crack of water and then nothing.
Nothing for quite a while.

"Bren," I called softly, "are you all right?" but no one
answered.

I found her glasses on the chair beside me and held them in my hands. "Brenda?"

Nothing.

"Brenda?"

"No fair calling," she said and gave me her drenched self. "Your turn," she said.

This time I stayed below the water for a long while and when I surfaced again my lungs were ready to pop. I threw my head back for air and above me saw the sky, low like a hand pushing down, and I began to swim as though to move out from under its pressure. I wanted to get back to Brenda, for I worried once again — and there was no evidence, was there? — that if I stayed away too long she would not be there when I returned. I wished that I had carried her glasses away with me, so she would have to wait for me to lead her back home. I was having crazy thoughts, I knew, and yet they did not seem uncalled for in the darkness and strangeness of that place. Oh how I wanted to call out to her from the pool, but I knew she would not answer and I forced myself to swim the length a third time, and then a fourth, but midway through the fifth I felt a weird fright again, had momentary thoughts of my own extinction, and that time when I came back I held her tighter than either of us expected.

"Let go, let go," she laughed, "my turn — "

"But Brenda — "

But Brenda was gone and this time it seemed as though she'd never come back. I settled back and waited for the sun to dawn over the ninth hole, prayed it would if only for the comfort of its light, and when Brenda finally returned to me I would not let her go, and her cold wetness crept into me somehow and made me shiver. "That's it, Brenda. Please, no more games," I said, and then when I spoke again I held her so tightly I almost dug my body into hers, "I love you," I said, "I do."

So the summer went on. I saw Brenda every evening: we went swimming, we went for walks, we went for rides, up through the mountains so far and so long that by the time we started back the fog had begun to emerge from the trees and push out into the road, and I would tighten my hands on the wheel and Brenda would put on her glasses and watch the white line for me. And we would eat — a few nights after my discovery of the fruit refrigerator Brenda led me to it herself. We would fill huge soup bowls with cherries, and in serving dishes for roast beef we would heap slices of watermelon. Then we would go up and out the back doorway of the basement and onto the back lawn and sit under the sporting-goods tree, the light from the TV room the only brightness we had out there. All we would hear for a while were just the two of us spitting pits. "I wish they would take root overnight and in the morning there'd just be watermelons and cherries."

"If they took root in this yard, sweetie, they'd grow refrigerators and Westinghouse Preferred. I'm not being nasty," I'd add quickly, and Brenda would laugh, and say she felt like a greengage plum, and I would disappear down into the basement and the cherry bowl would now be a greengage plum bowl, and then a nectarine bowl, and then a peach bowl, until, I have to admit it, I cracked my frail bowel, and would have to spend the following night, sadly, on the wagon. And then too we went out for corned beef sandwiches, pizza, beer and shrimp, ice cream sodas, and hamburgers. We went to the Lions Club Fair one night and Brenda won a Lions Club ashtray by shooting three baskets in a row. And when Ron came home from Milwaukee we went from time to time to see him play basketball in the semi-pro summer league, and it was those evenings that I felt a stranger with Brenda, for she knew all the players' names, and though for the most part they were gawky-limbed and dull, there was one named Luther Ferrari who was neither, and whom Brenda had dated for a whole year in high school. He was Ron's closest friend and I remembered his name from the Newark *News:* he was one of the great Ferrari brothers, All State all of them in at least two sports. It was Ferrari who called Brenda Buck, a nickname which apparently went back to her ribbon-winning days. Like Ron, Ferrari was exceedingly polite, as though it were some affliction of those over six feet three; he was gentlemanly towards me and gentle towards Brenda, and after a while I balked when the suggestion was made that we go to see Ron play. And then one night we discovered that at eleven o'clock the cashier of the Hilltop Theatre went home and the manager disappeared into his office, and so that summer we saw the last quarter of at least fifteen movies, and then when we were driving home — driving Brenda home, that is — we would try to reconstruct the beginnings of the films. Our favorite last quarter of a movie was *Ma and Pa Kettle in the City,* our favorite fruit, greengage plums, and our favorite, our only, people, each other. Of course we ran into others from time to time, some of Brenda's friends, and occasionally, one or two of mine. One night in August we even went to a bar out on Route 6 with Laura Simpson Stolowitch and her fiancé, but it was a dreary evening. Brenda and I seemed untrained in talking to others, and so we danced a great deal, which we realized was one thing we'd never done before. Laura's boyfriend drank stingers pompously and Simp — Brenda wanted me to call her Stolo but I didn't — Simp drank a tepid combination of something like ginger ale and soda. Whenever we returned to the table, Simp would be talking about "the dance" and her fiancé about "the film," until finally Brenda asked him "Which film?" and then we danced till closing time. And when we went back to Brenda's we filled a bowl with cherries which we carried into the TV room and ate sloppily for a while; and later, on the sofa, we loved each other and when I moved from the darkened room to the bathroom I could always feel cherry pits against my bare soles. At home, undressing for the second time that night, I would find red marks on the undersides of my feet.

And how did her parents take all of this? Mrs. Patimkin continued to smile at me and Mr. Patimkin continued to think I ate like a bird. When invited to dinner I would, for his benefit, eat twice what I wanted, but the truth seemed to be that after he'd characterized my appetite that first time, he never really bothered to look again. I might have eaten ten times my normal amount, have finally killed myself with food, he would still have considered me not a man but a sparrow. No one seemed distressed by my presence, though Julie had cooled considerably; consequently, when Brenda suggested to her father that at the end of August I spend a week of my vacation at the Patimkin house, he pondered a moment, decided on the five iron, made his approach shot, and said yes. And when she passed on to her mother the decision of Patimkin Sink, there wasn't much Mrs. Patimkin could do. So, through Brenda's craftiness, I was invited.

On that Friday morning that was to be my last day of work, my Aunt Gladys saw me packing my bag and she asked where I was going. I told her. She did not answer and I thought I saw awe in those red-rimmed hysterical eyes — I had come a long way since that day she'd said to me on the phone, "Fancy-shmancy."

"How long you going, I should know how to shop I wouldn't buy too much. You'll leave me with a refrigerator full of milk it'll go bad it'll stink up the refrigerator —"

"A week," I said.

"A *week?*" she said. "They got room for a week?"

"Aunt Gladys, they don't live over the store."

"I lived over a store I wasn't ashamed. Thank God we always had a roof. We never went begging in the streets," she told me as I packed the Bermudas I'd just bought, "and your cousin Susan we'll put through college, Uncle Max should live and be well. We didn't send her away to camp for August, she doesn't have shoes when she wants them, sweaters she doesn't have a drawerful —"

"I didn't say anything, Aunt Gladys."

"You don't get enough to eat here? You leave over sometimes I show your Uncle Max your plate it's a shame. A child in Europe could make a four-course meal from what you leave over."

"Aunt Gladys." I went over to her. "I get everything I want here. I'm just taking a vacation. Don't I deserve a vacation?"

She held herself to me and I could feel her trembling. "I told your mother I would take care of her Neil she shouldn't worry. And now you go running —"

I put my arms around her and kissed her on the top of her head. "C'mon," I said, "you're being silly. I'm not running away. I'm just going away for a week, on a vacation."

"You'll leave their telephone number God forbid you should get sick."

"Okay."

"Millburn they live?"

"Short Hills. I'll leave the number."

"Since when do Jewish people live in Short Hills? They couldn't be real Jews believe me."

"They're real Jews," I said.

"I'll see it I'll believe it." She wiped her eyes with the corner of her apron, just as I was zipping up the sides of the suitcase. "Don't close the bag yet. I'll make a little package with some fruit in it, you'll take with you."

"Okay, Aunt Gladys," and on the way to work that morning I ate the orange and the two peaches that she'd put in a bag for me.

A few hours later Mr. Scapello informed me that when I returned from my vacation after Labor Day, I would be hoisted up onto Martha Winney's stool. He himself, he said, had made the same move some twelve years ago, and so it appeared that if I could manage to maintain my balance I might someday be Mr. Scapello. I would also get an eight-dollar increase in salary which was five dollars more than the increase Mr. Scapello had received years before. He shook my hand and then started back up the long flight of marble stairs, his behind barging against his suit jacket like a hoop. No sooner had he left my side then I smelled spearmint and looked up to see the old man with veiny nose and jowls.

"Hello, young man," he said pleasantly. "Is the book back?"

"What book?"

"The Gauguin. I was shopping and I thought I'd stop

by to ask. I haven't gotten the card yet. It's two weeks already."

"No," I said, and as I spoke I saw that Mr. Scapello had stopped midway up the stairs and turned as though he'd forgotten to tell me something. "Look," I said to the old man, "it should be back any day." I said it with a finality that bordered on rudeness, and I alarmed myself, for suddenly I saw what would happen: the old man making a fuss, Mr. Scapello gliding down the stairs, Mr. Scapello scampering up to the stacks, Scapello scandalized, Scapello profuse, Scapello presiding at the ascension of John Mc-Kee to Miss Winney's stool. I turned to the old man, "Why don't you leave your phone number and I'll try to get a hold of it this afternoon — " but my attempt at concern and courtesy came too late, and the man growled some words about public servants, a letter to the Mayor, snotty kids, and left the library, thank God, only a second before Mr. Scapello returned to my desk to remind me that everyone was chipping in for a present for Miss Winney and that if I liked I should leave a half dollar on his desk during the day.

After lunch the colored kid came in. When he headed past the desk for the stairs, I called over to him. "Come here," I said. "Where are you going?"

"The heart section."

"What book are you reading?"

"That Mr. Go-again's book. Look, man, I ain't doing nothing wrong. I didn't do *no* writing in *any*thing. You could search me —"

"I know you didn't. Listen, if you like that book so much why don't you please take it home? Do you have a library card?"

"No, sir, I didn't take *nothing*."

"No, a library card is what we give to you so you can take books home. Then you won't have to come down here every day. Do you go to school?"

"Yes, sir. Miller Street School. But this here's summertime. It's okay I'm not in school. I ain't *supposed* to be in school."

"I know. As long as you go to school you can *have* a library card. You could take the book home."

"What you keep telling me take that book home for? At home somebody dee-*stroy* it."

"You could hide it someplace, in a desk —"

"Man," he said, squinting at me, "why don't you want me to come round here?"

"I didn't say you shouldn't."

"I *likes* to come here. I likes them stairs."

"I like them too," I said. "But the trouble is that someday somebody's going to take that book out."

He smiled. "Don't you worry," he said to me. "Ain't nobody done that yet," and he tapped off to the stairs and Stack Three.

Did I perspire that day! It was the coolest of the summer, but when I left work in the evening my shirt was sticking to my back. In the car I opened my bag, and while the rush-hour traffic flowed down Washington Street, I huddled in the back and changed into a clean shirt so that when I reached Short Hills I'd look as though I was deserving of an interlude in the suburbs. But driving up Central Avenue I could not keep my mind on my vacation, or for that matter on my driving: to the distress of pedestrians and motorists, I ground gears, overshot crosswalks, hesitated at green and red lights alike. I kept thinking that while I was on vacation that jowly bastard would return to the library, that the colored kid's book would disappear, that my new job would be taken away from me, that, in fact my old job — but then why should I worry about all that: the library wasn't going to be *my* life.

5

"Ron's getting married!" Julie screamed at me when I came through the door. "Ron's getting married!"

"Now?" I said.

"Labor Day! He's marrying Harriet, he's marrying Harriet." She began to sing it like a jump-rope song, nasal and rhythmic. "I'm going to be a sister-in-law!"

"Hi," Brenda said, "I'm going to be a sister-in-law."

"So I hear. When did it happen?"

"This afternoon he told us. They spoke long distance for forty minutes last night. She's flying here next week, and there's going to be a *huge* wedding. My parents are flittering all over the place. They've got to arrange everything in about a day or two. And my father's taking Ron in the business — but he's going to have to start at two hundred a week and then work himself up. That'll take till October."

"I thought he was going to be a gym teacher."

"He was. But now he has responsibilities . . ."

And at dinner Ron expanded on the subject of responsibilities and the future.

"We're going to have a boy," he said, to his mother's delight, "and when he's about six months old I'm going to sit him down with a basketball in front of him, and a football, and a baseball, and then whichever one he reaches for, that's the one we're going to concentrate on."

"Suppose he doesn't reach for any of them," Brenda said.

"Don't be funny, young lady," Mrs. Patimkin said.

"I'm going to be an aunt," Julie sang, and she stuck her tongue out at Brenda.

"When is Harriet coming?" Mr. Patimkin breathed through a mouthful of potatoes.

"A week from yesterday."

"Can she sleep in my room?" Julie cried. *"Can* she?"

"No, the guest room — " Mrs. Patimkin began, but then she remembered me — with a crushing side glance from those purple eyes, and said, "Of course."

Well, I did eat like a bird. After dinner my bag was carried — by me — up to the guest room which was across from Ron's room and right down the hall from Brenda. Brenda came along to show me the way.

"Let me see your bed, Bren."

"Later," she said.

"Can we? Up here?"

"I think so," she said. "Ron sleeps like a log."

"Can I stay the night?"

"I don't know."

"I could get up early and come back in here. We'll set the alarm."

"It'll wake everybody up."

"I'll remember to get up. I can do it."

"I better not stay up here with you too long," she said. "My mother'll have a fit. I think she's nervous about your being here."

"So am I. I hardly know them. Do you think I should really stay a whole week?"

"A whole week? Once Harriet gets here it'll be so chaotic you can probably stay two months."

"You think so?"

"Yes."

"Do you want me to?"

"Yes," she said, and went down the stairs so as to ease her mother's conscience.

I unpacked my bag and dropped my clothes into a drawer that was empty except for a packet of dress shields and a high school yearbook. In the middle of my unpacking, Ron came clunking up the stairs.

"Hi," he called into my room.

"Congratulations," I called back. I should have realized that any word of ceremony would provoke a handshake from Ron; he interrupted whatever it was he was about to do in his room, and came into mine.

"Thanks." He pumped me. "Thanks."

Then he sat down on my bed and watched me as I finished unpacking. I have one shirt with a Brooks Brothers label and I let it linger on the bed a while; the Arrows I heaped in the drawer. Ron sat there rubbing his forearm and grinning. After a while I was thoroughly unsettled by the silence.

"Well," I said, "that's something."

He agreed, to *what* I don't know.

"How does it feel?" I asked, after another longer silence.

"Better. Ferrari smacked it under the boards."

"Oh. Good," I said. "How does getting married feel?"

"Ah, okay, I guess."

I leaned against the bureau and counted stitches in the carpet.

Ron finally risked a journey into language. "Do you know anything about music?" he asked.

"Something, yes."

"You can listen to my phonograph if you want."

"Thanks, Ron. I didn't know you were interested in music.

"Sure. I got all the Andre Kostelanetz records ever made. You like Mantovani? I got all of him too. I like semi-classical a lot. You can hear my Columbus record if you want..." he dwindled off. Finally he shook my hand and left.

Downstairs I could hear Julie singing. "I'm going to be an a-a-aunt," and Mrs. Patimkin saying to her, "No, honey, you're going to be a sister-in-law. Sing that, sweetheart," but Julie continued to sing, "I'm going to be an a-a-aunt," and then I heard Brenda's voice joining hers, singing, "We're going to be an a-a-aunt," and then Julie joined that, and finally Mrs. Patimkin called to Mr. Patimkin, "Will you make her stop encouraging her..." and soon the duet ended.

And then I heard Mrs. Patimkin again. I couldn't make out the words but Brenda answered her. Their voices grew louder; finally I could hear perfectly. "I need a houseful of company at a time like this?" It was Mrs. Patimkin. "I asked you, Mother." "You asked your father. I'm the one you should have asked first. He doesn't know how much extra work this is for me..." "My God, Mother, you'd think we didn't have Carlota and Jenny." "Carlota and Jenny can't do everything. This is not the Salvation Army!" "What the hell does that mean?" "Watch your tongue, young lady. That may be very well for your college friends." "Oh, *stop* it, Mother!" "Don't raise your voice to me. When's the last time you lifted a finger to help around here?" "I'm not a slave ... I'm a daughter." "You ought to learn what a day's work means." "Why?" Brenda said. "*Why?*" "Because you're lazy,"

Mrs. Patimkin answered, "and you think the world owes you a living." "Whoever said *that?*" "You ought to earn some money and buy your own clothes." "Why? Good God, Mother, Daddy could live off the stocks alone, for God's sake. What are you complaining about?" "When's the last time you washed the dishes!" "Jesus Christ!" Brenda flared, "Carlota washes the dishes!" "Don't Jesus Christ me!" "Oh, Mother!" and Brenda was crying. "Why the hell are you like this!" "That's it," Mrs. Patimkin said "cry in front of your company . . ." "My *company* . . ." Brenda wept, "why don't you go yell at him too . . . why is everyone so nasty to me . . ."

From across the hall I heard Andre Kostelanetz let several thousand singing violins loose on "Night and Day." Ron's door was open and I saw he was stretched out, colossal, on his bed; he was singing along with the record. The words belonged to "Night and Day," but I didn't recognize Ron's tune. In a minute he picked up the phone and asked the operator for a Milwaukee number. While she connected him, he rolled over and turned up the volume on the record player, so that it would carry the nine hundred miles west.

I heard Julie downstairs. "Ha ha, Brenda's crying, ha ha, Brenda's crying."

And then Brenda was running up the stairs. "Your day'll come, you little bastard!" she called.

"*Brenda!*" Mrs. Patimkin called.

"*Mommy!*" Julie cried. "Brenda cursed at me!"

"What's going *on* here!" Mr. Patimkin shouted.

"You call *me*, Mrs. P?" Carlota shouted.

And Ron, in the other room, said, "Hello, Har, I told them . . ."

I sat down on my Brooks Brothers shirt and pronounced my own name out loud.

"Goddam her!" Brenda said to me as she paced up and down my room.

"Bren, do you think I should go —"

"Shhh..." She went to the door of my room and listened. "They're going visiting, thank God."

"Brenda —"

"Shhh... They've gone."

"Julie too?"

"Yes," she said. "Is Ron in his room? His door is closed."

"He went out."

"You can't hear anybody move around here. They all creep around in *sneakers*. Oh Neil."

"Bren, I asked you, maybe I should just stay through tomorrow and then go."

"Oh, it isn't you she's angry about."

"I'm not helping any."

"It's Ron, really. That he's getting married just has her flipped. And me. Now with that goody-good Harriet around she'll just forget I ever exist."

"Isn't that okay with you?"

She walked off to the window and looked outside. It was dark and cool; the trees rustled and flapped as though they were sheets that had been hung out to dry. Everything outside hinted at September, and for the first time I realized how close we were to Brenda's departure for school.

"Is it, Bren?" but she was not listening to me.

She walked across the room to a door at the far end of the room. She opened it.

"I thought that was a closet," I said.

"Come here."

She held the door back and we leaned into the darkness and could hear the strange wind hissing in the eaves of the house.

"What's in here?" I said.

"Money."

Brenda went into the room. When the puny sixty-watt bulb was twisted on, I saw that the place was full of old furniture — two wing chairs with hair-oil lines at the back, a sofa with a paunch in its middle, a bridge table, two bridge chairs with their stuffing showing, a mirror whose backing had peeled off, shadeless lamps, lampless shades, a coffee table with a cracked glass top, and a pile of rolled up shades.

"What is this?" I said.

"A storeroom. Our old furniture."

"How old?"

"From Newark," she said. "Come here." She was on her hands and knees in front of the sofa and was holding up its paunch to peek beneath.

"Brenda, what the hell are we doing here? You're getting filthy."

"It's not here."

"What?"

"The money. I told you."

I sat down on a wing chair, raising some dust. It had begun to rain outside, and we could smell the fall dampness coming through the vent that was outlined at the far end of the storeroom. Brenda got up from the floor and sat down on the sofa. Her knees and Bermudas were dirty and when she pushed her hair back she dirtied her forehead. There among the disarrangement and dirt I had the strange experience of seeing us, *both* of us, placed among disarrangement and dirt: we looked like a young couple who had just moved into a new apartment; we had suddenly taken stock of our furniture, finances, and future, and all we could feel any pleasure about was the clean smell of outside, which reminded us we were alive, but which, in a pinch, would not feed us.

"What money?" I said again.

"The hundred-dollar bills. From when I was a little girl . . ." and she breathed deeply. "When I was little and we'd just moved from Newark, my father took me up here one day. He took me into this room and told me that if anything should ever happen to him, he wanted me to know where there was some money that I should have. He said it wasn't for anybody else but me, and that I should never tell anyone about it, not even Ron. Or my mother."

"How much was it?"

"Three hundred-dollar bills. I'd never seen them before. I was nine, around Julie's age. I don't think we'd been living here a month. I remember I used to come up here about once a week, when no one was home but Carlota, and crawl under the sofa and make sure it was still here. And it always was. He never mentioned it once again. Never."

"Where is it? Maybe someone stole it."

"I don't know, Neil. I suppose he took it back."

"When it was gone," I said, "my God, didn't you tell him? Maybe Carlota — "

"I never knew it was gone, until just now. I guess I stopped looking at one time or another . . . And then I forgot about it. Or just didn't think about it. I mean I always had enough, I didn't need this. I guess one day *he* figured I wouldn't need it."

Brenda paced up to the narrow, dust-covered window and drew her initials on it.

"Why did you want it now?" I said.

"I don't know..." she said and went over and twisted the bulb off.

I didn't move from the chair and Brenda, in her tight shorts and shirt, seemed naked standing there a few feet away. Then I saw her shoulders shaking. "I wanted to find it and tear it up in little pieces and put the goddam pieces in her purse! If it was there, I swear it, I would have done it."

"I wouldn't have let you, Bren."

"Wouldn't you have?"

"No."

"Make love to me, Neil. Right now."

"Where?"

"Do it! *Here.* On this cruddy cruddy cruddy sofa."

And I obeyed her.

The next morning Brenda made breakfast for the two of us. Ron had gone off to his first day of work — I'd heard him singing in the shower only an hour after I'd returned to my own room; in fact, I had still been awake when the Chrysler had pulled out of the garage, carrying boss and son down to the Patimkin works in Newark. Mrs. Patimkin wasn't home either; she had taken her car and had gone off to the Temple to talk to Rabbi Kranitz about the wedding. Julie was on the back lawn playing at helping Carlota hang the clothes.

"You know what I want to do this morning?" Brenda said. We were eating a grapefruit, sharing it rather sloppily, for Brenda couldn't find a paring knife, and so we'd decided to peel it down like an orange and eat the segments separately.

"What?" I said.

"Run," she said. "Do you ever run?"

"You mean on a track? God, yes. In high school we had to run a mile every month. So we wouldn't be Momma's boys. I think the bigger your lungs get the more you're supposed to hate your mother."

"I want to run," she said, "and I want you to run. Okay?"

"Oh, Brenda . . ."

But an hour later, after a breakfast that consisted of another grapefruit, which apparently is all a runner is supposed to eat in the morning, we had driven the Volkswagen over to the high school, behind which was a quarter-mile track. Some kids were playing with a dog out in the grassy center of the track, and at the far end, near the woods, a figure in white shorts with slits in the side, and no shirt, was twirling, twirling, and then flinging a shot put as far as he could. After it left his hand he did a little eagle-eyed tap dance while he watched it arch and bend and land in the distance.

"You know," Brenda said, "you look like me. Except bigger."

We were dressed similarly, sneakers, sweat socks, khaki Bermudas, and sweat shirts, but I had the feeling that Brenda was not talking about the accidents of our dress — if they were accidents. She meant, I was sure, that I was somehow beginning to look the way she wanted me to. Like herself.

"Let's see who's faster," she said, and then we started along the track. Within the first eighth of a mile the three little boys and their dog were following us. As we passed the corner where the shot putter was, he waved at us; Brenda called "Hi!" and I smiled, which, as you may or may not know, makes one engaged in serious running feel inordinately silly. At the quarter mile the kids dropped off and retired to the grass, the dog turned and started the other way, and I had a tiny knife in my side. Still I was abreast of Brenda, who as we started on the second lap, called "Hi!" once again to the lucky shot putter, who was reclining on the grass now, watching us, and rubbing his shot like a crystal ball. Ah, I thought, there's the sport.

"How about us throwing the shot put?" I panted.

"After," she said, and I saw beads of sweat clinging to the last strands of hair that shagged off her ear. When we approached the half mile Brenda suddenly swerved off the track onto the grass and tumbled down; her departure surprised me and I was still running.

"Hey, Bob Mathias," she called, "let's lie in the sun . . ."

But I acted as though I didn't hear her and though my heart pounded in my throat and my mouth was dry as a drought, I made my legs move, and swore I would not stop until I'd finished one more lap. As I passed the shot putter for the third time, I called "Hi!"

She was excited when I finally pulled up alongside of her. "You're good," she said. My hands were on my hips and I was looking at the ground and sucking air — rather, air was sucking me, I didn't have much to say about it.

"Uh-huh," I breathed.

"Let's do this every morning," she said. "We'll get up and have two grapefruit, and then you'll come out here and run. I'll time you. In two weeks you'll break four minutes, won't you, sweetie? I'll get Ron's stop watch." She was so excited — she'd slid over on the grass and was pushing my socks up against my wet ankles and calves. She bit my kneecap.

"Okay," I said.

"Then we'll go back and have a real breakfast."

"Okay."

"You drive back," she said, and suddenly she was up and running ahead of me, and then we were headed back in the car.

And the next morning, my mouth still edgy from the grapefruit segments, we were at the track. We had Ron's stop watch and a towel for me, for when I was finished.

"My legs are a little sore," I said.

"Do some exercises," Brenda said. "I'll do them with you." She heaped the towel on the grass and together we did deep knee bends, and sit-ups, and push-ups, and some high-knee raising in place. I felt overwhelmingly happy.

"I'm just going to run a half today, Bren. We'll see what I do..." and I heard Brenda click the watch, and then when I was on the far side of the track, the clouds trailing above me like my own white, fleecy tail, I saw that Brenda was on the ground, hugging her knees, and alternately checking the watch and looking out at me. We were the only ones there, and it all reminded me of one of those scenes in race-horse movies, where an old trainer like Walter Brennan and a young handsome man clock the beautiful girl's horse in the early Kentucky morning, to see if it really is the fastest two-year-old alive. There were differences all right — one being simply that at the quarter mile Brenda shouted out to me, "A minute and fourteen

seconds," but it was pleasant and exciting and clean and
when I was finished Brenda was standing up and waiting
for me. Instead of a tape to break I had Brenda's sweet
flesh to meet, and I did, and it was the first time she said
that she loved me.

We ran — I ran — every morning, and by the end of
the week I was running a 7:02 mile, and always at the
end there was the little click of the watch and Brenda's
arms.

At night, I would read in my pajamas, while Brenda, in
her room, read, and we would wait for Ron to go to sleep.
Some nights we had to wait longer than others, and I would
hear the leaves swishing outside, for it had grown cooler at
the end of August, and the air-conditioning was turned off
at night and we were all allowed to open our windows.
Finally Ron would be ready for bed. He would stomp
around his room and then he would come to the door in
his shorts and T-shirt and go into the bathroom where he
would urinate loudly and brush his teeth. After he brushed
his teeth I would go in to brush mine. We would pass in
the hall and I would give him a hearty and sincere "Good-
night." Once in the bathroom, I would spend a moment
admiring my tan in the mirror; behind me I could see Ron's
jock straps hanging out to dry on the Hot and Cold knobs
of the shower. Nobody ever questioned their tastefulness
as adornment, and after a few nights I didn't even notice
them.

While Ron brushed his teeth and I waited in my bed for
my turn, I could hear the record player going in his room.
Generally, after coming in from basketball, he would call
Harriet — who was now only a few days away from us —
and then would lock himself up with *Sports Illustrated* and

Mantovani; however, when he emerged from his room for his evening toilet, it was not a Mantovani record I would hear playing, but something else, apparently what he'd once referred to as his Columbus record. I *imagined* that was what I heard, for I could not tell much from the last moments of sound. All I heard were bells moaning evenly and soft patriotic music behind them, and riding over it all, a deep kind of Edward R. Murrow gloomy voice: "*And so goodbye, Columbus,*" the voice intoned, "*. . . goodbye, Columbus . . . goodbye . . .*" Then there would be silence and Ron would be back in his room; the light would switch off and in only a few minutes I would hear him rumbling down into that exhilarating, restorative, vitamin-packed sleep that I imagined athletes to enjoy.

One morning near sneaking-away time I had a dream and when I awakened from it, there was just enough dawn coming into the room for me to see the color of Brenda's hair. I touched her in her sleep, for the dream had unsettled me: it had taken place on a ship, an old sailing ship like those you see in pirate movies. With me on the ship was the little colored kid from the library — I was the captain and he my mate, and we were the only crew members. For a while it was a pleasant dream; we were anchored in the harbor of an island in the Pacific and it was very sunny. Up on the beach there were beautiful bare-skinned Negresses, and none of them moved; but suddenly *we* were moving, our ship, out of the harbor, and the Negresses moved slowly down to the shore and began to throw leis at us and say "Goodbye, Columbus . . . goodbye, Columbus . . . goodbye . . ." and though we did not want to go, the little boy and I, the boat was moving and there was nothing we could do about it, and he shouted at me that it was my fault and I shouted it was his for not having a library card, but we were wasting our breath, for we were further and further from the island, and soon the natives were nothing at all. Space was all out of proportion in the dream, and things were sized and squared in no way I'd ever seen before, and I think it was that more than anything else that steered me into consciousness. I did not want to leave Brenda's side that morning, and for a while I played with the little point at the nape of her neck, where she'd had her hair cut. I stayed longer than I should have, and when finally I returned to my room I almost ran into Ron who was preparing for his day at Patimkin Kitchen and Bathroom Sinks.

6

That morning was supposed to have been my last at the Patimkin house; however, when I began to throw my things into my bag late in the day, Brenda told me I could unpack — somehow she'd managed to inveigle another week out of her parents, and I would be able to stay right through till Labor Day, when Ron would be married; then, the following morning Brenda would be off to school and I would go back to work. So we would be with each other until the summer's last moment.

This should have made me overjoyed, but as Brenda trotted back down the stairs to accompany her family to the airport — where they were to pick up Harriet — I was not joyful but disturbed, as I had been more and more with the thought that when Brenda went back to Radcliffe, that would be the end for me. I was convinced that even Miss Winney's stool was not high enough for me to see clear up to Boston. Nevertheless, I tossed my clothing back into the drawer and was able, finally, to tell myself that there'd been no hints of ending our affair from Brenda, and any suspicions I had, any uneasiness, was spawned in my own uncertain heart. Then I went into Ron's room to call my aunt.

"Hello?" she said.

"Aunt Gladys," I said, "how are you?"

"You're sick."

"No, I'm having a fine time. I wanted to call you, I'm going to stay another week."

"Why?"

"I told you. I'm having a good time. Mrs. Patimkin asked me to stay until Labor Day."

"You've got clean underwear?"

"I'm washing it at night. I'm okay, Aunt Gladys."

"By hand you can't get it clean."

"It's clean enough. Look, Aunt Gladys, I'm having a wonderful time."

"*Shmutz* he lives in and I shouldn't worry."

"How's Uncle Max?" I asked.

"What should he be? Uncle Max is Uncle Max. You, I don't like the way your voice sounds."

"Why? Do I sound like I've got on dirty underwear?"

"Smart guy. Someday you'll learn."

"What?"

"What do you mean *what*? You'll find out. You'll stay there too long you'll be too good for us."

"Never, sweetheart," I said.

"I'll see it I'll believe it."

"Is it cool in Newark, Aunt Gladys?"

"It's snowing," she said.

"Hasn't it been cool all week?"

"You sit around all day it's cool. For me it's not February, believe me."

"Okay, Aunt Gladys. Say hello to everybody."

"You got a letter from your mother."

"Good. I'll read it when I get home."

"You couldn't take a ride down you'll read it?"

"It'll wait. I'll drop them a note. Be a good girl," I said.

"What about your socks?"

"I go barefoot. Goodbye, honey." And I hung up.

Down in the kitchen Carlota was getting dinner ready. I was always amazed at how Carlota's work never seemed to get in the way of her life. She made household chores seem like illustrative gestures of whatever it was she was singing, even, if as now, it was "I Get a Kick out of You." She moved from the oven to the automatic dishwasher — she pushed buttons, turned dials, peeked in the glass-doored oven, and from time to time picked a big black grape out of a bunch that lay on the sink. She chewed and chewed, humming all the time, and then, with a deliberated casualness, shot the skin and the pit directly into the garbage disposal unit. I said hello to her as I went out the back door, and though she did not return the greeting, I felt a kinship with one who, like me, had been partially wooed and won on Patimkin fruit.

Out on the lawn I shot baskets for a while; then I picked up an iron and drove a cotton golf ball limply up into the sunlight; then I kicked a soccer ball towards the oak tree; then I tried shooting foul shots again. Nothing diverted me — I felt open-stomached, as though I hadn't eaten for months, and though I went back inside and came out with my own handful of grapes, the feeling continued, and I knew it had nothing to do with my caloric intake; it was only a rumor of the hollowness that would come when Brenda was away. The fact of her departure had, of course,

been on my mind for a while, but overnight it had taken
on a darker hue. Curiously, the darkness seemed to have
something to do with Harriet, Ron's intended, and I
thought for a time that it was simply the reality of Harriet's arrival that had dramatized the passing of time: we
had been talking about it and now suddenly it was here —
just as Brenda's departure would be here before we knew it.

But it was more than that: the union of Harriet and
Ron reminded me that separation need not be a permanent state. People could marry each other, even if they
were young! And yet Brenda and I had never mentioned
marriage, except perhaps for that night at the pool when
she'd said, "When you love me, everything will be all
right." Well, I loved her, and she me, and things didn't
seem all right at all. Or was I inventing troubles again? I
supposed I should really have thought my lot improved
considerably; yet, there on the lawn, the August sky seemed
too beautiful and temporary to bear, and I wanted Brenda
to marry me. Marriage, though, was not what I proposed
to her when she drove the car up the driveway, alone, some
fifteen minutes later. That proposal would have taken a
kind of courage that I did not think I had. I did not feel
myself prepared for any answer but "Hallelujah!" Any
other kind of yes wouldn't have satisfied me, and any
kind of no, even one masked behind the words, "Let's wait,
sweetheart," would have been my end. So I imagine that's
why I proposed the surrogate, which turned out finally to
be far more daring than I knew it to be at the time.

"Harriet's plane is late, so I drove home," Brenda called.

"Where's everyone else?"

"They're going to wait for her and have dinner at the
airport. I have to tell Carlota," and she went inside.

In a few minutes she appeared on the porch. She wore a yellow dress that cut a wide-bottomed U across her shoulders and neck, and showed where the tanned flesh began above her breasts. On the lawn she stepped out of her heels and walked barefoot over to where I was sitting under the oak tree.

"Women who wear high heels all the time get tipped ovaries," she said.

"Who told you that?"

"I don't remember. I like to think everything's ship-shape in there."

"Brenda, I want to ask you something . . ."

She yanked the blanket with the big O on it over to us and sat down.

"What?" she said.

"I know this is out of the blue, though really it's not . . . I want you to buy a diaphragm. To go to a doctor and get one."

She smiled. "Don't worry, sweetie, we're careful. Everything is okay."

"But that's the safest."

"We're safe. It'd be a waste."

"Why take chances?"

"But we *aren't*. How many things do you need."

"Honey, it isn't bulk I'm interested in. It's not even safety," I added.

"You just want me to own one, is that it? Like a walking stick, or a pith helmet — "

"Brenda, I want you to own one for . . . for the sake of pleasure."

"Pleasure? Whose? The doctor's?"

"Mine," I said.

She did not answer me, but rubbed her fingers along the ridge of her collarbone to wipe away the tiny globes of perspiration that had suddenly formed there.

"No, Neil, it's silly."

"Why?"

"Why? It just is."

"You know why it's silly, Brenda — because *I* asked you to do it?"

"That's sillier."

"If you asked *me* to buy a diaphragm we'd have to go straight to the Yellow Pages and find a gynecologist open on Saturday afternoon."

"I would never ask you to do that, baby."

"It's the truth," I said, though I was smiling. "It's the truth."

"It's not," she said, and got up and walked over to the basketball court, where she walked on the white lines that Mr. Patimkin had laid the day before.

"Come back here," I said.

"Neil, it's silly and I don't want to talk about it."

"Why are you being so selfish?"

"Selfish? You're the one who's being selfish. It's your pleasure . . ."

"That's right. My pleasure. Why not!"

"Don't raise your voice. Carlota."

"Then get the hell over here," I said.

She walked over to me, leaving white footprints on the grass. "I didn't think you were such a creature of the flesh," she said.

"Didn't you?" I said. "I'll tell you something that you ought to know. It's not even the pleasures of the flesh I'm talking about."

"Then frankly, I don't know *what* you're talking about. Why you're even bothering. Isn't what we use sufficient?"

"I'm bothering just because I want you to go to a doctor and get a diaphragm. That's all. No explanation. Just do it. Do it because I asked you to."

"You're not being reasonable — "

"Goddamit, Brenda!"

"Goddamit yourself!" she said and went up into the house.

I closed my eyes and leaned back and in fifteen minutes, or maybe less, I heard somebody stroking at the cotton golf ball. She had changed into shorts and a blouse and was still barefoot.

We didn't speak with each other, but I watched her bring the club back of her ear, and then swing through, her chin tilted up with the line of flight a regular golf ball would have taken.

"That's five hundred yards," I said.

She didn't answer but walked after the cotton ball and then readied for another swing.

"Brenda. Please come here."

She walked over, dragging the club over the grass.

"What?"

"I don't want to argue with you."

"Nor I with you," she said. "It was the first time."

"Was it such an awful thing for me to ask?"

She nodded.

"Bren, I know it was probably a surprise. It was for me. But we're not children."

"Neil, I just don't want to. It's not because you asked me to, either. I don't know where you get that from That's not it."

"Then why is it?"

"Oh everything. I just don't feel *old* enough for all that equipment."

"What does age have to do with it?"

"I don't mean age. I just mean — well, *me*. I mean it's so conscious a thing to do."

"Of course it's conscious. That's exactly it. Don't you see? It would change us."

"It would change me."

"Us. Together."

"Neil, how do you think I'd feel lying to some doctor."

"You can go to Margaret Sanger, in New York. They don't ask any questions."

"You've done this before?"

"No," I said. "I just know. I read Mary McCarthy."

"That's exactly right. That's just what I'd feel like, somebody out of *her*."

"Don't be dramatic," I said.

"You're the one who's being dramatic. You think there would be something affairish about it, then. Last summer I went with this whore who I sent out to buy — "

"Oh, Brenda, you're a selfish egotistical bitch! You're the one who's thinking about 'last summer,' about an end for us. In fact, that's the whole thing, isn't it — "

"That's right, I'm a bitch. I want this to end. That's why I ask you to stay another week, that's why I let you sleep with me in my own house. What's the *matter* with you! Why don't you and my mother take turns — one day she can plague me, the next you — "

"Stop it!"

"Go to hell, all of you!" Brenda said, and now she was

crying and I knew when she ran off I would not see her, as
I didn't, for the rest of the afternoon.

Harriet Ehrlich impressed me as a young lady singu-
larly unconscious of a motive in others or herself. All was
surfaces, and she seemed a perfect match for Ron, and too
for the Patimkins. Mrs. Patimkin, in fact, did just as
Brenda prophesied: Harriet appeared, and Brenda's
mother lifted one wing and pulled the girl in towards the
warm underpart of her body, where Brenda herself would
have liked to nestle. Harriet was built like Brenda, although a little chestier, and she nodded her head insist-
ently whenever anyone spoke. Sometimes she would even
say the last few words of your sentence with you, though
that was infrequent; for the most part she nodded and kept
her hands folded. All evening, as the Patimkins planned
where the newlyweds should live, what furniture they
should buy, how soon they should have a baby — all through
this I kept thinking that Harriet was wearing white gloves,
but she wasn't.

Brenda and I did not exchange a word or a glance;
we sat, listening, Brenda somewhat more impatient than
me. Near the end Harriet began calling Mrs. Patimkin
"Mother," and once, "Mother Patimkin," and that was
when Brenda went to sleep. I stayed behind, mesmerized
almost by the dissection, analysis, reconsideration, and
finally, the embracing of the trivial. At last Mr. and Mrs.
Patimkin tumbled off to bed, and Julie, who had fallen
asleep on her chair, was carried into her room by Ron.
That left us two non-Patimkins together.

"Ron tells me you have a very interesting job."

"I work in the library."

"I've always liked reading."

"That'll be nice, married to Ron."

"Ron likes music."

"Yes," I said. What had I *said*?

"You must get first crack at the best-sellers," she said.

"Sometimes." I said.

"Well," she said, flapping her hands on her knees, "I'm sure we'll all have a good time together. Ron and I hope you and Brenda will double with us soon."

"Not tonight." I smiled. "Soon. Will you excuse me?"

"Good night. I like Brenda very much."

"Thank you," I said as I started up the stairs.

I knocked gently on Brenda's door.

"I'm sleeping."

"Can I come in?" I asked.

Her door opened an inch and she said, "Ron will be up soon."

"We'll leave the door open. I only want to talk."

She let me in and I sat in the chair that faced the bed.

"How do you like your sister-in-law?"

"I've met her before."

"Brenda, you don't have to sound so damn terse."

She didn't answer and I just sat there yanking the string on the shade up and down.

"Are you still angry?" I asked at last.

"Yes."

"Don't be," I said. "You can forget about my suggestion. It's not worth it if this is what's going to happen."

"What did you expect to happen?"

"Nothing. I didn't think it would be so horrendous."

"That's because you can't understand my side."

"Perhaps."

"No perhaps about it."

"*Okay*," I said. "I just wish you'd realize what it is you're getting angry about. It's not my suggestion, Brenda."

"No? What is it?"

"It's me."

"Oh don't start that again, will you? I can't win, no matter what I say."

"Yes, you can," I said. "You have."

I walked out of her room, closing the door behind me for the night.

When I got downstairs the following morning there was a great deal of activity. In the living room I heard Mrs. Patimkin reading a list to Harriet while Julie ran in and out of rooms in search of a skate key. Carlota was vacuuming the carpet; every appliance in the kitchen was bubbling, twisting, and shaking. Brenda greeted me with a perfectly pleasant smile and in the dining room, where I walked to look out at the back lawn and the weather, she kissed me on the shoulder.

"Hello," she said.

"Hello."

"I have to go with Harriet this morning," Brenda told me. "So we can't run. Unless you want to go alone."

"No. I'll read or something. Where are you going?"

"We're going to New York. Shopping. She's going to buy a wedding dress. For after the wedding. To go away in."

"What are *you* going to buy?"

"A dress to be maid of honor in. If I go with Harriet then I can go to Bergdorf's without all that Ohrbach's business with my mother."

"Get me something, will you?" I said.

"Oh, Neil, are you going to bring that up again!"

"I was only *fooling*. I wasn't even thinking about that."

"Then why did you say it?"

"Oh Jesus!" I said, and went outside and drove my car down into Millburn Center where I had some eggs and coffee.

When I came back, Brenda was gone, and there were only Carlota, Mrs. Patimkin, and myself in the house. I tried to stay out of whichever rooms they were in, but finally Mrs. Patimkin and I wound up sitting opposite each other in the TV room. She was checking off names on a long sheet of paper she held; next to her, on the table, were two thin phone books which she consulted from time to time.

"No rest for the weary," she said to me.

I smiled hugely, embracing the proverb as though Mrs. Patimkin had just then coined it. "Yes. Of course," I said. "Would you like some help? Maybe I could help you check something."

"Oh, no," she said with a little head-shaking dismissal, "it's for Hadassah."

"Oh," I said.

I sat and watched her until she asked, "Is your mother in Hadassah?"

"I don't know if she is now. She was in Newark."

"Was she an active member?"

"I guess so, she was always planting trees in Israel for someone."

"Really?" Mrs. Patimkin said. "What's her name?"

"Esther Klugman. She's in Arizona now. Do they have Hadassah there?"

"Wherever there are Jewish women."

"Then I guess she is. She's with my father. They went there for their asthma. I'm staying with my aunt in Newark. She's not in Hadassah. My Aunt Sylvia is, though. Do you know her, Aaron Klugman and Sylvia? They belong to your club. They have a daughter, my cousin Doris — " I couldn't stop myself " — They live in Livingston. Maybe it isn't Hadassah my Aunt Sylvia belongs to. I think it's some TB organization. Or cancer. Muscular dystrophy, maybe. I know she's interested in *some* disease."

"That's very nice," Mrs. Patimkin said.

"Oh yes."

"They do very good work."

"I know."

Mrs. Patimkin, I thought, had begun to warm to me; she let the purple eyes stop peering and just look out at the world for a while without judging. "Are you interested in B'nai Brith?" she asked me. "Ron is joining, you know, as soon as he gets married."

"I think I'll wait till then," I said.

Petulantly, Mrs. Patimkin went back to her lists, and I realized it had been foolish of me to risk lightheartedness with her about Jewish affairs. "You're active in the Temple, aren't you?" I asked with all the interest I could muster.

"Yes," she said.

"What Temple do *you* belong to?" she asked in a moment.

"We used to belong to Hudson Street Synagogue. Since my parents left, I haven't had much contact."

I didn't know whether Mrs. Patimkin caught a false tone in my voice. Personally I thought I had managed my rueful confession pretty well, especially when I recalled the decade of paganism prior to my parents' departure. Regardless, Mrs. Patimkin asked immediately — and strategically it seemed — "We're all going to Temple Friday night. Why don't you come with us? I mean, are you orthodox or conservative?"

I considered. "Well, I haven't gone in a long time . . . I sort of switch . . ." I smiled. "I'm just Jewish," I said well-meaningly, but that too sent Mrs. Patimkin back to her Hadassah work. Desperately I tried to think of something that would convince her I wasn't an infidel. Finally I asked: "Do you know Martin Buber's work?"

"Buber . . . Buber," she said, looking at her Hadassah list. "Is he orthodox or conservative?" she asked.

". . . He's a philosopher."

"Is he *reformed?*" she asked, piqued either at my evasiveness or at the possibility that Buber attended Friday night services without a hat, and Mrs. Buber had only one set of dishes in her kitchen.

"Orthodox," I said faintly.

"That's very nice," she said.

"Yes."

"Isn't Hudson Street Synagogue orthodox?" she asked.

"I don't know."

"I thought you belonged."

"I was bar-mitzvahed there."

"And you don't know that it's orthodox?"

"Yes. I do. It is."

"Then *you* must be."

"Oh, yes, I am," I said. "What are you?" I popped, ushing.

"Orthodox. My husband is conservative," which meant,

I took it, that he didn't care. "Brenda is nothing, as you probably know."

"Oh?" I said. "No, I didn't know that."

"She was the best Hebrew student I've ever seen," Mrs. Patimkin said, "but then, of course, she got too big for her britches."

Mrs. Patimkin looked at me, and I wondered whether courtesy demanded that I agree. "Oh, I don't know," I said at last, "I'd say Brenda is conservative. Maybe a little reformed . . ."

The phone rang, rescuing me, and I spoke a silent orthodox prayer to the Lord.

"Hello," Mrs. Patimkin said. ". . . no . . . I can *not*, I have all the Hadassah calls to make . . ."

I acted as though I were listening to the birds outside, though the closed windows let no natural noises in.

"Have Ronald drive them up . . . But we can't wait, not if we want it on time . . ."

Mrs. Patimkin glanced up at me; then she put one hand over the mouthpiece. "Would you ride down to Newark for me?"

I stood. "Yes. Surely."

"Dear?" she said back into the phone, "Neil will come for it . . . No, *Neil*, Brenda's friend . . . Yes . . . Goodbye.

"Mr. Patimkin has some silver patterns I have to see. Would you drive down to his place and pick them up?"

"Of course."

"Do you know where the shop is?"

"Yes."

"Here," she said, handing a key ring to me, "take the Volkswagen."

"My car is right outside."

"Take these," she said.

Patimkin Kitchen and Bathroom Sinks was in the heart of the Negro section of Newark. Years ago, at the time of the great immigration, it had been the Jewish section, and still one could see the little fish stores, the kosher delicatessens, the Turkish baths, where my grandparents had shopped and bathed at the beginning of the century. Even the smells had lingered: whitefish, corned beef, sour tomatoes — but now, on top of these, was the grander greasier smell of auto wrecking shops, the sour stink of a brewery, the burning odor from a leather factory; and on the streets, instead of Yiddish, one heard the shouts of Negro children playing at Willie Mays with a broom handle and half a rubber ball. The neighborhood had changed: the old Jews like my grandparents had struggled and died, and their offspring had struggled and prospered, and moved further and further west, towards the edge of Newark, then out of it, and up the slope of the Orange Mountains, until they had reached the crest and started down the other side, pouring into Gentile territory as the Scotch-Irish had poured through the Cumberland Gap. Now, in fact, the Negroes were making the same migration, following the steps of the Jews, and those who remained in the Third Ward lived the most squalid of lives and dreamed in their fetid mattresses of the piny smell of Georgia nights.

I wondered, for an instant only, if I would see the colored kid from the library on the streets here. I didn't, of course, though I was sure he lived in one of the scabby, peeling buildings out of which dogs, children, and aproned women moved continually. On the top floors, windows were open, and the very old, who could no longer creak down the long stairs to the street, sat where they had been put, in the screenless windows, their elbows resting on fluffless pillows, and their heads tipping forward on their necks, watching the push of the young and the pregnant and the unemployed. Who would come after the Negroes? Who was left? No one, I thought, and someday these streets, where my grandmother drank hot tea from an old *jahrzeit* glass, would be empty and we would all of us have moved to the crest of the Orange Mountains, and wouldn't the dead stop kicking at the slats in their coffins then?

I pulled the Volkswagen up in front of a huge garage door that said across the front of it:

PATIMKIN KITCHEN AND BATHROOM SINKS
"Any Size — Any Shape"

Inside I could see a glass-enclosed office; it was in the center of an immense warehouse. Two trucks were being loaded in the rear, and Mr. Patimkin, when I saw him, had a cigar in his mouth and was shouting at someone. It was Ron, who was wearing a white T-shirt that said Ohio State Athletic Association across the front. Though he was taller than Mr. Patimkin, and almost as stout, his hands hung weakly at his sides like a small boy's; Mr. Patimkin's cigar locomoted in his mouth. Six Negroes were loading one of the trucks feverishly, tossing — my stomach dropped — sink bowls at one another.

Ron left Mr. Patimkin's side and went back to directing the men. He thrashed his arms about a good deal, and though on the whole he seemed rather confused, he didn't appear to be at all concerned about anybody dropping a sink. Suddenly I could see myself directing the Negroes —

I would have an ulcer in an hour. I could almost hear the
enamel surfaces shattering on the floor. And I could hear
myself: "Watch it, you guys. Be careful, will you?
Whoops! Oh, please be — *watch* it! Watch! Oh!" Suppose Mr. Patimkin should come up to me and say, "Okay,
boy, you want to marry my daughter, let's see what you
can do." Well, he would see: in a moment that floor would
be a shattered mosaic, a crunchy path of enamel. "Klugman, what kind of worker are you? You work like you
eat!" "That's right, that's right, I'm a sparrow, let me go."
"Don't you even know how to load and unload?" "Mr.
Patimkin, even breathing gives me trouble, sleep tires me
out, let me go, let me go . . ."

Mr. Patimkin was headed back to the fish bowl to answer a ringing phone, and I wrenched myself free of my
reverie and headed towards the office too. When I entered,
Mr. Patimkin looked up from the phone with his eyes; the
sticky cigar was in his free hand — he moved it at me, a
greeting. From outside I heard Ron call in a high voice,
"You can't all go to lunch at the same time. We haven't
got all day!"

"Sit down," Mr. Patimkin shot at me, though when he
went back to his conversation I saw there was only one
chair in the office, his. People did not sit at Patimkin
Sink — here you earned your money the hard way, standing up. I busied myself looking at the several calendars
that hung from filing cabinets; they showed illustrations
of women so dreamy, so fantastically thighed and uddered,
that one could not think of them as pornographic. The
artist who had drawn the calendar girls for "Lewis Construction Company," and "Earl's Truck and Auto Repair," and "Grossman and Son, Paper Box" had been
painting some third sex I had never seen.

"Sure, sure, sure," Mr. Patimkin said into the phone. "Tomorrow, don't tell me tomorrow. Tomorrow the world could blow up."

At the other end someone spoke. Who was it? Lewis from the construction company? Earl from truck repair?

"I'm running a business, Grossman, not a charity."

So it was Grossman being browbeaten at the other end.

"Shit on that," Mr. Patimkin said. "You're not the only one in town, my good friend," and he winked at me.

Ah-ha, a conspiracy against Grossman. Me and Mr. Patimkin. I smiled as collusively as I knew how.

"All right then, we're here till five . . . No later."

He wrote something on a piece of paper. It was only a big X.

"My kid'll be here," he said. "Yea, he's in the business."

Whatever Grossman said on the other end, it made Mr. Patimkin laugh. Mr. Patimkin hung up without a goodbye.

He looked out the back to see how Ron was doing. "Four years in college he can't unload a truck."

I didn't know what to say but finally chose the truth. "I guess I couldn't either."

"You could learn. What am I, a genius? I learned. Hard work never killed anybody."

To that I agreed.

Mr. Patimkin looked at his cigar. "A man works hard he's got something. You don't get anywhere sitting on your behind, you know . . . The biggest men in the country worked hard, believe me. Even Rockefeller. Success don't come easy . . ." He did not say this so much as he mused it out while he surveyed his dominion. He was not a man enamored of words, and I had the feeling that what had tempted him into this barrage of universals was probably the combination of Ron's performance and my presence — me, the outsider who might one day be an insider. But did Mr. Patimkin even consider that possibility? I did not know; I only knew that these few words he did speak could hardly transmit all the satisfaction and surprise he felt about the life he had managed to build for himself and his family.

He looked out at Ron again. "Look at him, if he played basketball like that they'd throw him the hell off the court." But he was smiling when he said it.

He walked over to the door. "Ronald, let them go to lunch."

Ron shouted back, "I thought I'd let some go now, and some later."

"Why?"

"Then somebody'll always be —"

"No fancy deals here," Mr. Patimkin shouted. "We all go to lunch at once."

Ron turned back. "All right, boys, lunch!"

His father smiled at me. "Smart boy? Huh?" He tapped his head. "That took brains, huh? He ain't got the stomach for business. He's an idealist," and then I think Mr. Patimkin suddenly realized who *I* was, and eagerly corrected himself so as not to offend. "That's all right, you know, if you're a schoolteacher, or like you, you know, a student or something like that. Here you need a little of the *gonif* in you. You know what that means? *Gonif*?"

"Thief," I said.

"You know more than my own kids. They're *goyim*, my kids, that's how much they understand." He watched the Negro loading gang walk past the office and shouted out to them, "You guys know how long an hour is? All right, you'll be back in an hour!"

Ron came into the office and of course shook my hand. "Do you have that stuff for Mrs. Patimkin?" I asked.

"Ronald, get him the silver patterns." Ron turned away and Mr. Patimkin said, "When I got married we had forks and knives from the five and ten. This kid needs gold to eat off," but there was no anger; far from it.

I drove to the mountains in my own car that afternoon, and stood for a while at the wire fence watching the deer lightly prance, coyly feed, under the protection of signs that read, DO NOT FEED THE DEER, *By Order of South Mountain Reservation.* Alongside me at the fence were dozens of kids; they giggled and screamed when the deer licked the popcorn from their hands, and then were sad when their own excitement sent the young loping away towards the far end of the field where their tawny-skinned mothers stood regally watching the traffic curl up the mountain road. Young white-skinned mothers, hardly older than I, and in many instances younger, chatted in their convertibles behind me, and looked down from time to time to see what their children were about. I had seen them before, when Brenda and I had gone out for a bite in the afternoon, or had driven up here for lunch: in clotches of three and four they sat in the rustic hamburger joints that dotted the Reservation area while their children gobbled hamburgers and malteds and were given dimes to feed the jukebox. Though none of the little ones were old enough to read the song titles, almost all of them could holler out the words, and they did, while the mothers, a few of whom I recognized as high school mates of mine, compared suntans, supermarkets, and vacations. They looked immortal sitting there. Their hair would always stay the color they desired, their clothes the right texture and shade; in their homes they would have simple Swedish modern when that was fashionable, and if huge, ugly baroque ever came back, out would go the long, midget-legged marble coffee table and in would come Louis Quatorze. These were the goddesses, and if I were Paris I could not have been able to choose among them, so microscopic were the differences. Their fates had collapsed them into one. Only Brenda shone. Money and comfort would not erase her singleness — they hadn't yet, or had they? What was I loving, I wondered, and since I am not one to stick scalpels into myself, I wiggled my hand in the fence and allowed a tiny-nosed buck to lick my thoughts away.

When I returned to the Patimkin house, Brenda was in the living room looking more beautiful than I had ever seen her. She was modeling her new dress for Harriet and her mother. Even Mrs. Patimkin seemed softened by the sight of her; it looked as though some sedative had been injected into her, and so relaxed the Brenda-hating muscles around her eyes and mouth.

Brenda, without glasses, modeled in place; when she looked at me it was a kind of groggy, half-waking look I got, and though others might have interpreted it as sleepiness it sounded in my veins as lust. Mrs. Patimkin told her finally that she'd bought a very nice dress and I told her she looked lovely and Harriet told her she was very beautiful and that *she* ought to be the bride, and then there was an uncomfortable silence while all of us wondered who ought to be the groom.

Then when Mrs. Patimkin had led Harriet out to the

kitchen, Brenda came up to me and said, "I *ought* to be the bride."

"You ought, sweetheart." I kissed her, and suddenly she was crying.

"What is it, honey?" I said.

"Let's go outside."

On the lawn, Brenda was no longer crying but her voice sounded very tired.

"Neil, I called Margaret Sanger Clinic," she said. "When I was in New York."

I didn't answer.

"Neil, they *did* ask if I was married. God, the woman sounded like my mother . . ."

"What did you say?"

"I said *no*."

"What did she say?"

"I don't know. I hung up." She walked away and around the oak tree. When she appeared again she'd stepped out of her shoes and held one hand on the tree, as though it were a Maypole she were circling.

"You can call them back," I said.

She shook her head. "No, I can't. I don't even know why I called in the first place. We were shopping and I just walked away, looked up the number, and called."

"Then you can go to a doctor."

She shook again.

"Look, Bren," I said, rushing to her, "we'll go together, to a doctor. In New York —"

"I don't want to go to some dirty little office — "

"We won't. We'll go to the most posh gynecologist in New York. One who gets *Harper's Bazaar* for the reception room. How does that sound?"

She bit her lower lip.

"You'll come with me?" she asked.

"I'll come with you."

"To the office?"

"Sweetie, your husband wouldn't come to the office."

"No?"

"He'd be working."

"But you're not," she said.

"I'm on vacation," I said, but I had answered the wrong question. "Bren, I'll wait and when you're all done we'll buy a drink. We'll go out to dinner."

"Neil, I shouldn't have called Margaret Sanger — it's not right."

"It is, Brenda. It's the most right thing we can do." She walked away and I was exhausted from pleading. Somehow I felt I could have convinced her had I been a bit more crafty; and yet I did not want it to be craftiness that changed her mind. I was silent when she came back, and perhaps it was just that, my *not* saying anything, that prompted her finally to say, "I'll ask Mother Patimkin if she wants us to take Harriet too . . ."

7

I shall never forget the heat and mugginess of that afternoon we drove into New York. It was four days after the day she'd called Margaret Sanger — she put it off and put it off, but finally on Friday, three days before Ron's wedding and four before her departure, we were heading through the Lincoln Tunnel, which seemed longer and fumier than ever, like Hell with tiled walls. Finally we were in New York and smothered again by the thick day. I pulled around the policeman who directed traffic in his shirt sleeves and up onto the Port Authority roof to park the car.

"Do you have cab fare?" I said.

"Aren't you going to come with me?"

"I thought I'd wait in the bar. Here, downstairs."

"You can wait in Central Park. His office is right across the street."

"Bren, what's the diff — " But when I saw the look that invaded her eyes I gave up the air-conditioned bar to accompany her across the city. There was a sudden shower while our cab went crosstown, and when the rain stopped the streets were sticky and shiny, and below the pavement was the rumble of the subways, and in all it was like entering the ear of a lion.

The doctor's office was in the Squibb Building, which is across from Bergdorf Goodman's and so was a perfect place for Brenda to add to her wardrobe. For some reason we had never once considered her going to a doctor in Newark, perhaps because it was too close to home and might allow for possibilities of discovery. When Brenda got to the revolving door she looked back at me; her eyes were very watery, even with her glasses, and I did not say a word, afraid what a word, any word, might do. I kissed her hair and motioned that I would be across the street by the Plaza fountain, and then I watched her revolve through the doors. Out on the street the traffic moved slowly as though the humidity were a wall holding everything back. Even the fountain seemed to be bubbling boiling water on the people who sat at its edge, and in an instant I decided against crossing the street, and turned south on Fifth and began to walk the steaming pavement towards St. Patrick's. On the north steps a crowd was gathered; everyone was watching a model being photographed. She was wearing a lemon-colored dress and had her feet pointed like a ballerina, and as I passed into the church I heard some lady say, "If I ate cottage cheese *ten* times a day, I couldn't be that skinny."

It wasn't much cooler inside the church, though the stillness and the flicker of the candles made me think it was. I took a seat at the rear and while I couldn't bring myself to kneel, I did lean forward onto the back of the bench before me, and held my hands together and closed my eyes. I wondered if I looked like a Catholic, and in my wonderment I began to make a little speech to myself. Can I call the self-conscious words I spoke prayer? At any rate, I called my audience God. God, I said, I am twenty-three years old. I want to make the best of things. Now the doctor is about to wed Brenda to me, and I am not entirely certain this is all for the best. What is it I love, Lord? Why have I chosen? Who is Brenda? The race is to the swift. Should I have stopped to think?

I was getting no answers, but I went on. If we meet You at all, God, it's that we're carnal, and acquisitive, and thereby partake of You. I am carnal, and I know You approve, I just know it. But how carnal can I get? I am acquisitive. Where do I turn now in my acquisitiveness? Where do we meet? Which prize is You?

It was an ingenious meditation, and suddenly I felt ashamed. I got up and walked outside, and the noise of Fifth Avenue met me with an answer:

Which prize do you think, *schmuck?* Gold dinnerware, sporting-goods trees, nectarines, garbage disposals, bumpless noses, Patimkin Sink, Bonwit Teller —

But damn it, God, that *is* You!

And God only laughed, that clown.

On the steps around the fountain I sat in a small arc of

a rainbow that the sun had shot through the spray of the water. And then I saw Brenda coming out of the Squibb Building. She carried nothing with her, like a woman who's only been window shopping, and for a moment I was glad that in the end she had disobeyed my desire.

As she crossed the street, though, that little levity passed, and then I was myself again.

She walked up before me and looked down at where I sat; when she inhaled she filled her entire body, and then let her breath out with a "Whew!"

"Where is it?" I said.

My answer, at first, was merely that victorious look of hers, the one she'd given Simp the night she'd beaten her, the one I'd gotten the morning I finished the third lap alone. At last she said, "I'm wearing it."

"Oh, Bren."

"He said shall I wrap it or will you take it with you?"

"Oh Brenda, I love you."

We slept together that night, and so nervous were we about our new toy that we performed like kindergartners, or (in the language of that country) like a lousy double-play combination. And then the next day we hardly saw one another at all, for with the last-minute wedding preparations came scurrying, telegramming, shouting, crying, rushing — in short, lunacy. Even the meals lost their Patimkin fullness, and were tortured out of Kraft cheese, stale onion rolls, dry salami, a little chopped liver, and fruit cocktail. It was hectic all weekend, and I tried as best I could to keep clear of the storm, at whose eye, Ron, clumsy and smiling, and Harriet, flittering and courteous, were being pulled closer and closer together. By Sunday night fatigue had arrested hysteria and all of the Patimkins, Brenda included, had gone off to an early sleep. When Ron went into the bathroom to brush his teeth I decided to go in and brush mine. While I stood over the sink he checked his supports for dampness; then he hung them on the shower knobs and asked me if I would like to listen to his records for a while. It was not out of boredom and loneliness that I accepted; rather a brief spark of lockerroom comradery had been struck there among the soap and the water and the tile, and I thought that perhaps Ron's invitation was prompted by a desire to spend his last moments as a Single Man with another Single Man. If I was right, then it was the first real attestation he'd given to my masculinity. How could I refuse?

I sat on the unused twin bed.

"You want to hear Mantovani?"

"Sure," I said.

"Who do you like better, him or Kostelanetz?"

"It's a toss-up."

Ron went to his cabinet. "Hey, how about the Columbus record? Brenda ever play it for you?"

"No. I don't think so."

He extracted a record from its case, and like a giant with a sea shell, placed it gingerly on the phonograph. Then he smiled at me and leaned back onto his bed. His arms were behind his head and his eyes fixed on the ceiling. "They give this to all the seniors. With the yearbook —" but he hushed as soon as the sound began. I watched Ron and listened to the record.

At first there was just a roll of drums, then silence, then another drum roll — and then softly, a marching song, the melody of which was very familiar. When the song ended, I heard the bells, soft, loud, then soft again. And finally there came a Voice, bowel-deep and historic, the kind one associates with documentaries about the rise of Fascism.

"The year, 1956. The season, fall. The place, Ohio State University ..."

Blitzkrieg! Judgment Day! The Lord had lowered his baton, and the Ohio State Glee Club were lining out the Alma Mater as if their souls depended on it. After one desperate chorus, they fell, still screaming, into bottomless oblivion, and the Voice resumed:

"The leaves had begun to turn and redden on the trees. Smoky fires line Fraternity Row, as pledges rake the leaves and turn them to a misty haze. Old faces greet new ones, new faces meet old, and another year has begun ..."

Music. Glee Club in great comeback. Then the Voice: "The place, the banks of the Olentangy. The event, Homecoming Game, 1956. The opponent, the ever dangerous Illini ..."

Roar of crowd. New voice — Bill Stern: "Illini over the ball. The snap. Linday fading to pass, he finds a receiver, he passes long *long* down field — and IT'S INTERCEPTED BY NUMBER 43, HERB CLARK OF OHIO STATE! Clark evades one tackler, he evades another as he comes up to midfield. Now he's picking up blockers, he's down to the 45, the 40, the 35 — "

And as Bill Stern egged on Clark, and Clark, Bill Stern, Ron, on his bed, with just a little body-english, eased Herb Clark over the goal.

"And it's the Buckeyes ahead now, 21 to 19. *What a game!*"

The Voice of History baritoned in again: "But the season

was up and down, and by the time the first snow had covered the turf, it was the sound of dribbling and the cry *Up and In!* that echoed through the fieldhouse..."

Ron closed his eyes.

"The Minnesota game," a new, high voice announced, "and for some of our seniors, their last game for the red and white . . . The players are ready to come out on the floor and into the spotlight. There'll be a big hand of appreciation from this capacity crowd for some of the boys who won't be back next year. Here comes Larry Gardner, big Number 7, out onto the floor, Big Larry from Akron, Ohio . . ."

"Larry — " announced the P.A. system; "Larry," the crowd roared back.

"And here comes Ron Patimkin dribbling out. Ron, Number 11, from Short Hills, New Jersey. Big Ron's last game, and it'll be some time before Buckeye fans forget him . . ."

Big Ron tightened on his bed as the loudspeaker called his name; his ovation must have set the nets to trembling. Then the rest of the players were announced, and then basketball season was over, and it was Religious Emphasis Week, the Senior Prom (Billy May blaring at the gymnasium roof), Fraternity Skit Night, E. E. Cummings reading to students (verse, silence, applause); and then, finally, commencement:

"The campus is hushed this day of days. For several thousand young men and women it is a joyous yet a solemn occasion. And for their parents a day of laughter and a day of tears. It is a bright green day, it is June the seventh of the year one thousand nine hundred and fifty-seven and for these young Americans the most stirring day of their lives. For many this will be their last glimpse of the campus, of Columbus, for many many years. Life calls us, and anxiously if not nervously we walk out into the world and away from the pleasures of these ivied walls. But not from its memories. They will be the concomitant, if not the fundament, of our lives. We shall choose husbands and wives, we shall choose jobs and homes, we shall sire children and grandchildren, but we will not forget you, Ohio State. In the years ahead we will carry with us always memories of thee, Ohio State . . ."

Slowly, softly, the OSU band begins the Alma Mater, and then the bells chime that last hour. Soft, very soft, for it is spring.

There was goose flesh on Ron's veiny arms as the Voice continued. "We offer ourselves to you then, world, and come at you in search of Life. And to you, Ohio State, to you Columbus, we say thank you, thank you and goodbye. We will miss you, in the fall, in the winter, in the spring, but some day we shall return. Till then, goodbye, Ohio State, goodbye, red and white, goodbye, Columbus . . . goodbye, Columbus . . . goodbye . . ."

Ron's eyes were closed. The band was upending its last truckload of nostalgia, and I tiptoed from the room, in step with the 2163 members of the Class of '57.

I closed my door, but then opened it and looked back at Ron: he was still humming on his bed. Thee! I thought, my brother-in-law!

The wedding.

Let me begin with the relatives.

There was Mrs. Patimkin's side of the family: her sister Molly, a tiny buxom hen whose ankles swelled and ringed her shoes, and who would remember Ron's wedding if for no other reason than she'd martyred her feet in three-inch heels, and Molly's husband, the butter and egg man, Harry Grossbart, who had earned his fortune with barley and corn in the days of Prohibition. Now he was active in the Temple and whenever he saw Brenda he swatted her on the can; it was a kind of physical bootlegging that passed, I guess, for familial affection. Then there was Mrs. Patimkin's brother, Marty Kreiger, the Kosher Hot-Dog King, an immense man, as many stomachs as he had chins, and already, at fifty-five, with as many heart attacks as chins and stomachs combined. He had just come back from a health cure in the Catskills, where he said he'd eaten nothing but All-Bran and had won $1500 at gin rummy. When the photographer came by to take pictures, Marty put his hand on his wife's pancake breasts and said, "Hey, how about a picture of this!" His wife, Sylvia, was a frail, spindly woman with bones like a bird's. She had cried throughout the ceremony, and sobbed openly, in fact, when the rabbi had pronounced Ron and Harriet "man and wife in the eyes of God and the State of New Jersey." Later, at dinner, she had hardened enough to slap her husband's hand as it reached out for a cigar. However, when he reached across to hold her breast she just looked aghast and said nothing.

Also there were Mrs. Patimkin's twin sisters, Rose and Pearl, who both had white hair, the color of Lincoln convertibles, and nasal voices, and husbands who followed after them but talked only to each other, as though, in fact, sister had married sister, and husband had married husband. The husbands, named Earl Klein and Manny Kartzman, sat next to each other during the ceremony, then at dinner, and once, in fact, while the band was playing between courses, they rose, Klein and Kartzman, as though to dance, but instead walked to the far end of the hall where together they paced off the width of the floor. Earl, I learned later, was in the carpet business, and apparently he was trying to figure how much money he would make if the Hotel Pierre favored him with a sale.

On Mr. Patimkin's side there was only Leo, his half-brother. Leo was married to a woman named Bea whom nobody seemed to talk to. Bea kept hopping up and down during the meal and running over to the kiddie table to see if her little girl, Sharon, was being taken care of. "I told her not to take the kid. Get a baby-sitter, I said." Leo told me this while Brenda danced with Ron's best man, Ferrari. "She says what are we, millionaires? No, for Christ sake, but my brother's kids gets married, I can have a little celebration. No, we gotta *shlep* the kid with us. Aah, it gives her something to do! . . ." He looked around the hall. Up on the stage Harry Winters (né Weinberg) was leading his band in a medley from *My Fair Lady*; on the floor, all ages, all sizes, all shapes were dancing. Mr. Patimkin was dancing with Julie, whose dress had slipped down from her shoulders to reveal her soft small back, and long neck, like Brenda's. He danced in little squares and was making considerable effort not to step on Julie's toes. Harriet, who was, as everyone said, a beautiful bride, was dancing with her father. Ron danced with Harriet's mother, Brenda with Ferrari, and I had sat down for a while in the empty chair beside Leo so as not to get maneuvered into dancing with Mrs. Patimkin, which seemed to be the direction towards which things were moving.

"You're Brenda's boy friend? Huh?" Leo said.

I nodded — earlier in the evening I'd stopped giving blushing explanations. "You gotta deal there, boy," Leo said, "you don't louse it up."

"She's very beautiful," I said.

Leo poured himself a glass of champagne, and then waited as though he expected a head to form on it; when one didn't, he filled the glass to the brim.

"Beautiful, not beautiful, what's the difference. I'm a practical man. I'm on the bottom, so I gotta be. You're Aly Khan you worry about marrying movie stars. I wasn't born yesterday . . . You know how old I was when I got married? Thirty-five years old. I don't know what the hell kind of hurry I was in." He drained his glass and refilled it. "I'll tell you something, one good thing happened to me in my whole life. Two maybe. Before I came back from overseas I got a letter from my wife — she wasn't my wife then. My mother-in-law found an apartment for us in Queens. Sixty-two fifty a month it cost. That's the last good thing that happened."

"What was the first?"

"What first?"

"You said *two* things," I said.

"I don't remember. I say two because my wife tells me I'm sarcastic and a cynic. That way maybe she won't think I'm such a wise guy."

I saw Brenda and Ferrari separate, and so excused myself and started for Brenda, but just then Mr. Patimkin separated from Julie and it looked as though the two men were going to switch partners. Instead the four of them stood on the dance floor and when I reached them they were laughing and Julie was saying, "What's so funny!" Ferrari said "Hi" to me and whisked Julie away, which sent her into peals of laughter.

Mr. Patimkin had one hand on Brenda's back and suddenly the other one was on mine. "You kids having a good
time?" he said.

We were sort of swaying, the three of us, to "Get Me to
the Church on Time."

Brenda kissed her father. "Yes," she said. "I'm so
drunk my head doesn't even need my neck."

"It's a fine wedding, Mr. Patimkin."

"You want anything just ask me . . ." he said, a little
drunken himself. "You're two good kids . . . How do you
like that brother of yours getting married? . . . Huh? . . . Is
that a girl or is that a girl?"

Brenda smiled, and though she apparently thought her
father had spoken of her, I was sure he'd been referring to
Harriet.

"You like weddings, Daddy?" Brenda said.

"I like my kids' weddings . . ." He slapped me on the
back. "You two kids, you want anything? Go have a good
time. Remember," he said to Brenda, "you're my
honey . . ." Then he looked at me. "Whatever my Buck
wants is good enough for me. There's no business too big
it can't use another head."

I smiled, though not directly at him, and beyond I could
see Leo sopping up champagne and watching the three of
us; when he caught my eye he made a sign with his hand,
a circle with his thumb and forefinger, indicating, "That a
boy, that a boy!"

After Mr. Patimkin departed, Brenda and I danced
closely, and we only sat down when the waiters began to cir-
culate with the main course. The head table was noisy,
particularly at our end where the men were almost all team-
mates of Ron's, in one sport or another; they ate a fan
tastic number of rolls. Tank Feldman, Ron's roommate,

who had flown in from Toledo, kept sending the waiter
back for rolls, for celery, for olives, and always to the
squealing delight of Gloria Feldman, his wife, a nervous,
undernourished girl who continually looked down the front
of her gown as though there was some sort of construction
project going on under her clothes. Gloria and Tank, in
fact, seemed to be self-appointed precinct captains at our
end. They proposed toasts, burst into wild song, and continually referred to Brenda and me as "love birds." Brenda
smiled at this with her eyeteeth and I brought up a cheery
look from some fraudulent auricle of my heart.

And the night continued: we ate, we drank, we danced
— Rose and Pearl did the Charleston with one another
(while their husbands examined woodwork and chande-
liers), and then I did the Charleston with none other than
Gloria Feldman, who made coy, hideous faces at me all
the time we danced. Near the end of the evening, Brenda,
who'd been drinking champagne like her Uncle Leo, did a
Rita Hayworth tango with herself, and Julie fell asleep on
some ferns she'd whisked off the head table and made into
a mattress at the far end of the hall. I felt a numbness
creep into my hard palate, and by three o'clock people
were dancing in their coats, shoeless ladies were wrapping
hunks of wedding cake in napkins for their children's
lunch, and finally Gloria Feldman made her way over to our
end of the table and said, freshly, "Well, our little Radcliffe
smarty, what have *you* been doing all summer?"

"Growing a penis."

Gloria smiled and left as quickly as she'd come, and
Brenda without another word headed shakily away for the
ladies' room and the rewards of overindulgence. No sooner
had she left than Leo was beside me, a glass in one hand, a
new bottle of champagne in the other.

"No sign of the bride and groom?" he said, leering. He'd lost most of his consonants by this time and was doing the best he could with long, wet vowels. "Well, you're next, kid, I see it in the cards ... You're nobody's sucker ..." And he stabbed me in the side with the top of the bottle, spilling champagne onto the side of my rented tux. He straightened up, poured more onto his hand and glass, but then suddenly he stopped. He was looking into the lights which were hidden beneath a long bank of flowers that adorned the front of the table. He shook the bottle in his hand as though to make it fizz. "The son of a bitch who invented the fluorescent bulb should drop dead!" He set the bottle down and drank.

Up on the stage Harry Winters brought his musicians to a halt. The drummer stood up, stretched, and they all began to open up cases and put their instruments away. On the floor, relatives, friends, associates, were holding each other around the waists and the shoulders, and small children huddled around their parents' legs. A couple of kids ran in and out of the crowd, screaming at tag, until one was grabbed by an adult and slapped soundly on the behind. He began to cry, and couple by couple the floor emptied. Our table was a tangle of squashed everything: napkins, fruits, flowers; there were empty whiskey bottles, droopy ferns, and dishes puddled with unfinished cherry jubilee, gone sticky with the hours. At the end of the table Mr. Patimkin was sitting next to his wife, holding her hand. Opposite them, on two bridge chairs that had been pulled up, sat Mr. and Mrs. Ehrlich. They spoke quietly and evenly, as though they had known each other for years and years. Everything had slowed down now, and from time to time people would come up to the Patimkins and Ehrlichs, wish them *mazel tov,* and then drag themselves and their families out into the September night, which was cool and windy, someone said, and reminded me that soon would come winter and snow.

"They never wear out, those things, you know that." Leo was pointing to the fluorescent lights that shone through the flowers. "They last for years. They could make a car like that if they wanted, that could never wear out. It would run on water in the summer and snow in the winter. But they wouldn't do it, the big boys ... Look at me," Leo said, splashing his suit front with champagne, "I sell a good bulb. You can't get the kind of bulb I sell in the drugstores. It's a quality bulb. But I'm the little guy. I don't even own a car. His brother, and I don't even own an automobile. I take a train wherever I go. I'm the only guy I know who wears out three pairs of rubbers every winter. Most guys get new ones when they lose the old ones. I wear them out, like shoes. Look," he said, leaning into me, "I could sell a crappy bulb, it wouldn't break my heart. But it's not good business."

The Ehrlichs and Patimkins scraped back their chairs and headed away, all except Mr. Patimkin who came down the table towards Leo and me.

He slapped Leo on the back. "Well, how you doing, *shtarke?*"

"All right, Ben. All right . . ."

"You have a good time?"

"You had a nice affair, Ben, it must've cost a pretty penny, believe me . . ."

Mr. Patimkin laughed. "When I make out my income tax I go to see Leo. He knows just how much money I spent . . . You need a ride home?" he asked me.

"No, thanks. I'm waiting for Brenda. We have my car."

"Good night," Mr. Patimkin said.

I watched him step down off the platform that held the head table, and then start towards the exit. Now the only people in the hall — the shambles of a hall — were myself, Leo, and his wife and child who slept, both of them, with their heads pillowed on a crumpled tablecloth at a table down on the floor before us. Brenda still wasn't around.

"When you got it," Leo said, rubbing his fingers together, "you can afford to talk like a big shot. Who needs a guy like me any more. Salesmen, you spit on them. You can go to the supermarket and buy anything. Where my wife shops you can buy sheets and pillowcases. Imagine, a grocery store! Me, I sell to gas stations, factories, small businesses, all up and down the east coast. Sure, you can sell a guy in a gas station a crappy bulb that'll burn out in a week. For inside the pumps I'm talking, it takes a certain kind of bulb. A utility bulb. All right, so you sell him a crappy bulb, and then a week later he puts in a new one, and while he's screwing it in he still remembers your name. Not me. I sell a quality bulb. It lasts a month, five weeks, before it even flickers, then it gives you another couple days, dim maybe, but so you shouldn't go blind. It hangs on, it's a quality bulb. Before it even burns out you notice it's getting darker, so you put a new one in. What people don't like is when one minute it's sunlight and the next dark. Let it glimmer a few days and they don't feel so bad. Nobody ever throws out my bulb — they figure they'll save them, can always use them in a pinch. Sometimes I say to a guy, you ever throw out a bulb you bought from Leo Patimkin? You gotta use psychology. That's why I'm sending my kid to college. You don't know a little psychology these days, you're licked . . ."

He lifted an arm and pointed out to his wife; then he

slumped down in his seat. "Aaach!" he said, and drank off half a glass of champagne. "I'll tell you, I go as far as New London, Connecticut. That's as far as I'll go, and when I come home at night I stop first for a couple drinks. Martinis. Two I have, sometimes three. That seems fair, don't it? But to her a little sip or a bathtubful, it smells the same. She says it's bad for the kid if I come home smelling. The kid's a baby, for God's sake, she thinks that's the way I'm *supposed* to smell. A forty-eight-year-old man with a three-year-old kid! She'll give me a thrombosis that kid. My wife, she wants me to come home early and play with the kid before she goes to bed. Come home, she says, and *I'll* make you a drink. Hah! I spend all day sniffing gas, leaning under hoods with grimy *poilishehs* in New London, trying to force a lousy bulb into a socket —I'll screw it in myself, I tell them — and she thinks I want to come home and drink a martini from a jelly glass! How long are you going to stay in bars, she says. Till a Jewish girl is Miss Rheingold!

"Look," he went on after another drink, "I love my kid like Ben loves his Brenda. It's not that I don't want to play with her. But if I play with the kid and then at night get into bed with my wife, then she can't expect fancy things from me. It's one or the other. I'm no movie star."

Leo looked at his empty glass and put it on the table; he tilted the bottle up and drank the champagne like soda water. "How much do you think I make a week?" he said.

"I don't know."

"Take a guess."

"A hundred dollars."

"Sure, and tomorrow they're gonna let the lions out of the cage in Central Park. What do you think I make?"

"I can't tell."

"A cabdriver makes more than me. That's a fact. My wife's brother is a cabdriver, *he* lives in Kew Gardens. And he don't take no crap, no sir, not those cabbies. Last week it was raining one night and I said the hell with it, I'm taking a cab. I'd been all day in Newton, Mass. I don't usually go so far, but on the train in the morning I said to myself, stay on, go further, it'll be a change. And I know all the time I'm kidding myself. I wouldn't even make up the extra fare it cost me. But I stay on. And at night I still had a couple boxes with me, so when the guy pulls up at Grand Central there's like a genie inside me says get in. I even threw the bulbs in, not even caring if they broke. And this cabbie says, Whatya want to do, buddy, rip the leather? Those are brand new seats I got. No, I said. Jesus Christ, he says, some goddam people. I get in and give him a Queens address which ought to shut him up, but no, all the way up the Drive he was Jesus Christing me. It's hot in the cab, so I open a window and *then* he turns around and says, Whatya want to do, give me a cold in the neck? I just got over a goddam cold . . ." Leo looked at me, bleary-eyed. "This city is crazy! If I had a little money I'd get out of here in a minute. I'd go to California. They don't need bulbs out there it's so light. I went to New Guinea during the war from San Francisco. *There*," he burst, "there is the other good thing that happened to me, that night in San Francisco with this Hannah Schreiber. That's the both of them, you asked me I'm telling you — the apartment my mother-in-law got us, and this Hannah Schreiber. One night was all. I went to a B'nai Brith dance for servicemen in the basement of some big temple, and I met her. I wasn't married then, so don't make faces."

"I'm not."

"She had a nice little room by herself. She was going to school to be a teacher. Already I knew something was up because she let me feel inside her slip in the cab. Listen to me, I sound like I'm always in cabs. Maybe two other times in my life. To tell the truth I don't even enjoy it. All the time I'm riding I'm watching the meter. Even the pleasures I can't enjoy!"

"What about Hannah Schreiber?"

He smiled, flashing some gold in his mouth. "How do you like that name? She was only a girl, but she had an old lady's name. In the room she says to me she believes in oral love. I can still hear her: Leo Patimkin, I believe in oral love. I don't know what the hell she means. I figure she was one of those Christian Scientists or some cult or something. So I said, But what about for soldiers, guys going overseas who may get killed, God forbid." He shrugged his shoulders. "The smartest guy in the world I wasn't. But that's twenty years almost, I was still wet behind the ears. I'll tell you, every once in a while my wife — you know, she does for me what Hannah Schreiber did. I don't like to force her, she works hard. That to her is like a cab to me. I wouldn't force her. I can remember every time, I'll bet. Once after a Seder, my mother was still living, she should rest in peace. My wife was up to here with Mogen David. In fact, *twice* after Seders. Aachhh! Everything good in my life I can count on my fingers! God forbid some one should leave me a million dollars, I wouldn't even have to take off my shoes. I got a whole other hand yet."

He pointed to the fluorescent bulbs with the nearly empty champagne bottle. "You call that a light? That's a light to *read* by? It's purple, for God's sake! Half the

blind men in the world ruined themselves by those damn
things. You know who's behind them? The optometrists!
I'll tell you, if I could get a couple hundred for all my stock
and the territory, I'd sell tomorrow. That's right, Leo A.
Patimkin, one semester accounting, City College nights,
will sell equipment, territory, good name. I'll buy two
inches in the *Times*. The territory is from here to everywhere. I go where I want, my own boss, no one tells me
what to do. You know the Bible? 'Let there be light —
and there's Leo Patimkin!' That's my trademark, I'll sell
that too. I tell them that slogan, the *poilishehs*, they think
I'm making it up. What good is it to be smart unless you're
in on the ground floor! I got more brains in my pinky than
Ben got in his whole *head*. Why is it he's on top and I'm on
the bottom! *Why!* Believe me, if you're born lucky, you're
lucky!" And then he exploded into silence.

I had the feeling that he was going to cry, so I leaned
over and whispered to him, "You better go home." He
agreed, but I had to raise him out of his seat and steer him
by one arm down to his wife and child. The little girl
could not be awakened, and Leo and Bea asked me to watch
her while they went out into the lobby to get their coats.
When they returned, Leo seemed to have dragged himself
back to the level of human communication. He shook my
hand with real feeling. I was very touched.

"You'll go far," he said to me. "You're a smart boy,
you'll play it safe. Don't louse things up."

"I won't."

"Next time we see you it'll be *your* wedding," and he
winked at me. Bea stood alongside, muttering goodbye
all the while he spoke. He shook my hand again and then
picked the child out of her seat, and they turned towards

the door. From the back, round-shouldered, burdened, child-carrying, they looked like people fleeing a captured city.

Brenda, I discovered, was asleep on a couch in the lobby. It was almost four o'clock and the two of us and the desk clerk were the only ones in the hotel lobby. At first I did not waken Brenda, for she was pale and wilted and I knew she had been sick. I sat beside her, smoothing her hair back off her ears. How would I ever come to know her, I wondered, for as she slept I felt I knew no more of her than what I could see in a photograph. I stirred her gently and in a half-sleep she walked beside me out to the car.

It was almost dawn when we came out of the Jersey side of the Lincoln Tunnel. I switched down to my parking lights, and drove on to the Turnpike, and there out before me I could see the swampy meadows that spread for miles and miles, watery, blotchy, smelly, like an oversight of God. I thought of that other oversight, Leo Patimkin, half-brother to Ben. In a few hours he would be on a train heading north, and as he passed Scarsdale and White Plains, he would belch and taste champagne and let the flavor linger in his mouth. Alongside him on the seat, like another passenger, would be cartons of bulbs. He would get off at New London, or maybe, inspired by the sight of his half-brother, he would stay on again, hoping for some new luck further north. For the world was Leo's territory, every city, every swamp, every road and highway. He could go on to Newfoundland if he wanted, Hudson Bay, and on up to Thule, and then slide down the other side of the globe and rap on frosted windows on the Russian steppes, if he wanted. But he wouldn't. Leo was forty-eight years old and he had learned. He pursued discomfort and sorrow, all right, but if you had a heartful by the time you reached New London, what new awfulness could you look forward to in Vladivostok?

The next day the wind was blowing the fall in and the branches of the weeping willow were fingering at the Patimkin front lawn. I drove Brenda to the train at noon, and she left me.

8

Autumn came quickly. It was cold and in Jersey the leaves turned and fell overnight. The following Saturday I took a ride up to see the deer, and did not even get out of the car, for it was too brisk to be standing at the wire fence, and so I watched the animals walk and run in the dimness of the late afternoon, and after a while everything, even the objects of nature, the trees, the clouds, the grass, the weeds, reminded me of Brenda, and I drove back down to Newark. Already we had sent our first letters and I had called her late one night, but in the mail and on the phone we had some difficulty discovering one another; we had not the style yet. That night I tried her again, and someone on her floor said she was out and would not be in till late.

Upon my return to the library I was questioned by Mr. Scapello about the Gauguin book. The jowly gentleman *had* sent a nasty letter about my discourtesy, and I was only able to extricate myself by offering a confused story in an indignant tone. In fact, I even managed to turn it around so that Mr. Scapello was apologizing to me as he led me up to my new post, there among the encyclopedias, the bibliographies, the indexes and guides. My bullying surprised me, and I wondered if some of it had not been learned from Mr. Patimkin that morning I'd heard him giving Grossman an earful on the phone. Perhaps I was more of a business-man than I thought. Maybe I could learn to become a Patimkin with ease ...

Days passed slowly; I never did see the colored kid again, and when, one noon, I looked in the stacks, Gauguin was gone, apparently charged out finally by the jowly man. I wondered what it had been like that day the colored kid had discovered the book was gone. Had he cried? For some reason I imagined that he had blamed it on me, but then I realized that I was confusing the dream I'd had with reality. Chances were he had discovered someone else, Van Gogh, Vermeer ... But no, they were not his kind of artists. What had probably happened was that he'd given up on the library and gone back to playing Willie Mays in the streets. He was better off, I thought. No sense carrying dreams of Tahiti in your head, if you can't afford the fare.

Let's see, what else did I do? I ate, I slept, I went to the movies, I sent broken-spined books to the bindery — I did everything I'd ever done before, but now each activity was surrounded by a fence, existed alone, and my life consisted of jumping from one fence to the next. There was no flow, for that had been Brenda.

And then Brenda wrote saying that she could be coming in for the Jewish holidays which were only a week away. I was so overjoyed I wanted to call Mr. and Mrs. Patimkin, just to tell them of my pleasure. However, when I got to the phone and had actually dialed the first two letters, I knew that at the other end there would be silence; if there was anything said, it would only be Mrs. Patimkin asking, "What is it you want?" Mr. Patimkin had probably for-gotten my name.

That night, after dinner, I gave Aunt Gladys a kiss and told her she shouldn't work so hard.

"In less than a week it's Rosh Hashana and he thinks I should take a vacation. Ten people I'm having. What do you think, a chicken cleans itself? Thank God, the holidays come once a year, I'd be an old woman before my time."

But then it was only nine people Aunt Gladys was having, for only two days after her letter Brenda called.

"Oy, Gut!" Aunt Gladys called. "Long *distance!*"

"Hello?" I said.

"Hello, sweetie?"

"Yes," I said.

"What *is* it?" Aunt Gladys tugged at my shirt. "What is it?"

"It's for me."

"Who?" Aunt Gladys said, pointing into the receiver.

"Brenda," I said.

"Yes?" Brenda said.

"Brenda?" Aunt Gladys said. "What does she call long distance, I almost had a heart attack."

"Because she's in Boston," I said. "Please, Aunt Gladys . . ."

And Aunt Gladys walked off, mumbling, "These kids . . ."

"Hello," I said again into the phone.

"Neil, how are you?"

"I love you."

"Neil, I have bad news. I can't come in this week."

"But, honey, it's the Jewish holidays."

"Sweet*heart*," she laughed.

"Can't you say that, for an excuse?"

"I have a test Saturday, and a paper, and you know if I went home I wouldn't get anything done . . ."

"You would."

"Neil, I just *can't*. My mother'd make me go to Temple, and I wouldn't even have enough time to see *you*."

"Oh God, Brenda."

"Sweetie?"

"Yes?"

"Can't you come up here?" she asked.

"I'm working."

"The Jewish holidays," she said.

"Honey, I can't. Last year I didn't take them off, I can't all—"

"You can say you had a conversion."

"Besides, my aunt's having all the family for dinner, and you know what with my parents — "

"Come up, Neil."

"I can't just take two days off, Bren. I just got promoted and a raise — "

"The hell with the raise."

"Baby, it's my job."

"Forever?" she said.

"No."

"Then come. I've got a hotel room."

"For me?"

"For us."

"Can you do that?"

"No and yes. People do it."

"Brenda, you tempt me."

"Be tempted."

"I could take a train Wednesday right from work."

"You could stay till Sunday night."

"Bren, I can't. I still have to be back to work on Saturday."

"Don't you ever get a day *off?*" she said.

"Tuesdays," I said glumly.

"God."

"And Sunday," I added.

Brenda said something but I did not hear her, for Aunt Gladys called, "You talk all day long distance?"

"Quiet!" I shouted back to her.

"Neil, will you?"

"Damn it, yes," I said.

"Are you angry?"

"I don't think so. I'm going to come up."

"Till Sunday."

"We'll see."

"Don't feel upset, Neil. You sound upset. It is the Jewish holidays. I mean you *should* be off."

"That's right," I said. "I'm an orthodox Jew, for God's sake, I ought to take advantage of it."

"That's right," she said.

"Is there a train around six?"

"Every hour, I think."

"Then I'll be on the one that leaves at six."

"I'll be at the station," she said. "How will I know you?"

"I'll be disguised as an orthodox Jew."

"Me too," she said.

"Good night, love," I said.

Aunt Gladys cried when I told her I was going away for Rosh Hashana.

"And I was preparing a big meal," she said.

"You can still prepare it."

"What will I tell your mother?"

"I'll tell her, Aunt Gladys. Please. You have no right to get upset . . ."

"Someday you'll have a family you'll know what it's like."

"I have a family now."

"What's a matter," she said, blowing her nose, "That girl couldn't come home to see her family it's the holidays?"

"She's in school, she just can't — "

"If she loved her family she'd find time. We don't live six hundred years."

"She does love her family."

"Then one day a year you could break your heart and pay a visit."

"Aunt Gladys, you don't understand."

"Sure," she said, "when I'm twenty-three years old I'll understand everything."

I went to kiss her and she said, "Go away from me, go run to Boston . . ."

The next morning I discovered that Mr. Scapello didn't want me to leave on Rosh Hashana either, but I unnerved him, I think, by hinting that his coldness about my taking the two days off might just be so much veiled anti-Semitism, so on the whole he was easier to manage. At lunch time I took a walk down to Penn Station and picked up a train schedule to Boston. That was my bedtime reading for the next three nights.

She did not look like Brenda, at least for the first minute. And probably to her I did not look like me. But we kissed and held each other, and it was strange to feel the thickness of our coats between us.

"I'm letting my hair grow," she said in the cab, and that in fact was all she said. Not until I helped her out of the cab did I notice the thin gold band shining on her left hand.

She hung back, strolling casually about the lobby while I signed the register "Mr. and Mrs. Neil Klugman," and then in the room we kissed again.

"Your heart's pounding," I said to her.

"I know," she said.

"Are you nervous?"

"No."

"Have you done this before?" I said.

"I read Mary McCarthy."

She took off her coat and instead of putting it in the closet, she tossed it across the chair. I sat down on the bed; she didn't.

"What's the matter?"

Brenda took a deep breath and walked over to the window, and I thought that perhaps it would be best for me to ask nothing — for us to get used to each other's presence in quiet. I hung her coat and mine in the empty closet, and left the suitcases — mine and hers — standing by the bed.

Brenda was kneeling backwards in the chair, looking out the window as though out the window was where she'd rather be. I came up behind her and put my hands around her body and held her breasts, and when I felt the cool draft that swept under the sill, I realized how long it had been since that first warm night when I had put my arms around her and felt the tiny wings beating in her back. And then I realized why I'd really come to Boston — it had been long enough. It was time to stop kidding about marriage.

"Is something the matter?" I said.

"Yes."

It wasn't the answer I'd expected; I wanted no answer really, only to soothe her nervousness with my concern.

But I asked, "What is it? Why didn't you mention it on the phone?"

"It only happened today."

"School?"

"Home. They found out about us."

I turned her face up to mine. "That's okay. I told my aunt I was coming here too. What's the difference?"

"About the summer. About our sleeping together."

"Oh?"

"Yes."

". . . Ron?"

"No."

"That night, you mean, did Julie —"

"No," she said, "it wasn't *anybody*."

"I don't get it."

Brenda got up and walked over to the bed where she sat down on the edge. I sat in the chair.

"My mother found the thing."

"The diaphragm?"

She nodded.

"When?" I asked.

"The other day, I guess." She walked to the bureau and opened her purse. "Here, you can read them in the order I got them." She tossed an envelope at me; it was dirty-edged and crumpled, as though it had been in and out of her pockets a good many times. "I got this one this morning," she said. "Special delivery."

I took out the letter and read:

PATIMKIN KITCHEN AND BATHROOM SINKS

"Any Size — Any Shape"

Dear Brenda —

Don't pay any Attention to your Mother's Letter when you get it. I love you honey if you want a coat I'll buy You a coat. You could always have anything you wanted. We have every faith in you so you won't be too upset by what your mother says in her Letter. Of course she is a little hystericall because of the shock and she has been Working so hard for Hadassah. She is a Woman and it is hard for her to understand some of the Shocks in life. Of course I can't say We weren't all surprised because from the beginning I was nice to him and Thought he would appreciate the nice vacation we supplied for him. Some People never turn out the way you hope and pray but I am willing to forgive and call Buy Gones, Buy Gones, You have always up till now been a good Buck and got good scholastic Grades and Ron has always been what we wanted a Good Boy, most important, and a Nice boy. This late in my life believe me I am not going to start hating my own flesh and blood. As for your mistake it takes Two to make a mistake and now that you will be away at school and from him and what you got involved in you will probably do all right I have every faith you will. You have to have faith in your children like in a Business or any serious undertaking and there is nothing that is so bad that we can't forgive especially when Our own flesh and blood is involved. We have a nice close nitt family and why not???? Have a nice Holiday and in Temple I will say a Prayer for you as I do every year. On Monday I want you to go into Boston and buy a coat.

Whatever you need because I know how Cold it gets up where you are ... Give my regards to Linda and remember to bring her home with you on Thanksgiving like last year. You two had such a nice time. I have always never said bad things about any of your friends or Rons and that this should happen is only the exception that proves the rule. Have a Happy Holiday.

YOUR FATHER

And then it was signed BEN PATIMKIN, but that was crossed out and written beneath "Your Father" were again, like an echo, the words, "Your Father."

"Who's Linda?" I asked.

"My roommate, last year." She tossed another envelope to me. "Here. I got this one in the afternoon. Air Mail."

The letter was from Brenda's mother. I started to read it and then put it down a moment. "You got this *after?*"

"Yes," she said. "When I got his I didn't know what was happening. Read hers."

I began again.

Dear Brenda:

I don't even know how to begin. I have been crying all morning and have had to skip my board meeting this afternoon because my eyes are so red. I never thought this would happen to a daughter of mine. I wonder if you know what I mean, if it is at least on your conscience, so I won't have to degrade either of us with a description. All I can say is that this morning when I was cleaning out the drawers and putting away your summer clothing I came upon something in your bottom drawer, *under* some sweaters which you probably remember leaving there. I cried the minute I saw it and I haven't stopped crying yet. Your father called a while ago and now he is driving home because he heard how upset I was on the phone.

I don't know what we ever did that you should reward us this way. We gave you a nice home and all the love and respect a child needs. I always was proud when you were a little girl that you could take care of yourself so well. You took care of Julie so beautifully it was a treat to see, when you were only fourteen years old. But you drifted away from your family, even though we sent you to the best schools and gave you the best money could buy. Why you should reward us this way is a question I'll carry with me to the grave.

About your friend I have no words. He is his parents' responsibility and I cannot imagine what kind of home life he had that he could act that way. Certainly that was a fine way to repay us for the hospitality we were nice enough to show to him, a perfect stranger. That the two of you should be carrying on like that in our very house I will never in my life be able to understand. Times certainly have changed since I was a girl that this kind of thing could go on. I keep asking myself if at least you didn't think of us while you were doing that. If not for me, how could you do this to your father? God forbid Julie should ever learn of this.

God only knows what you have been doing all these years we put our trust in you.

You have broken your parents' hearts and you should know that. This is some thank you for all we gave you.

MOTHER

She only signed "Mother" once, and that was in an extraordinarily miniscule hand, like a whisper.

"Brenda," I said.

"What?"

"Are you starting to cry?"

"No. I cried already."

"Don't start again."

"I'm trying not to, for God's sake."

"Okay . . . Brenda, can I ask you one question?"

"What?"

"Why did you leave it home?"

"Because I didn't plan on using it here, that's why."

"Suppose I'd come up. I mean I have come up, what about that?"

"I thought I'd come down first."

"So then couldn't you have carried it down then? Like a toothbrush?"

"Are you trying to be funny?"

"No. I'm just asking you why you left it home."

"I told you," Brenda said. "I thought I'd come home."

"But, Brenda, that doesn't make any sense. Suppose you did come home, and then you came back again. Wouldn't you have taken it with you then?"

"I don't *know*."

"Don't get angry," I said.

"You're the one who's angry."

"I'm upset, I'm not angry."

"I'm upset then too."

I did not answer but walked to the window and looked out. The stars and moon were out, silver and hard, and from the window I could see over to the Harvard campus where lights burned and then seemed to flicker when the trees blew across them.

"Brenda . . ."

"What?"

"Knowing how your mother feels about you, wasn't it silly to leave it home? Risky?"

"What does how she feels about me have to do with it?"

"You can't trust her."

"Why can't I?"

"Don't you see. You *can't*."

"Neil, she was only cleaning out the drawers."

"Didn't you know she would?"

"She never did before. Or maybe she did. Neil, I couldn't think of everything. We slept together night after night and nobody heard or noticed — "

"Brenda, why the hell are you willfully confusing things?"

"I'm not!"

"Okay," I said softly. "All right."

"It's you who's confusing things," Brenda said. "You act as though I wanted her to find it."

I didn't answer.

"Do you believe *that?*" she said, after neither of us had spoken for a full minute.

"I don't know."

"Oh, Neil, you're *crazy*."

"What was crazier than leaving that damn thing around?"

"It was an oversight."

"Now it's an oversight, before it was deliberate."

"It was an oversight about the drawer. It wasn't an oversight about leaving it," she said.

"Brenda, sweetheart, wouldn't the safest, smartest, easiest, simplest thing been to have taken it with you? Wouldn't it?"

"It didn't make any difference either way."

"Brenda, this is the most frustrating argument of my life!"

"You keep making it seem as though I *wanted* her to

find it. Do you think I need this? Do you? I can't even go home any more."

"Is that so?"

"Yes!"

"No," I said. "You can go home — your father will be waiting with two coats and a half-dozen dresses."

"What about my mother?"

"It'll be the same with her."

"Don't be absurd. How can I face them!"

"Why can't you face them? Did you do anything wrong?"

"Neil, look at the reality of the thing, will you?"

"*Did* you do anything wrong?"

"Neil, *they* think it's wrong. They're my parents."

"But do you think it's wrong — "

"That doesn't *matter*."

"It does to me, Brenda . . ."

"Neil, why are *you* confusing things? You keep accusing me of things."

"Damn it, Brenda, you're guilty of some things."

"W*hat?*"

"Of leaving that damn diaphragm there. How can you call it an oversight!"

"Oh, Neil, don't start any of that psychoanalytic crap!"

"Then why else did you do it? You wanted her to find it!"

"Why?"

"I don't know, Brenda, *why?*"

"Oh!" she said, and she picked up the pillow and threw it back on to the bed.

"What happens now, Bren?" I said.

"What does that mean?"

"Just that. What happens now?"

She rolled over on to the bed and buried her head in it.

"Don't start crying," I said.

"I'm *not.*"

I was still holding the letters and took Mr. Patimkin's from its envelope.

"Why does your father capitalize all these letters?"

She didn't answer.

" 'As for your mistake,' " I read aloud to Brenda, " 'it takes Two to make a mistake and now that you will be away at school and from him and what you got involved in you will probably do all right I have every faith you will. Your father. Your father.' "

She turned and looked at me; but silently.

" 'I have always never said bad things about any of your friends or Rons and that this should happen is only the exception that proves the rule. Have a Happy Holiday.' " I stopped; in Brenda's face there was positively no threat of tears; she looked, suddenly, solid and decisive. "Well, what are you going to do?" I asked.

"Nothing."

"Who are you going to bring home Thanksgiving — Linda?" I said, "or me?"

"Who *can* I bring home, Neil?"

"I don't know, who can you?"

"Can I bring you home?"

"I don't know," I said, "can you?"

"Stop repeating the question!"

"I sure as hell can't give you the answer."

"Neil, be realistic. After this, can I bring you home? Can you see us all sitting around the table?"

"I can't if you can't, and I can if you can."

"Are you going to speak Zen, for God's sake!"

"Brenda, the choices aren't mine. You can bring Linda or me. You can go home or not go home. That's another choice. Then you don't even have to worry about choosing between me and Linda."

"Neil, you don't understand. They're still my parents. They did send me to the best schools, didn't they? They have given me everything I've wanted, haven't they?"

"Yes."

"Then how can I not go home? I *have* to go home."

"Why?"

"You don't understand. Your parents don't bother you any more. You're lucky."

"Oh, sure. I live with my crazy aunt, that's a real bargain."

"Families are different. You don't understand."

"Goddamit, I understand more than you think. I understand why the hell you left that thing lying around. Don't you? Can't you put two and two together?"

"Neil, what are you talking about! You're the one who doesn't understand. You're the one who from the very beginning was accusing me of things? Remember? Isn't it so? Why don't you have your eyes fixed? Why don't you have this fixed, that fixed? As if it were my fault that I *could* have them fixed. You kept acting as if I was going to run away from you every minute. And now you're doing it again, telling me I planted that thing on purpose."

"I loved you, Brenda, so I cared."

"I loved *you*. That's why I got that damn thing in the first place."

And then we heard the tense in which we'd spoken and we settled back into ourselves and silence.

A few minutes later I picked up my bag and put on my

coat. I think Brenda was crying too when I went out the door.

Instead of grabbing a cab immediately, I walked down the street and out towards the Harvard Yard which I had never seen before. I entered one of the gates and then headed out along a path, under the tired autumn foliage and the dark sky. I wanted to be alone, in the dark; not because I wanted to think about anything, but rather because, for just a while, I wanted to think about nothing. I walked clear across the Yard and up a little hill and then I was standing in front of the Lamont Library, which, Brenda had once told me, had Patimkin Sinks in its rest rooms. From the light of the lamp on the path behind me I could see my reflection in the glass front of the building. Inside, it was dark and there were no students to be seen, no librarians. Suddenly, I wanted to set down my suitcase and pick up a rock and heave it right through the glass, but of course I didn't. I simply looked at myself in the mirror the light made of the window. I was only that substance, I thought, those limbs, that face that I saw in front of me. I looked, but the outside of me gave up little information about the inside of me. I wished I could scoot around to the other side of the window, faster than light or sound or Herb Clark on Homecoming Day, to get behind that image and catch whatever it was that looked through those eyes. What was it inside me that had turned pursuit and clutching into love, and then turned it inside out again? What was it that had turned winning into losing, and losing — who knows — into winning? I was sure I had loved Brenda, though standing there, I knew I couldn't any longer. And I knew it would be a long while before I made love to anyone the way I had made love to her. With anyone else, could I summon up such a passion? Whatever spawned my love for her, had that spawned such lust too? If she had only been slightly *not* Brenda . . . but then would I have loved her? I looked hard at the image of me, at that darkening of the glass, and then my gaze pushed through it, over the cool floor, to a broken wall of books, imperfectly shelved.

I did not look very much longer, but took a train that got me into Newark just as the sun was rising on the first day of the Jewish New Year. I was back in plenty of time for work.

THE

CONVERSION

OF THE JEWS

Y ou're a real one for opening your mouth in the first place," Itzie said. "What do you open your mouth all the time for?"

"I didn't bring it up, Itz, I didn't," Ozzie said.

"What do you care about Jesus Christ for anyway?"

"I didn't bring up Jesus Christ. He did. I didn't even know what he was talking about. Jesus is historical, he kept saying. Jesus is historical." Ozzie mimicked the monumental voice of Rabbi Binder.

"Jesus was a person that lived like you and me," Ozzie continued. "That's what Binder said — "

"Yeah? . . . So what! What do I give two cents whether he lived or not. And what do you gotta open your mouth!" Itzie Lieberman favored closed-mouthedness, especially when it came to Ozzie Freedman's questions. Mrs. Freedman had to see Rabbi Binder twice before about Ozzie's questions and this Wednesday at four-thirty would be the third time. Itzie preferred to keep *his* mother in the kitchen; he settled for behind-the-back subtleties such as gestures, faces, snarls and other less delicate barnyard noises.

"He was a real person, Jesus, but he wasn't like God, and we don't believe he is God." Slowly, Ozzie was explaining Rabbi Binder's position to Itzie, who had been absent from Hebrew School the previous afternoon.

"The Catholics," Itzie said helpfully, "they believe in Jesus Christ, that he's God." Itzie Lieberman used "the Catholics" in its broadest sense — to include the Protestants.

Ozzie received Itzie's remark with a tiny head bob, as though it were a footnote, and went on. "His mother was Mary, and his father probably was Joseph," Ozzie said. "But the New Testament says his real father was God."

"His *real* father?"

"Yeah," Ozzie said, "that's the big thing, his father's supposed to be God."

"Bull."

"That's what Rabbi Binder says, that it's impossible — "

"Sure it's impossible. That stuff's all bull. To have a baby you gotta get laid," Itzie theologized. "Mary hadda get laid."

"That's what Binder says: 'The only way a woman can have a baby is to have intercourse with a man.'"

"He said *that*, Ozz?" For a moment it appeared that Itzie had put the theological question aside. "He said that, intercourse?" A little curled smile shaped itself in the lower half of Itzie's face like a pink mustache. "What you guys do, Ozz, you laugh or something?"

"I raised my hand."

"Yeah? Whatja say?"

"That's when I asked the question."

Itzie's face lit up. "Whatja ask about — intercourse?"

"No, I asked the question about God, how if He could create the heaven and earth in six days, and make all the animals and the fish and the light in six days — the light especially, that's what always gets me, that He could make the light. Making fish and animals, that's pretty good — "

"That's damn good." Itzie's appreciation was honest but unimaginative: it was as though God had just pitched a one-hitter.

"But making light . . . I mean when you think about it, it's really something," Ozzie said. "Anyway, I asked Binder if He could make all that in six days, and He could *pick* the six days he wanted right out of nowhere, why couldn't He let a woman have a baby without having intercourse."

"You said intercourse, Ozz, to Binder?"

"Yeah."

"Right in class?"

"Yeah."

Itzie smacked the side of his head.

"I mean, no kidding around," Ozzie said, "that'd really be nothing. After all that other stuff, that'd practically be nothing."

Itzie considered a moment. "What'd Binder say?"

"He started all over again explaining how Jesus was historical and how he lived like you and me but he wasn't God. So I said I under*stood* that. What I wanted to know was different."

What Ozzie wanted to know was always different. The first time he had wanted to know how Rabbi Binder could call the Jews "The Chosen People" if the Declaration of Independence claimed all men to be created equal. Rabbi Binder tried to distinguish for him between political equality and spiritual legitimacy, but what Ozzie wanted to know, he insisted vehemently, was different. That was the first time his mother had to come.

Then there was the plane crash. Fifty-eight people had

been killed in a plane crash at La Guardia. In studying a casualty list in the newspaper his mother had discovered among the list of those dead eight Jewish names (his grandmother had nine but she counted Miller as a Jewish name); because of the eight she said the plane crash was "a tragedy." During free-discussion time on Wednesday Ozzie had brought to Rabbi Binder's attention this matter of "some of his relations" always picking out the Jewish names. Rabbi Binder had begun to explain cultural unity and some other things when Ozzie stood up at his seat and said that what he wanted to know was different. Rabbi Binder insisted that he sit down and it was then that Ozzie shouted that he wished all fifty-eight were Jews. That was the second time his mother came.

"And he kept explaining about Jesus being historical, and so I kept asking him. No kidding, Itz, he was trying to make me look stupid."

"So what he finally do?"

"Finally he starts screaming that I was deliberately simple-minded and a wise guy, and that my mother had to come, and this was the last time. And that I'd never get bar-mitzvahed if he could help it. Then, Itz, then he starts talking in that voice like a statue, real slow and deep, and he says that I better think over what I said about the Lord. He told me to go to his office and think it over." Ozzie leaned his body towards Itzie. "Itz, I thought it over for a solid hour, and now I'm convinced God could do it."

Ozzie had planned to confess his latest transgression to his mother as soon as she came home from work. But it was a Friday night in November and already dark, and when Mrs. Freedman came through the door she tossed off her coat, kissed Ozzie quickly on the face, and went to the kitchen table to light the three yellow candles, two for the Sabbath and one for Ozzie's father.

When his mother lit the candles she would move her two arms slowly towards her, dragging them through the air, as though persuading people whose minds were half made up. And her eyes would get glassy with tears. Even when his father was alive Ozzie remembered that her eyes had gotten glassy, so it didn't have anything to do with his dying. It had something to do with lighting the candles.

As she touched the flaming match to the unlit wick of a Sabbath candle, the phone rang, and Ozzie, standing only a foot from it, plucked it off the receiver and held it muffled to his chest. When his mother lit candles Ozzie felt there should be no noise; even breathing, if you could manage it, should be softened. Ozzie pressed the phone to his breast and watched his mother dragging whatever she was dragging, and he felt his own eyes get glassy. His mother was a round, tired, gray-haired penguin of a woman whose gray skin had begun to feel the tug of gravity and the weight of her own history. Even when she was dressed up she didn't look like a chosen person. But when she lit candles she looked like something better; like a woman who knew momentarily that God could do anything.

After a few mysterious minutes she was finished. Ozzie hung up the phone and walked to the kitchen table where she was beginning to lay the two places for the four-course Sabbath meal. He told her that she would have to see Rabbi Binder next Wednesday at four-thirty, and then he told her why. For the first time in their life together she hit Ozzie across the face with her hand.

All through the chopped liver and chicken soup part of

the dinner Ozzie cried; he didn't have any appetite for the rest.

On Wednesday, in the largest of the three basement class-rooms of the synagogue, Rabbi Marvin Binder, a tall, hand-some, broad-shouldered man of thirty with thick strong-fibered black hair, removed his watch from his pocket and saw that it was four o'clock. At the rear of the room Yakov Blotnik, the seventy-one-year-old custodian, slowly polished the large window, mumbling to himself, unaware that it was four o'clock or six o'clock, Monday or Wednesday. To most of the students Yakov Blotnik's mumbling, along with his brown curly beard, scythe nose, and two heel-trailing black cats, made of him an object of wonder, a for-eigner, a relic, towards whom they were alternately fearful and disrespectful. To Ozzie the mumbling had always seemed a monotonous, curious prayer; what made it curi-ous was that old Blotnik had been mumbling so steadily for so many years, Ozzie suspected he had memorized the prayers and forgotten all about God.

"It is now free-discussion time," Rabbi Binder said. "Feel free to talk about any Jewish matter at all — re-ligion, family, politics, sports — "

There was silence. It was a gusty, clouded November afternoon and it did not seem as though there ever was or could be a thing called baseball. So nobody this week said a word about that hero from the past, Hank Greenberg — which limited free discussion considerably.

And the soul-battering Ozzie Freedman had just re-ceived from Rabbi Binder had imposed its limitation. When it was Ozzie's turn to read aloud from the Hebrew book the rabbi had asked him petulantly why he didn't read more rapidly. He was showing no progress. Ozzie said he could read faster but that if he did he was sure not to understand what he was reading. Nevertheless, at the rabbi's repeated suggestion Ozzie tried, and showed a great talent, but in the midst of a long passage he stopped short and said he didn't understand a word he was reading, and started in again at a drag-footed pace. Then came the soul-battering.

Consequently when free-discussion time rolled around none of the students felt too free. The rabbi's invitation was answered only by the mumbling of feeble old Blotnik.

"Isn't there anything at all you would like to discuss?" Rabbi Binder asked again, looking at his watch. "No questions or comments?"

There was a small grumble from the third row. The rabbi requested that Ozzie rise and give the rest of the class the advantage of his thought.

Ozzie rose. "I forget it now," he said, and sat down in his place.

Rabbi Binder advanced a seat towards Ozzie and poised himself on the edge of the desk. It was Itzie's desk and the rabbi's frame only a dagger's-length away from his face snapped him to sitting attention.

"Stand up again, Oscar," Rabbi Binder said calmly, "and try to assemble your thoughts."

Ozzie stood up. All his classmates turned in their seats and watched as he gave an unconvincing scratch to his forehead.

"I can't assemble any," he announced, and plunked himself down.

"Stand up!" Rabbi Binder advanced from Itzie's desk to the one directly in front of Ozzie; when the rabbinical back was turned Itzie gave it five-fingers off the tip of his nose, causing a small titter in the room. Rabbi Binder was too absorbed in squelching Ozzie's nonsense once and for all to bother with titters. "Stand up, Oscar. What's your question about?"

Ozzie pulled a word out of the air. It was the handiest word. "Religion."

"Oh, now you remember?"

"Yes."

"What is it?"

Trapped, Ozzie blurted the first thing that came to him. "Why can't He make anything He wants to make!"

As Rabbi Binder prepared an answer, a final answer, Itzie, ten feet behind him, raised one finger on his left hand, gestured it meaningfully towards the rabbi's back, and brought the house down.

Binder twisted quickly to see what had happened and in the midst of the commotion Ozzie shouted into the rabbi's back what he couldn't have shouted to his face. It was a loud, toneless sound that had the timbre of something stored inside for about six days.

"You don't know! You don't know anything about God!"

The rabbi spun back towards Ozzie. "What?"

"You don't know — you don't — "

"Apologize, Oscar, apologize!" It was a threat.

"You don't — "

Rabbi Binder's hand flicked out at Ozzie's cheek. Perhaps it had only been meant to clamp the boy's mouth shut, but Ozzie ducked and the palm caught him squarely on the nose.

The blood came in a short, red spurt on to Ozzie's shirt front.

The next moment was all confusion. Ozzie screamed, "You bastard, you bastard!" and broke for the classroom door. Rabbi Binder lurched a step backwards, as though his own blood had started flowing violently in the opposite direction, then gave a clumsy lurch forward and bolted out the door after Ozzie. The class followed after the rabbi's huge blue-suited back, and before old Blotnik could turn from his window, the room was empty and everyone was headed full speed up the three flights leading to the roof.

If one should compare the light of day to the life of man: sunrise to birth; sunset — the dropping down over the edge — to death; then as Ozzie Freedman wiggled through the trapdoor of the synagogue roof, his feet kicking backwards bronco-style at Rabbi Binder's outstretched arms — at that moment the day was fifty years old. As a rule, fifty or fifty-five reflects accurately the age of late afternoons in November, for it is in that month, during those hours, that one's awareness of light seems no longer a matter of seeing, but of hearing: light begins clicking away. In fact, as Ozzie locked shut the trapdoor in the rabbi's face, the sharp click of the bolt into the lock might momentarily have been mistaken for the sound of the heavier gray that had just throbbed through the sky.

With all his weight Ozzie kneeled on the locked door; any instant he was certain that Rabbi Binder's shoulder would fling it open, splintering the wood into shrapnel and catapulting his body into the sky. But the door did not move and below him he heard only the rumble of feet, first loud then dim, like thunder rolling away.

A question shot through his brain. "Can this be *me?*" For a thirteen-year-old who had just labeled his religious leader a bastard, twice, it was not an improper question.

Louder and louder the question came to him —"Is it me? It is me?" — until he discovered himself no longer kneeling, but racing crazily towards the edge of the roof, his eyes crying, his throat screaming, and his arms flying everywhichway as though not his own.

"Is it me? Is it me Me ME ME ME! It has to be me — but is it!"

It is the question a thief must ask himself the night he jimmies open his first window, and it is said to be the question with which bridegrooms quiz themselves before the altar.

In the few wild seconds it took Ozzie's body to propel him to the edge of the roof, his self-examination began to grow fuzzy. Gazing down at the street, he became confused as to the problem beneath the question: was it, is-it-me-who-called-Binder-a-bastard? or, is-it-me-prancing-around-on-the-roof? However, the scene below settled all, for there is an instant in any action when whether it is you or somebody else is academic. The thief crams the money in his pockets and scoots out the window. The bridegroom signs the hotel register for two. And the boy on the roof finds a streetful of people gaping at him, necks stretched backwards, faces up, as though he were the ceiling of the Hayden Planetarium. Suddenly you know it's you.

"Oscar! Oscar Freedman!" A voice rose from the center of the crowd, a voice that, could it have been seen, would have looked like the writing on scroll. "Oscar Freedman, get down from there. Immediately!" Rabbi Binder was pointing one arm stiffly up at him; and at the end of that arm, one finger aimed menacingly. It was the attitude of a dictator, but one — the eyes confessed all — whose personal valet had spit neatly in his face.

Ozzie didn't answer. Only for a blink's length did he look towards Rabbi Binder. Instead his eyes began to fit together the world beneath him, to sort out people from places, friends from enemies, participants from spectators. In little jagged starlike clusters his friends stood around Rabbi Binder, who was still pointing. The topmost point on a star compounded not of angels but of five adolescent boys was Itzie. What a world it was, with those stars below, Rabbi Binder below ... Ozzie, who a moment earlier hadn't been able to control his own body, started to feel the meaning of the word control: he felt Peace and he felt Power.

"Oscar Freedman, I'll give you three to come down."

Few dictators give their subjects three to do anything; but, as always, Rabbi Binder only looked dictatorial.

"Are you ready, Oscar?"

Ozzie nodded his head yes, although he had no intention in the world — the lower one of the celestial one he'd just entered — of coming down even if Rabbi Binder should give him a million.

"All right then," said Rabbi Binder. He ran a hand through his black Samson hair as though it were the gesture prescribed for uttering the first digit. Then, with his other hand cutting a circle out of the small piece of sky around him, he spoke. "One!"

There was no thunder. On the contrary, at that moment, as though "one" was the cue for which he had been waiting, the world's least thunderous person appeared on the synagogue steps. He did not so much come out the synagogue door as lean out, onto the darkening air. He clutched at the doorknob with one hand and looked up at the roof.

"Oy!"

Yakov Blotnik's old mind hobbled slowly, as if on crutches, and though he couldn't decide precisely what the boy was doing on the roof, he knew it wasn't good — that is, it wasn't-good-for-the-Jews. For Yakov Blotnik life had fractionated itself simply: things were either good-for-the-Jews or no-good-for-the-Jews.

He smacked his free hand to his in-sucked cheek, gently. "Oy, Gut!" And then quickly as he was able, he jacked down his head and surveyed the street. There was Rabbi Binder (like a man at an auction with only three dollars in his pocket, he had just delivered a shaky "Two!"); there were the students, and that was all. So far it-wasn't-so-bad-for-the-Jews. But the boy had to come down immediately, before anybody saw. The problem: how to get the boy off the roof?

Anybody who has ever had a cat on the roof knows how to get him down. You call the fire department. Or first you call the operator and you ask her for the fire department. And the next thing there is great jamming of brakes and clanging of bells and shouting of instructions. And then the cat is off the roof. You do the same thing to get a boy off the roof.

That is, you do the same thing if you are Yakov Blotnik and you once had a cat on the roof.

When the engines, all four of them, arrived, Rabbi Binder had four times given Ozzie the count of three. The big hook-and-ladder swung around the corner and one of the firemen leaped from it, plunging headlong towards the yellow fire hydrant in front of the synagogue. With a huge wrench he began to unscrew the top nozzle. Rabbi Binder raced over to him and pulled at his shoulder.

"There's no fire . . ."

The fireman mumbled back over his shoulder and, heat-edly, continued working at the nozzle.

"But there's no fire, there's no fire . . ." Binder shouted. When the fireman mumbled again, the rabbi grasped his face with both his hands and pointed it up at the roof.

To Ozzie it looked as though Rabbi Binder was trying to tug the fireman's head out of his body, like a cork from a bottle. He had to giggle at the picture they made: it was a family portrait — rabbi in black skullcap, fireman in red fire hat, and the little yellow hydrant squatting beside like a kid brother, bareheaded. From the edge of the roof Ozzie waved at the portrait, a one-handed, flapping, mock-ing wave; in doing it his right foot slipped from under him. Rabbi Binder covered his eyes with his hands.

Firemen work fast. Before Ozzie had even regained his balance, a big, round, yellowed net was being held on the synagogue lawn. The firemen who held it looked up at Ozzie with stern, feelingless faces.

One of the firemen turned his head towards Rabbi Binder. "What, is the kid nuts or something?"

Rabbi Binder unpeeled his hands from his eyes, slowly, painfully, as if they were tape. Then he checked: nothing on the sidewalk, no dents in the net.

"Is he gonna jump, or what?" the fireman shouted.

In a voice not at all like a statue, Rabbi Binder finally answered. "Yes, Yes, I think so . . . He's been threatening to . . ."

Threatening to? Why, the reason he was on the roof, Ozzie remembered, was to get away; he hadn't even thought about jumping. He had just run to get away, and the truth was that he hadn't really headed for the roof as much as he'd been chased there.

"What's his name, the kid?"

"Freedman," Rabbi Binder answered. "Oscar Freedman."

The fireman looked up at Ozzie. "What is it with you, Oscar? You gonna jump, or what?"

Ozzie did not answer. Frankly, the question had just arisen.

"Look, Oscar, if you're gonna jump, jump — and if you're not gonna jump, don't jump. But don't waste our time, willya?"

Ozzie looked at the fireman and then at Rabbi Binder. He wanted to see Rabbi Binder cover his eyes one more time.

"I'm going to jump."

And then he scampered around the edge of the roof to the corner, where there was no net below, and he flapped his arms at his sides, swishing the air and smacking his palms to his trousers on the downbeat. He began screaming like some kind of engine, "Wheeeee ... wheeeeee," and leaning way out over the edge with the upper half of his body. The firemen whipped around to cover the ground with the net. Rabbi Binder mumbled a few words to Somebody and covered his eyes. Everything happened quickly, jerkily, as in a silent movie. The crowd, which had arrived with the fire engines, gave out a long, Fourth-of-July fireworks oooh-aahhh. In the excitement no one had paid the crowd much heed, except, of course, Yakov Blotnik, who swung from the doorknob counting heads. "Fier und tsvansik ... finf und tsvantsik ... Oy, Gut!" It wasn't like this with the cat.

Rabbi Binder peeked through his fingers, checked the sidewalk and net. Empty. But there was Ozzie racing to the other corner. The firemen raced with him but were unable to keep up. Whenever Ozzie wanted to he might jump and splatter himself upon the sidewalk, and by the time the firemen scooted to the spot all they could do with their net would be to cover the mess.

"Wheeeee . . . wheeeee . . ."

"Hey, Oscar," the winded fireman yelled, "What the hell is this, a game or something?"

"Wheeeee . . . wheeeee . . ."

"Hey, Oscar — "

But he was off now to the other corner, flapping his wings fiercely. Rabbi Binder couldn't take it any longer — the fire engines from nowhere, the screaming suicidal boy, the net. He fell to his knees, exhausted, and with his hands curled together in front of his chest like a little dome, he pleaded, "Oscar, stop it, Oscar. Don't jump, Oscar. Please come down . . . Please don't jump."

And further back in the crowd a single voice, a single young voice, shouted a lone word to the boy on the roof.

"Jump!"

It was Itzie. Ozzie momentarily stopped flapping.

"Go ahead, Ozz — jump!" Itzie broke off his point of the star and courageously, with the inspiration not of a wise-guy but of a disciple, stood alone. "Jump, Ozz, jump!"

Still on his knees, his hands still curled, Rabbi Binder twisted his body back. He looked at Itzie, then, agonizingly, back to Ozzie.

"Oscar, Don't jump! Please, Don't Jump . . . please please . . ."

"Jump!" This time it wasn't Itzie but another point of the star. By the time Mrs. Freedman arrived to keep her four-thirty appointment with Rabbi Binder, the whole little upside down heaven was shouting and pleading for Ozzie to jump, and Rabbi Binder no longer was pleading with him not to jump, but was crying into the dome of his hands.

Understandably Mrs. Freedman couldn't figure out what her son was doing on the roof. So she asked.

"Ozzie, my Ozzie, what are you doing? My Ozzie, what is it?"

Ozzie stopped wheeeeeing and slowed his arms down to a cruising flap, the kind birds use in soft winds, but he did not answer. He stood against the low, clouded, darkening sky — light clicked down swiftly now, as on a small gear — flapping softly and gazing down at the small bundle of a woman who was his mother.

"What are you doing, Ozzie?" She turned towards the kneeling Rabbi Binder and rushed so close that only a paper-thickness of dusk lay between her stomach and his shoulders.

"What is my baby doing?"

Rabbi Binder gaped up at her but he too was mute. All that moved was the dome of his hands; it shook back and forth like a weak pulse.

"Rabbi, get him down! He'll kill himself. Get him down, my only baby . . ."

"I can't," Rabbi Binder said, "I can't . . ." and he turned his handsome head towards the crowd of boys behind him. "It's them. Listen to them."

And for the first time Mrs. Freedman saw the crowd of boys, and she heard what they were yelling.

"He's doing it for them. He won't listen to me. It's them." Rabbi Binder spoke like one in a trance.

"For them?"

"Yes."

"Why for them?"

"They want him to ..."

Mrs. Freedman raised her two arms upward as though she were conducting the sky. "For them he's doing it!" And then in a gesture older than pyramids, older than prophets and floods, her arms came slapping down to her sides. "A martyr I have. Look!" She tilted her head to the roof. Ozzie was still flapping softly. "My martyr."

"Oscar, come down, *please*," Rabbi Binder groaned.

In a startlingly even voice Mrs. Freedman called to the boy on the roof. "Ozzie, come down, Ozzie. Don't be a martyr, my baby."

As though it were a litany, Rabbi Binder repeated her words. "Don't be a martyr, my baby. Don't be a martyr."

"Gawhead, Ozz — *be* a Martin!" It was Itzie. "Be a Martin, be a Martin," and all the voices joined in singing for Martindom, whatever *it* was. "Be a Martin, be a Martin ..."

Somehow when you're on a roof the darker it gets the less you can hear. All Ozzie knew was that two groups wanted two new things: his friends were spirited and musical about what they wanted; his mother and the rabbi were even-toned, chanting, about what they didn't want. The rabbi's voice was without tears now and so was his mother's.

The big net stared up at Ozzie like a sightless eye. The big, clouded sky pushed down. From beneath it looked like a gray corrugated board. Suddenly, looking up into that unsympathetic sky, Ozzie realized all the strangeness of what these people, his friends, were asking: they wanted him to jump, to kill himself; they were singing about it now — it made them that happy. And there was an even greater strangeness: Rabbi Binder was on his knees, trembling. If there was a question to be asked now it was not "Is it me?" but rather "Is it us? . . . Is it us?"

Being on the roof, it turned out, was a serious thing. If he jumped would the singing become dancing? Would it? What would jumping stop? Yearningly, Ozzie wished he could rip open the sky, plunge his hands through, and pull out the sun; and on the sun, like a coin, would be stamped JUMP or DON'T JUMP.

Ozzie's knees rocked and sagged a little under him as though they were setting him for a dive. His arms tightened, stiffened, froze, from shoulders to fingernails. He felt as if each part of his body were going to vote as to whether he should kill himself or not — and each part as though it were independent of *him*.

The light took an unexpected click down and the new darkness, like a gag, hushed the friends singing for this and the mother and rabbi chanting for that.

Ozzie stopped counting votes, and in a curiously high voice, like one who wasn't prepared for speech, he spoke.

"Mamma?"

"Yes, Oscar."

"Mamma, get down on your knees, like Rabbi Binder."

"Oscar — "

"Get down on your knees," he said, "or I'll jump."

Ozzie heard a whimper, then a quick rustling, and when he looked down where his mother had stood he saw the top of a head and beneath that a circle of dress. She was kneeling beside Rabbi Binder.

He spoke again. "Everybody kneel." There was the sound of everybody kneeling.

Ozzie looked around. With one hand he pointed towards the synagogue entrance. "Make *him* kneel."

There was a noise, not of kneeling, but of body-and-cloth stretching. Ozzie could hear Rabbi Binder saying in a gruff whisper, ". . . or he'll *kill* himself," and when next he looked there was Yakov Blotnik off the doorknob and for the first time in his life upon his knees in the Gentile posture of prayer.

As for the firemen — it is not as difficult as one might imagine to hold a net taut while you are kneeling.

Ozzie looked around again; and then he called to Rabbi Binder.

"Rabbi?"

"Yes, Oscar."

"Rabbi Binder, do you believe in God."

"Yes."

"Do you believe God can do Anything?" Ozzie leaned his head out into the darkness. "Anything?"

"Oscar, I think — "

"Tell me you believe God can do Anything."

There was a second's hesitation. Then: "God can do Anything."

"Tell me you believe God can make a child without intercourse."

"He can."

"Tell me!"

"God," Rabbi Binder admitted, "can make a child without intercourse."

"Mamma, you tell me."

"God can make a child without intercourse," his mother said.

"Make *him* tell me." There was no doubt who *him* was.

In a few moments Ozzie heard an old comical voice say something to the increasing darkness about God.

Next, Ozzie made everybody say it. And then he made them all say they believed in Jesus Christ — first one at a time, then all together.

When the catechizing was through it was the beginning of evening. From the street it sounded as if the boy on the roof might have sighed.

"Ozzie?" A woman's voice dared to speak. "You'll come down now?"

There was no answer, but the woman waited, and when a voice finally did speak it was thin and crying, and exhausted as that of an old man who has just finished pulling the bells.

"Mamma, don't you see — you shouldn't hit me. He shouldn't hit me. You shouldn't hit me about God, Mamma. You should never hit anybody about God — "

"Ozzie, please come down now."

"Promise me, promise me you'll never hit anybody about God."

He had asked only his mother, but for some reason everyone kneeling in the street promised he would never hit anybody about God.

Once again there was silence.

"I can come down now, Mamma," the boy on the roof finally said. He turned his head both ways as though checking the traffic lights. "Now I can come down . . ."

And he did, right into the center of the yellow net that glowed in the evening's edge like an overgrown halo.

DEFENDER

OF

THE FAITH

In May of 1945, only a few weeks after the fighting had ended in Europe, I was rotated back to the States, where I spent the remainder of the war with a training company at Camp Crowder, Missouri. We had been racing across Germany so swiftly during the late winter and spring that when I boarded the plane that drizzly morning in Berlin, I couldn't believe our destination lay to the west. My mind might inform me otherwise, but there was an inertia of the spirit that told me we were flying to a new front where we would disembark and continue our push eastward — eastward until we'd circled the globe, marching through villages along whose twisting, cobbled streets crowds of the enemy would watch us take possession of what up till then they'd considered their own. I had changed enough in two years not to mind the trembling of the old people, the crying of the very young, the uncertain fear in the eyes of the once-arrogant. After two years I had been fortunate enough to develop an infantryman's heart which, like his feet, at first aches and swells, but finally grows horny enough for him to travel the weirdest paths without feeling a thing.

Captain Paul Barrett was to be my C. O. at Camp Crowder. The day I reported for duty he came out of his office to shake my hand. He was short, gruff, and fiery, and indoors or out he wore his polished helmet liner down on his little eyes. In Europe he had received a battlefield commission and a serious chest wound, and had been returned to the States only a few months before. He spoke easily to me, but was, I thought, unnecessarily abusive towards the troops. At the evening formation, he introduced me.

"Gentlemen," he called. "Sergeant Thurston, as you know, is no longer with this Company. Your new First Sergeant is Sergeant Nathan Marx here. He is a veteran of the European theater and consequently will take no shit."

I sat up late in the orderly room that evening, trying halfheartedly to solve the riddle of duty rosters, personnel forms, and morning reports. The CQ slept with his mouth open on a mattress on the floor. A trainee stood reading the next day's duty roster, which was posted on the bulletin board directly inside the screen door. It was a warm evening and I could hear the men's radios playing dance music over in the barracks.

The trainee, who I knew had been staring at me whenever I looked groggily into the forms, finally took a step in my direction.

"Hey, Sarge — we having a G.I. party tomorrow night?" A G.I. party is a barracks-cleaning.

"You usually have them on Friday nights?"

"Yes," and then he added mysteriously, "that's the whole thing."

"Then you'll have a G.I. party."

He turned away and I heard him mumbling. His

shoulders were moving and I wondered if he was crying.

"What's your name, soldier?" I asked.

He turned, not crying at all. Instead his green-speckled eyes, long and narrow, flashed like fish in the sun. He walked over to me and sat on the edge of my desk.

He reached out a hand. "Sheldon," he said.

"Stand on your own two feet, Sheldon."

Climbing off the desk, he said, "Sheldon Grossbart." He smiled wider at the intimacy into which he'd led me.

"You against cleaning the barracks Friday night, Grossbart? Maybe we shouldn't have G.I. parties — maybe we should get a maid." My tone startled me: I felt like a Charlie McCarthy, with every top sergeant I had ever known as my Edgar Bergen.

"No, Sergeant." He grew serious, but with a seriousness that seemed only to be the stifling of a smile. "It's just G.I. parties on Friday night, of all nights . . ."

He slipped up to the corner of the desk again — not quite sitting, but not quite standing either. He looked at me with those speckled eyes flashing and then made a gesture with his hand. It was very slight, no more than a rotation back and forth of the wrist, and yet it managed to exclude from our affairs everything else in the orderly room, to make the two of us the center of the world. It seemed, in fact, to exclude everything about the two of us except our hearts. "Sergeant Thurston was one thing," he whispered, an eye flashing to the sleeping CQ "but we thought with you here, things might be a little different."

"We?"

"The Jewish personnel."

"Why?" I said, harshly.

He hesitated a moment, and then, uncontrollably, his

hand went up to his mouth. "I mean . . ." he said.

"What's on your mind?" Whether I was still angry at
the "Sheldon" business or something else, I hadn't a
chance to tell — but clearly I was angry.

". . . we thought you . . . Marx, you know, like Karl Marx.
The Marx brothers. Those guys are all . . . M-A-R-X,
isn't that how you spell it, Sergeant?"

"M-A-R-X."

"Fishbein said — " He stopped. "What I mean to say,
Sergeant — " His face and neck were red, and his mouth
moved but no words came out. In a moment, he raised
himself to attention, gazing down at me. It was as though
he had suddenly decided he could expect no more sympathy
from me than from Thurston, the reason being that I was
of Thurston's faith and not his. The young man had
managed to confuse himself as to what my faith really was,
but I felt no desire to straighten him out. Very simply, I
didn't like him.

When I did nothing but return his gaze, he spoke, in an
altered tone. "You see, Sergeant," he explained to me,
"Friday nights, Jews are supposed to go to services."

"Did Sergeant Thurston tell you you couldn't go to
them when there was a G.I. party?"

"No."

"Did he say you had to stay and scrub the floors?"

"No, Sergeant."

"Did the Captain say you had to stay and scrub the
floors?"

"That isn't it, Sergeant. It's the other guys in the barracks." He leaned toward me. "They think we're goofing
off. But we're not. That's when Jews go to services, Friday
night. We have to."

"Then go."

"But the other guys make accusations. They have no right."

"That's not the Army's problem, Grossbart. It's a personal problem you'll have to work out yourself."

"But it's un*fair*."

I got up to leave. "There's nothing I can do about it," I said.

Grossbart stiffened in front of me. "But this is a matter of *religion*, sir."

"Sergeant."

"I mean 'Sergeant,' " he said, almost snarling.

"Look, go see the chaplain. The I.G. You want to see Captain Barrett, I'll arrange an appointment."

"No, no. I don't want to make trouble, Sergeant. That's the first thing they throw up to you. I just want my rights!"

"Damn it, Grossbart, stop whining. You have your rights. You can stay and scrub floors or you can go to *shul* — "

The smile swam in again. Spittle gleamed at the corners of his mouth. "You mean church, Sergeant."

"I mean *shul*, Grossbart!" I walked past him and outside. Near me I heard the scrunching of a guard's boots on gravel. In the lighted windows of the barracks the young men in T-shirts and fatigue pants were sitting on their bunks, polishing their rifles. Suddenly there was a light rustling behind me. I turned and saw Grossbart's dark frame fleeing back to the barracks, racing to tell his Jewish friends that they were right — that like Karl and Harpo, I was one of them.

The next morning, while chatting with the Captain, I recounted the incident of the previous evening, as if to unburden myself of it. Somehow in the telling it seemed to the Captain that I was not so much explaining Grossbart's position as defending it.

"Marx, I'd fight side by side with a nigger if the fellow proved to me he was a man. I pride myself," the Captain said looking out the window, "that I've got an open mind. Consequently, Sergeant, nobody gets special treatment here, for the good *or* the bad. All a man's got to do is prove himself. A man fires well on the range, I give him a weekend pass. He scores high in PT, he gets a weekend pass. He *earns* it." He turned from the window and pointed a finger at me. "You're a Jewish fellow, am I right, Marx?"

"Yes, sir."

"And I admire you. I admire you because of the ribbons on your chest, not because you had a hem stitched on your dick before you were old enough to even know you had one. I judge a man by what he shows me on the field of battle, Sergeant. It's what he's got *here*," he said, and then, though I expected he would point to his heart, he jerked a thumb towards the buttons straining to hold his blouse across his belly. "Guts," he said.

"Okay, sir, I only wanted to pass on to you how the men felt."

"Mr. Marx, you're going to be old before your time if you worry about how the men feel. Leave that stuff to the Chaplain — pussy, the clap, church picnics with the little girls from Joplin, that's all his business, not yours. Let's us train these fellas to shoot straight. If the Jewish personnel feels the other men are accusing them of goldbricking ... well, I just don't know. Seems awful funny how suddenly the Lord is calling so loud in Private Grossman's ear he's just got to run to church."

"Synagogue," I said.

"Synagogue is right, Sergeant. I'll write that down for handy reference. Thank you for stopping by."

That evening, a few minutes before the company gathered outside the orderly room for the chow formation, I called the CQ, Corporal Robert LaHill, in to see me. LaHill was a dark burly fellow whose hair curled out of his clothes wherever it could. He carried a glaze in his eyes that made one think of caves and dinosaurs. "LaHill," I said, "when you take the formation, remind the men that they're free to attend church services *whenever* they are held, provided they report to the orderly room before they leave the area."

LaHill didn't flicker; he scratched his wrist, but gave no indication that he'd heard or understood.

"LaHill," I said, "*church.* You remember? Church, priest, Mass, confession . . ."

He curled one lip into a ghastly smile; I took it for a signal that for a second he had flickered back up into the human race.

"Jewish personnel who want to attend services this evening are to fall out in front of the orderly room at 1900." And then I added, "By order of Captain Barrett."

A little while later, as a twilight softer than any I had seen that year dropped over Camp Crowder, I heard LaHill's thick, inflectionless voice outside my window: "Give me your ears, troopers. Toppie says for me to tell you that at 1900 hours all Jewish personnel is to fall out in front here if they wants to attend the Jewish Mass."

At seven o'clock, I looked out of the orderly-room window and saw three soldiers in starched khakis standing alone on the dusty quadrangle. They looked at their watches and fidgeted while they whispered back and forth. It was getting darker, and alone on the deserted field they looked tiny. When I walked to the door I heard the noises of the G.I. party coming from the surrounding barracks — bunks being pushed to the wall, faucets pounding water into buckets, brooms whisking at the wooden floors. In the windows big puffs of cloth moved round and round, cleaning the dirt away for Saturday's inspection. I walked outside and the moment my foot hit the ground I thought I heard Grossbart, who was now in the center, call to the other two, "Ten-*hut*!" Or maybe when they all three jumped to attention, I imagined I heard the command.

At my approach, Grossbart stepped forward. "Thank you, sir," he said.

"Sergeant, Grossbart," I reminded him. "You call officers 'Sir.' I'm not an officer. You've been in the Army three weeks — you know that."

He turned his palms out at his sides to indicate that, in truth, he and I lived beyond convention. "Thank you, anyway," he said.

"Yes," the tall boy behind him said. "Thanks a lot."

And the third whispered, "Thank you," but his mouth barely fluttered so that he did not alter by more than a lip's movement, the posture of attention.

"For what?" I said.

Grossbart snorted, happily. "For the announcement before. The Corporal's announcement. It helped. It made it . . ."

"Fancier." It was the tall boy finishing Grossbart's sentence.

Grossbart smiled. "He means formal, sir. Public," he

said to me. "Now it won't seem as though we're just taking off, goldbricking, because the work has begun."

"It was by order of Captain Barrett," I said.

"Ahh, but you pull a little weight..." Grossbart said. "So we thank you." Then he turned to his companions. "Sergeant Marx, I want you to meet Larry Fishbein."

The tall boy stepped forward and extended his hand. I shook it. "You from New York?" he asked.

"Yes."

"Me too." He had a cadaverous face that collapsed inward from his cheekbone to his jaw, and when he smiled — as he did at the news of our communal attachment — revealed a mouthful of bad teeth. He blinked his eyes a good deal, as though he were fighting back tears. "What borough?" he asked.

I turned to Grossbart. "It's five after seven. What time are services?"

"*Shul*," he smiled, "is in ten minutes. I want you to meet Mickey Halpern. This is Nathan Marx, our Sergeant."

The third boy hopped forward. "Private Michael Halpern." He saluted.

"Salute officers, Halpern." The boy dropped his hand, and in his nervousness checked to see if his shirt pockets were buttoned on the way down.

"Shall I march them over, sir?" Grossbart asked, "or are you coming along?"

From behind Grossbart, Fishbein piped up. "Afterwards they're having refreshments. A Ladies' Auxiliary from St. Louis, the rabbi told us last week."

"The chaplain," whispered Halpern.

"You're welcome to come along," Grossbart said.

To avoid his plea, I looked away, and saw, in the windows

of the barracks, a cloud of faces staring out at the four of us.

"Look, hurry out of here, Grossbart."

"Okay, then," he said. He turned to the others. "Double time, *march!*" and they started off, but ten feet away Grossbart spun about, and running backwards he called to me, "Good *shabus,* sir." And then the three were swallowed into the Missouri dusk.

Even after they'd disappeared over the parade grounds, whose green was now a deep twilight blue, I could hear Grossbart singing the double-time cadence, and as it grew dimmer and dimmer it suddenly touched some deep memory — as did the slant of light — and I was remembering the shrill sounds of a Bronx playground, where years ago, beside the Grand Concourse, I had played on long spring evenings such as this. Those thin fading sounds . . . It was a pleasant memory for a young man so far from peace and home, and it brought so very many recollections with it that I began to grow exceedingly tender about myself. In fact, I indulged myself to a reverie so strong that I felt within as though a hand had opened and was reaching down inside. It had to reach so very far to touch me. It had to reach past those days in the forests of Belgium and the dying I'd refused to weep over; past the nights in those German farmhouses whose books we'd burned to warm us, and which I couldn't bother to mourn; past those endless stretches when I'd shut off all softness I might feel for my fellows, and managed even to deny myself the posture of a conqueror — the swagger that I, as a Jew, might well have worn as my boots whacked against the rubble of Münster, Braunschweig, and finally Berlin.

But now one night noise, one rumor of home and time past, and memory plunged down through all I had anesthetized and came to what I suddenly remembered to be myself. So it was not altogether curious that in search of more of me I found myself following Grossbart's tracks to Chapel No. 3 where the Jewish services were being held.

I took a seat in the last row, which was empty. Two rows in front sat Grossbart, Fishbein, and Halpern, each holding a little white dixie cup. Fishbein was pouring the contents of his cup into Grossbart's, and Grossbart looked mirthful as the liquid drew a purple arc between his hand and Fishbein's. In the glary yellow light, I saw the chaplain on the pulpit chanting the first line of the responsive reading. Grossbart's prayerbook remained closed on his lap; he swished the cup around. Only Halpern responded in prayer. The fingers of his right hand were spread wide across the cover of the book, and his cap was pulled down low onto his brow so that it was round like a *yarmulke* rather than long and pointed. From time to time, Grossbart wet his lips at the cup's edge; Fishbein, his long yellow face, a dying light bulb, looked from here to there, leaning forward at the neck to catch sight of the faces down the row, in front — then behind. He saw me and his eyelids beat a tattoo. His elbow slid into Grossbart's side, his neck inclined towards his friend, and then, when the congregation responded, Grossbart's voice was among them. Fishbein looked into his book now too; his lips, however, didn't move.

Finally it was time to drink the wine. The chaplain smiled down at them as Grossbart swigged in one long gulp, Halpern sipped, meditating, and Fishbein faked devotion with an empty cup.

At last the chaplain spoke: "As I look down amongst the congregation —" he grinned at the word, "this night, I

see many new faces, and I want to welcome you to Friday
night services here at Camp Crowder. I am Major Leo Ben
Ezra, your chaplain . . ." Though an American, the chaplain spoke English very deliberately, syllabically almost, as
though to communicate, above all, to the lip-readers in the
audience. "I have only a few words to say before we adjourn
to the refreshment room where the kind ladies of the
Temple Sinai, St. Louis, Missouri, have a nice setting for
you."

Applause and whistling broke out. After a momentary
grin, the chaplain raised his palms to the congregation, his
eyes flicking upward a moment, as if to remind the troops
where they were and Who Else might be in attendance. In
the sudden silence that followed, I thought I heard Grossbart's cackle — "Let the goyim clean the floors!" Were
those the words? I wasn't sure, but Fishbein, grinning,
nudged Halpern. Halpern looked dumbly at him, then
went back to his prayerbook, which had been occupying
him all through the rabbi's talk. One hand tugged at the
black kinky hair that stuck out under his cap. His lips
moved.

The rabbi continued. "It is about the food that I want
to speak to you for a moment. I know, I know, I know,"
he intoned, wearily, "how in the mouths of most of you
the *trafe* food tastes like ashes. I know how you gag, some
of you, and how your parents suffer to think of their children eating foods unclean and offensive to the palate.
What can I tell you? I can only say close your eyes and
swallow as best you can. Eat what you must to live and
throw away the rest. I wish I could help more. For those
of you who find this impossible, may I ask that you try and
try, but then come to see me in private where, if your re-

vulsion is such, we will have to seek aid from those higher up."

A round of chatter rose and subsided; then everyone sang "Ain Kelohanoh", after all those years I discovered I still knew the words.

Suddenly, the service over, Grossbart was upon me. "Higher up? He means the General?"

"Hey, Shelly," Fishbein interrupted, "he means God." He smacked his face and looked at Halpern. "How high can you go!"

"Shhh!" Grossbart said. "What do you think, Sergeant?"

"I don't know. You better ask the chaplain."

"I'm going to. I'm making an appointment to see him in private. So is Mickey."

Halpern shook his head. "No, no, Sheldon . . ."

"You have rights, Mickey. They can't push us around."

"It's okay. It bothers my mother, not me . . ."

Grossbart looked at me. "Yesterday he threw up. From the hash. It was all ham and God knows what else."

"I have a cold — that was why," Halpern said. He pushed his *yamalkah* back into a cap.

"What about you, Fishbein?" I asked. "You kosher too?"

He flushed, which made the yellow more gray than pink. "A little. But I'll let it ride. I have a very strong stomach. And I don't eat a lot anyway . . ." I continued to look at him, and he held up his wrist to re-enforce what he'd just said. His watch was tightened to the last hole and he pointed that out to me. "So I don't mind."

"But services are important to you?" I asked him.

He looked at Grossbart. "Sure, sir."

"Sergeant."

"Not so much at home," said Grossbart, coming between us, "but away from home it gives one a sense of his Jewishness."

"We have to stick together," Fishbein said.

I started to walk towards the door; Halpern stepped back to make way for me.

"That's what happened in Germany," Grossbart was saying, loud enough for me to hear. "They didn't stick together. They let themselves get pushed around."

I turned. "Look, Grossbart, this is the Army, not summer camp."

He smiled. "So?" Halpern tried to sneak off, but Grossbart held his arm. "So?" he said again.

"Grossbart," I asked, "how old are you?"

"Nineteen."

"And you?" I said to Fishbein.

"The same. The same month even."

"And what about him?" I pointed to Halpern, who'd finally made it safely to the door.

"Eighteen," Grossbart whispered. "But he's like he can't tie his shoes or brush his teeth himself. I feel sorry for him."

"I feel sorry for all of us, Grossbart, but just act like a man. Just don't overdo it."

"Overdo what, sir?"

"The sir business. Don't overdo that," I said, and I left him standing there. I passed by Halpern but he did not look up. Then I was outside, black surrounded me — but behind I heard Grossbart call, "Hey, Mickey, *liebschen*, come on back. Refreshments!"

Liebschen! My grandmother's word for me!

One morning, a week later, while I was working at my

desk, Captain Barrett shouted for me to come into his office. When I entered, he had his helmet liner squashed down so that I couldn't even see his eyes. He was on the phone, and when he spoke to me, he cupped one hand over the mouthpiece.

"Who the fuck is Grossbart?"

"Third platoon, Captain," I said. "A trainee."

"What's all this stink about food? His mother called a goddam congressman about the food . . ." He uncovered the mouthpiece and slid his helmet up so I could see the curl of his bottom eyelash. "Yes, sir," he said into the phone. "Yes, sir. I'm still here, sir. I'm asking Marx here right now . . ."

He covered the mouthpiece again and looked back to me. "Lightfoot Harry's on the phone," he said, between his teeth. "This congressman calls General Lyman who calls Colonel Sousa who calls the Major who calls me. They're just dying to stick this thing on me. What's a matter," he shook the phone at me, "I don't feed the troops? What the hell is this?"

"Sir, Grossbart is strange . . ." Barrett greeted that with a mockingly indulgent smile. I altered my approach. "Captain, he's a very orthodox Jew and so he's only allowed to eat certain foods."

"He throws up, the congressman said. Every time he eats something his mother says he throws up!"

"He's accustomed to observing the dietary laws, Captain."

"So why's his old lady have to call the White House!"

"Jewish parents, sir, they're apt to be more protective than you expect. I mean Jews have a very close family life. A boy goes away from home, sometimes the mother is liable to get very upset. Probably the boy *mentioned* something in a letter and his mother misinterpreted."

"I'd like to punch him one right in the mouth. There's a goddam war on and he wants a silver platter!"

"I don't think the boy's to blame, sir. I'm sure we can straighten it out by just asking him. Jewish parents worry — "

"*All* parents worry, for Christ sake. But they don't get on their high horse and start pulling strings — "

I interrupted, my voice higher, tighter than before. "The home life, Captain, is so very important . . . but you're right, it may sometimes get out of hand. It's a very wonderful thing, Captain, but because it's so close, this kind of thing — "

He didn't listen any longer to my attempt to present both myself and Lightfoot Harry with an explanation for the letter. He turned back to the phone. "Sir?" he said. "Sir, Marx here tells me Jews have a tendency to be pushy. He says he thinks he can settle it right here in the Company . . . Yes, sir . . . I *will* call back, sir, soon as I can . . ." He hung up. "Where are the men, Sergeant?"

"On the range."

With a whack on the top, he crushed his helmet over his eyes, and charged out of his chair. "We're going for a ride."

The Captain drove and I sat beside him. It was a hot spring day and under my newly starched fatigues it felt as though my armpits were melting down onto my sides and chest. The roads were dry and by the time we reached the firing range, my teeth felt gritty with dust though my mouth had been shut the whole trip. The Captain slammed the brakes on and told me to get the hell out and find Grossbart.

I found him on his belly, firing wildly at the 500 feet target. Waiting their turns behind him were Halpern and Fishbein. Fishbein, wearing a pair of rimless G.I. glasses I hadn't seen on him before, gave the appearance of an old peddler who would gladly have sold you the rifle and cartridges that were slung all over him. I stood back by the ammo boxes, waiting for Grossbart to finish spraying the distant targets. Fishbein straggled back to stand near me.

"Hello, Sergeant Marx."

"How are you?" I mumbled.

"Fine, thank you. Sheldon's really a good shot."

"I didn't notice."

"I'm not so good, but I think I'm getting the hang of it now . . . Sergeant, I don't mean to, you know, ask what I shouldn't . . ." The boy stopped. He was trying to speak intimately but the noise of the shooting necessitated that he shout at me.

"What is it?" I asked. Down the range I saw Captain Barrett standing up in the jeep, scanning the line for me and Grossbart.

"My parents keep asking and asking where we're going. Everybody says the Pacific. I don't care, but my parents . . . If I could relieve their minds I think I could concentrate more on my shooting."

"I don't know where, Fishbein. Try to concentrate anyway."

"Sheldon says you might be able to find out — "

"I don't know a thing, Fishbein. You just take it easy, and don't let Sheldon — "

"*I'm* taking it easy, Sergeant. It's at home —"

Grossbart had just finished on the line and was dusting his fatigues with one hand. I left Fishbein's sentence in the middle.

"Grossbart, the Captain wants to see you."

He came toward us. His eyes blazed and twinkled. "Hi!"

"Don't point that goddam rifle!"

"I wouldn't shoot you, Sarge." He gave me a smile wide as a pumpkin as he turned the barrel aside.

"Damn you, Grossbart — this is no joke! Follow me."

I walked ahead of him and had the awful suspicion that behind me Grossbart was *marching*, his rifle on his shoulder, as though he were a one-man detachment.

At the jeep he gave the Captain a rifle salute. "Private Sheldon Grossbart, sir."

"At ease, Grossman." The captain slid over to the empty front seat, and crooking a finger, invited Grossbart closer.

"Bart, sir. Sheldon Gross*bart*. It's a common error." Grossbart nodded to me — *I* understand, he indicated. I looked away, just as the mess truck pulled up to the range, disgorging a half dozen K.P.'s with rolled-up sleeves. The mess sergeant screamed at them while they set up the chow line equipment.

"Grossbart, your mama wrote some congressman that we don't feed you right. Do you know that?" the Captain said.

"It was my father, sir. He wrote to Representative Franconi that my religion forbids me to eat certain foods."

"What religion is that, Grossbart?"

"Jewish."

"Jewish, *sir*," I said to Grossbart.

"Excuse me, sir. 'Jewish, sir.' "

"What have you been living on?" the Captain asked.
"You've been in the Army a month already. You don't look
to me like you're falling to pieces."

"I eat because I have to, sir. But Sergeant Marx will tes-
tify to the fact that I don't eat one mouthful more than I
need to in order to survive."

"Marx," Barrett asked, "is that so?"

"I've never seen Grossbart eat, sir," I said.

"But you heard the rabbi," Grossbart said. "He told us
what to do, and I listened."

The Captain looked at me. "Well, Marx?"

"I still don't know what he eats and doesn't eat, sir."

Grossbart raised his rifle, as though to offer it to me.
"But, Sergeant —"

"Look, Grossbart, just answer the Captain's questions!"
I said sharply.

Barrett smiled at me and I resented it. "All right, Grossbart," he said, "What is it you want? The little piece of
paper? You want out?"

"No, sir. Only to be allowed to live as a Jew. And for
the others, too."

"What others?"

"Fishbein, sir, and Halpern."

"They don't like the way we serve either?"

"Halpern throws up, sir. I've seen it."

"I thought *you* throw up."

"Just once, sir. I didn't know the sausage was sausage."

"We'll give menus, Grossbart. We'll show training films
about the food, so you can identify when we're trying to
poison you."

Grossbart did not answer. Out before me, the men had been organized into two long chow lines. At the tail end of one I spotted Fishbein — or rather, his glasses spotted me. They winked sunlight back at me like a friend. Halpern stood next to him, patting inside his collar with a khaki handkerchief. They moved with the line as it began to edge up towards the food. The mess sergeant was still screaming at the K.P.'s, who stood ready to ladle out the food, bewildered. For a moment I was actually terrorized by the thought that somehow the mess sergeant was going to get involved in Grossbart's problem.

"Come over here, Marx," the Captain said to me. "Marx, you're a Jewish fella, am I right?"

I played straight man. "Yes, sir."

"How long you been in the Army? Tell this boy."

"Three years and two months."

"A year in combat, Grossbart. Twelve goddam months in combat all through Europe. I admire this man," the Captain said, snapping a wrist against my chest. But do you hear him peeping about the food? Do you? I want an answer, Grossbart. Yes or no."

"No, sir."

"And why not? He's a Jewish fella."

"Some things are more important to some Jews than other things to other Jews."

Barrett blew up. "Look, Grossbart, Marx here is a good man, a goddam *hero*. When you were sitting on your sweet ass in high school, Sergeant Marx was killing Germans. Who does more for the Jews, you by throwing up over a lousy piece of sausage, a piece of firstcut meat — or Marx by killing those Nazi bastards? If I was a Jew, Grossbart, I'd kiss this man's feet. He's a goddam hero, you know that?

And *he* eats what we give him. Why do you have to cause trouble is what I want to know! What is it you're buckin' for, a discharge?"

"No, sir."

"I'm talking to a *wall!* Sergeant, get him out of my way." Barrett pounced over to the driver's seat. "I'm going to see the chaplain!" The engine roared, the jeep spun around, and then, raising a whirl of dust, the Captain was headed back to camp.

For a moment, Grossbart and I stood side by side, watching the jeep. Then he looked at me and said, "I don't want to start trouble. That's the first thing they toss up to us."

When he spoke I saw that his teeth were white and straight, and the sight of them suddenly made me understand that Grossbart actually did have parents: that once upon a time someone had taken little Sheldon to the dentist. He was someone's son. Despite all the talk about his parents, it was hard to believe in Grossbart as a child, an heir — as related by blood to anyone, mother, father, or, above all, to me. This realization led me to another.

"What does your father do, Grossbart?" I asked, as we started to walk back towards the chow line.

"He's a tailor."

"An American?"

"Now, yes. A son in the Army," he said, jokingly.

"And your mother?" I asked.

He winked. "A *ballabusta* — she practically sleeps with a dustcloth in her hand."

"She's also an immigrant?"

"All she talks is Yiddish, still "

"And your father too?"

"A little English. 'Clean,' 'Press,' 'Take the pants in . . .' That's the extent of it. But they're good to me . . ."

"Then, Grossbart — " I reached out and stopped him. He turned towards me and when our eyes met his seemed to jump back, shiver in their sockets. He looked afraid. "Grossbart, then you were the one who wrote that letter, weren't you?"

It took only a second or two for his eyes to flash happy again. "Yes." He walked on, and I kept pace. "It's what my father *would* have written if he had known how. It was his name, though. *He* signed it. He even mailed it. I sent it home. For the New York postmark."

I was astonished, and he saw it. With complete seriousness, he thrust his right arm in front of me. "Blood is blood, Sergeant," he said, pinching the blue vein in his wrist.

"What the hell *are* you trying to do, Grossbart? I've seen you eat. Do you know that? I told the Captain I don't know what you eat, but I've seen you eat like a hound at chow."

"We work hard, Sergeant. We're in training. For a furnace to work, you've got to feed it coal."

"If you wrote the letter, Grossbart, then why did you say you threw up all the time?"

"I was really talking about Mickey there. But he would never write, Sergeant, though I pleaded with him. He'll waste away to nothing if I don't help. Sergeant, I used my name, my father's name, but it's Mickey and Fishbein too I'm watching out for."

"You're a regular Messiah, aren't you?"

We were at the chow line now.

"That's a good one, Sergeant." He smiled. "But who knows? Who can tell? Maybe you're the Messiah . . . a

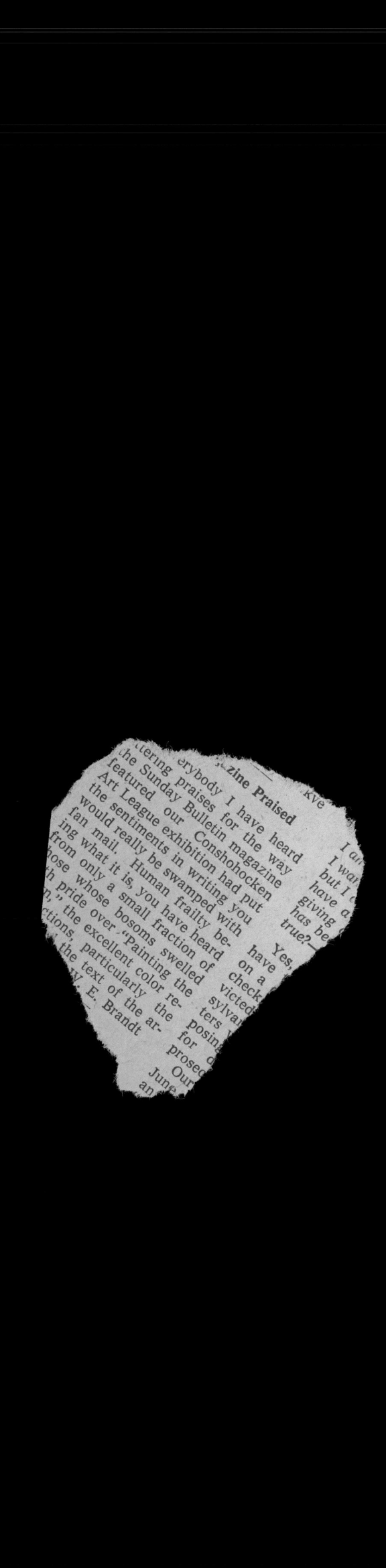

...zine Praised

...kve

...tering praises for the way ...erybody I have heard ...he Sunday Bulletin magazine featured our Conshohocken Art League exhibition had put the sentiments in writing you would really be swamped with fan mail. Human frailty be- ing what it is, you have heard from only a small fraction of ...ose whose bosoms swelled ...h pride over "Painting the ...," the excellent color re- ...tions, particularly the ...the text of the ar-

...W. E. Brandt

I a...
I wa...
but I...
have a...
giving...
has be...
true?

Yes,
have
on a
check...
victed
sylva...
ters
for d...
posing
prosec...

Our
June
an

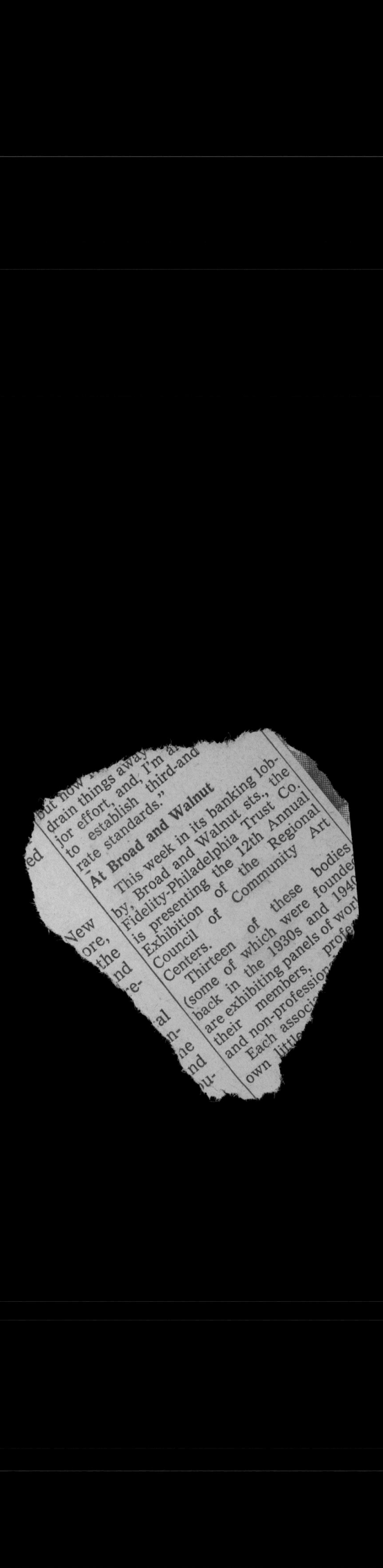

but now ... away ...
drain effort, and, I'm a ...
jor effort, and, I'm a ...
to establish third-and
rate standards."

At Broad and Walnut

This week in its banking lob-
by, Broad and Walnut sts., the
Fidelity-Philadelphia Trust Co.
is presenting the 12th Annual
Exhibition of the Regional
Council of Community Art
Centers.

Thirteen of these bodies
(some of which were founde...
back in the 1930s and 194...
are exhibiting panels of wor...
their members, and non-profession...

Each associa...
own little...

New
ore,
the
nd
e-
al
n-
he
nd
hu-
ed

little bit. What Mickey says is the Messiah is a collective idea. He went to Yeshivah, Mickey, for a while. He says *together* we're the Messiah. Me a little bit, you a little bit . . . You should hear that kid talk, Sergeant, when he gets going."

"Me a little bit, you a little bit. You'd like to believe that, wouldn't you, Grossbart? That makes everything so clean for you."

"It doesn't seem too bad a thing to believe, Sergeant. It only means we should all give a little, is all . . ."

I walked off to eat my rations with the other noncoms.

Two days later a letter addressed to Captain Barrett passed over my desk. It had come through the chain of command — from the office of Congressman Franconi, where it had been received, to General Lyman, to Colonel Sousa, to Major Lamont, to Captain Barrett. I read it over twice while the Captain was at the officers' mess. It was dated May 14th, the day Barrett had spoken with Grossbart on the rifle range.

Dear Congressman:

First let me thank you for your interest in behalf of my son, Private Sheldon Grossbart. Fortunately, I was able to speak with Sheldon on the phone the other night, and I think I've been able to solve our problem. He is, as I mentioned in my last letter, a very religious boy, and it was only with the greatest difficulty that I could persuade him that the religious thing to do — what God Himself would want Sheldon to do — would be to suffer the pangs of religious remorse for the good of his country and all mankind. It took some doing, Congressman, but finally he saw the light. In fact, what he said (and I wrote down the words on a scratch pad so as never to forget), what he said was, "I guess you're right, Dad. So many millions of my fellow Jews gave up their lives to the enemy, the least I can do is live for a while minus a bit of my heritage so as to help end this struggle and regain for all the children of God dignity and humanity." That, Congressman, would make any father proud.

By the way, Sheldon wanted me to know — and to pass on to you — the name of a soldier who helped him reach this decision: SERGEANT NATHAN MARX. Sergeant Marx is a combat veteran who is Sheldon's First Sergeant. This man has helped Sheldon over some of the first hurdles he's had to face in the Army, and is in part responsible for Sheldon's changing his mind about the dietary laws. I know Sheldon would appreciate any recognition Marx could receive.

Thank you and good luck. I look forward to seeing your name on the next election ballot.

Respectfully,

SAMUEL E. GROSSBART

Attached to the Grossbart communiqué was a communiqué addressed to General Marshall Lyman, the post commander, and signed by Representative Charles E. Franconi of the House of Representatives. The communiqué informed General Lyman that Sergeant Nathan Marx was a credit to the U.S. Army and the Jewish people.

What was Grossbart's motive in recanting? Did he feel he'd gone too far? Was the letter a strategic retreat — a crafty attempt to strengthen what he considered our alliance? Or had he actually changed his mind, via an imaginary dialogue between Grossbart *père* and *fils?* I was puzzled, but only for a few days — that is, only until I realized that whatever his reasons, he had actually decided to disappear from my life: he was going to allow himself to become just another trainee. I saw him at inspection but he never winked; at chow formations but he never flashed me a sign; on Sundays, with the other trainees, he would sit around watching the noncoms' softball team, for whom I pitched, but not once did he speak an unnecessary or unusual word to me. Fishbein and Halpern retreated from sight too, at Grossbart's command I was sure. Apparently he'd seen that wisdom lay in turning back before he plunged us over into the ugliness of privilege undeserved. Our separation allowed me to forgive him our past encounters, and, finally, to admire him for his good sense.

Meanwhile, free of Grossbart, I grew used to my job and my administrative tasks. I stepped on a scale one day and discovered I had truly become a noncombatant: I had gained seven pounds. I found patience to get past the first three pages of a book. I thought about the future more and more, and wrote letters to girls I'd known before the war — I even got a few answers. I sent away to Columbia for a Law School catalogue. I continued to follow the war in the Pacific, but it was not my war and I read of bombings and battles like a civilian. I thought I could see the end in sight and sometimes at night I dreamed that I was walking on streets of Manhattan — Broadway, Third Avenue, and 116th Street, where I had lived those three years I'd attended Columbia College. I curled myself around these dreams and I began to be happy.

And then one Saturday when everyone was away and I

was alone in the orderly room reading a month-old copy of
The Sporting News, Grossbart reappeared.

"You a baseball fan, Sergeant?"

I looked up. "How are you?"

"Fine," Grossbart said. "They're making a soldier out
of me."

"How are Fishbein and Halpern?"

"Coming along," he said. "We've got no training this
afternoon. They're at the movies."

"How come you're not with them?"

"I wanted to come over and say hello."

He smiled — a shy, regular-guy smile, as though he and
I well knew that our friendship drew its sustenance from
unexpected visits, remembered birthdays, and borrowed
lawnmowers. At first it offended me, and then the feeling
was swallowed by the general uneasiness I felt at the thought
that everyone on the post was locked away in a dark movie
theater and I was here alone with Grossbart. I folded my
paper.

"Sergeant," he said, "I'd like to ask a favor. It is a favor
and I'm making no bones about it."

He stopped, allowing me to refuse him a hearing —
which, of course, forced me into a courtesy I did not intend. "Go ahead."

"Well, actually it's two favors."

I said nothing.

"The first one's about these rumors. Everybody says
we're going to the Pacific."

"As I told your friend Fishbein, I don't know. You'll
just have to wait to find out. Like everybody else."

"You think there's a chance of any of us going East?"

"Germany," I said, "maybe."

"I meant New York."

"I don't think so, Grossbart. Offhand."

"Thanks for the information, Sergeant," he said.

"It's not information, Grossbart. Just what I surmise."

"It certainly would be good to be near home. My parents . . . you know." He took a step towards the door and then turned back. "Oh the other thing. May I ask the other?"

"What is it?"

"The other thing is — I've got relatives in St. Louis and they say they'll give me a whole Passover dinner if I can get down there. God, Sergeant, that'd mean an awful lot to me."

I stood up. "No passes during basic, Grossbart."

"But we're off from now till Monday morning, Sergeant. I could leave the post and no one would even know."

"I'd know. You'd know."

"But that's all. Just the two of us. Last night I called my aunt and you should have heard her. 'Come, come,' she said. 'I got gefilte fish, *chrain*, the works!' Just a day, Sergeant, I'd take the blame if anything happened."

"The captain isn't here to sign a pass."

"You could sign."

"Look, Grossbart — "

"Sergeant, for two months practically I've been eating *trafe* till I want to die."

"I thought you'd made up your mind to live with it. To be minus a little bit of heritage."

He pointed a finger at me. "You!" he said. "That wasn't for you to read!"

"I read it. So what."

"That letter was addressed to a congressman."

"Grossbart, don't feed me any crap. You *wanted* me to read it."

"Why are you persecuting me, Sergeant?"

"Are you kidding!"

"I've run into this before," he said, "but never from my own!"

"Get out of here, Grossbart! Get the hell out of my sight!"

He did not move. "Ashamed, that's what you are. So you take it out on the rest of us. They say Hitler himself was half a Jew. Seeing this, I wouldn't doubt it!"

"What are you trying to do with me, Grossbart? What are you after? You want me to give you special privileges, to change the food, to find out about your orders, to give you weekend passes."

"You even talk like a goy!" Grossbart shook his fist. "Is this a weekend pass I'm asking for? Is a Seder sacred or not?"

Seder! It suddenly occurred to me that Passover had been celebrated weeks before. I confronted Grossbart with the fact.

"That's right," he said. "Who says no? A month ago, and I was in the field eating hash! And now all I ask is a simple favor — a Jewish boy I thought would understand. My aunt's willing to go out of her way — to make a Seder a month later — " He turned to go, mumbling.

"Come back here!" I called. He stopped and looked at me. "Grossbart, why can't you be like the rest? Why do you have to stick out like a sore thumb? Why do you beg for special treatment?"

"Because I'm a Jew, Sergeant. I *am* different. Better, maybe not. But different."

"This is a war, Grossbart. For the time being *be* the same."

"I refuse."

"What?"

"I refuse. I can't stop being me, that's all there is to it." Tears came to his eyes. "It's a hard thing to be a Jew. But now I see what Mickey says — it's a harder thing to stay one." He raised a hand sadly toward me. "Look at you."

"Stop crying!"

"Stop this, stop that, stop the other thing! You stop, Sergeant. Stop closing your heart to your own!" And wiping his face with his sleeve, he ran out the door. "The least we can do for one another ... the least ..."

An hour later I saw Grossbart headed across the field. He wore a pair of starched khakis and carried only a little leather ditty bag. I went to the door and from the outside felt the heat of the day. It was quiet — not a soul in sight except over by the mess hall four K.P.'s sitting round a pan, sloped forward from the waists, gabbing and peeling potatoes in the sun.

"Grossbart!" I called.

He looked toward me and continued walking.

"Grossbart, get over here!"

He turned and stepped into his long shadow. Finally he stood before me.

"Where are you going?" I said.

"St. Louis. I don't care."

"You'll get caught without a pass."

"So I'll get caught without a pass."

"You'll go to the stockade."

"I'm in the stockade." He made an about-face and headed off.

1 let him go only a step: "Come back here," I said, and he followed me into the office, where I typed out a pass and signed the Captain's name and my own initials after it.

He took the pass from me and then, a moment later, he reached out and grabbed my hand. "Sergeant, you don't know how much this means to me."

"Okay. Don't get in any trouble."

"I wish I could show you how much this means to me."

"Don't do me any favors. Don't write any more congressmen for citations."

Amazingly, he smiled. "You're right. I won't. But let me do something."

"Bring me a piece of that gefilte fish. Just get out of here."

"I will! With a slice of carrot and a little horseradish. I won't forget."

"All right. Just show your pass at the gate. And don't tell *anybody*."

"I won't. It's a month late, but a good Yom Tov to you."

"Good Yom Tov, Grossbart," I said.

"You're a good Jew, Sergeant. You like to think you have a hard heart, but underneath you're a fine decent man. I mean that."

Those last three words touched me more than any words from Grossbart's mouth had the right to. "All right, Grossbart. Now call me 'sir' and get the hell out of here."

He ran out the door and was gone. I felt very pleased with myself — it was a great relief to stop fighting Grossbart. And it had cost me nothing. Barrett would never find out, and if he did, I could manage to invent some excuse. For a while I sat at my desk, comfortable in my decision. Then the screen door flew back and Grossbart burst in again. "Sergeant!" he said. Behind him I saw Fishbein and Halpern, both in starched khakis, both carrying ditty bags exactly like Grossbart's.

"Sergeant, I caught Mickey and Larry coming out of the movies. I almost missed them."

"Grossbart, did I say tell no one?"

"But my aunt said I could bring friends. That I should, in fact."

"I'm the Sergeant, Grossbart — not your aunt!"

Grossbart looked at me in disbelief; he pulled Halpern up by his sleeve. "Mickey, tell the Sergeant what this would mean to you."

"Grossbart, for God's sake, spare us —"

"Tell him what you told me, Mickey. How much it would mean."

Halpern looked at me and, shrugging his shoulders, made his admission. "A lot."

Fishbein stepped forward without prompting. "This would mean a great deal to me and my parents, Sergeant Marx."

"No!" I shouted.

Grossbart was shaking his head. "Sergeant, I could see you denying me, but how you can deny Mickey, a Yeshivah boy, that's beyond me."

"I'm not denying Mickey anything. You just pushed a little too hard, Grossbart. *You* denied him."

"I'll give him my pass, then," Grossbart said. "I'll give him my aunt's address and a little note. At least let him go."

In a second he had crammed the pass into Halpern's

pants' pocket. Halpern looked at me, Fishbein too. Grossbart was at the door, pushing it open. "Mickey, bring me a
piece of gefilte fish at least." And then he was outside
again.

The three of us looked at one another and then I said,
"Halpern, hand that pass over."

He took it from his pocket and gave it to me. Fishbein
had now moved to the doorway, where he lingered. He
stood there with his mouth slightly open and then pointed
to himself. "And me?" he asked.

His utter ridiculousness exhausted me. I slumped down
in my seat and felt pulses knocking at the back of my
eyes. "Fishbein," I said, "you understand I'm not trying
to deny you anything, don't you? If it was my Army I'd
serve gefilte fish in the mess hall. I'd sell kugel in the PX,
honest to God."

Halpern smiled.

"You understand, don't you, Halpern?"

"Yes, Sergeant."

"And you, Fishbein? I don't want enemies. I'm just
like you — I want to serve my time and go home. I miss the
same things you miss."

"Then, Sergeant," Fishbein interrupted, "Why don't
you come too?"

"Where?"

"To St. Louis. To Shelley's aunt. We'll have a regular
Seder. Play hide-the-matzah." He gave a broad, black-
toothed smile.

I saw Grossbart in the doorway again, on the other side
of the screen.

"Pssst!" He waved a piece of paper. "Mickey, here's the
address. Tell her I couldn't get away."

Halpern did not move. He looked at me and I saw the

shrug moving up his arms into his shoulders again. I took the cover off my typewriter and made out passes for him and Fishbein. "Go," I said, "the three of you."

I thought Halpern was going to kiss my hand.

That afternoon, in a bar in Joplin, I drank beer and listened with half an ear to the Cardinal game. I tried to look squarely at what I'd become involved in, and began to wonder if perhaps the struggle with Grossbart wasn't much my fault as his. What was I that I had to *muster* generous feelings? Who was I to have been feeling so grudging, so tight-hearted? After all, I wasn't being asked to move the world. Had I a right, then, or a reason, to clamp down on Grossbart, when that meant clamping down on Halpern, too? And Fishbein, that ugly agreeable soul, wouldn't he suffer in the bargain also? Out of the many recollections that had tumbled over me these past few days, I heard from some childhood moment my grandmother's voice: "What are you making a *tsimas?*" It was what she would ask my mother when, say, I had cut myself with a knife and her daughter was busy bawling me out. I would need a hug and a kiss and my mother would moralize! But my grandmother knew — mercy overrides justice. I should have known it, too. Who was Nathan Marx to be such a pennypincher with kindness? Surely, I thought, the Messiah himself — if he should ever come — won't niggle over nickels and dimes. God willing, he'll hug and kiss.

The next day, while we were playing softball over on the Parade Grounds, I decided to ask Bob Wright, who was noncom in charge over at Classification and Assignment, where he thought our trainees would be sent when their cycle ended in two weeks. I asked casually, between innings, and he said, "They're pushing them all into the

Pacific. Shulman cut the orders on your boys the other day."

The news shocked me, as though I were father to Halpern, Fishbein, and Grossbart.

That night I was just sliding into sleep when someone tapped on the door. "What is it?"

"Sheldon."

He opened the door and came in. For a moment I felt his presence without being able to see him. "How was it?" I asked, as though to the darkness.

He popped into sight before me. "Great, Sergeant." I felt my springs sag; Grossbart was sitting on the edge of the bed. I sat up.

"How about you?" he asked. "Have a nice weekend?"

"Yes."

He took a deep paternal breath. "The others went to sleep ..." We sat silently for a while, as a homey feeling invaded my ugly little cubicle: the door was locked, the cat out, the children safely in bed.

"Sergeant, can I tell you something? Personal?"

I did not answer and he seemed to know why. "Not about me. About Mickey. Sergeant, I never felt for anybody like I feel for him. Last night I heard Mickey in the bed next to me. He was crying so, it could have broken your heart. Real sobs."

"I'm sorry to hear that."

"I had to talk to him to stop him. He held my hand, Sergeant — he wouldn't let it go. He was almost hysterical. He kept saying if he only knew where we were going. Even if he knew it *was* the Pacific, that would be better than nothing. Just to know."

Long ago, someone had taught Grossbart the sad law

that only lies can get the truth. Not that I couldn't believe in Halpern's crying — his eyes *always* seemed red-rimmed. But, fact or not, it became a lie when Grossbart uttered it. He was entirely strategic. But then — it came with the force of indictment — so was I! There are strategies of aggression, but there are strategies of retreat, as well. And so, recognizing that I, myself, had not been without craft and guile, I told him what I knew. "It is the Pacific."

He let out a small gasp, which was not a lie. "I'll tell him. I wish it was otherwise."

"So do I."

He jumped on my words. "You mean you think you could do something? A change maybe?"

"No, I couldn't do a thing."

"Don't you know anybody over at C & A?"

"Grossbart, there's nothing I can do. If your orders are for the Pacific then it's the Pacific."

"But Mickey."

"Mickey, you, me — everybody, Grossbart. There's nothing to be done. Maybe the war'll end before you go. Pray for a miracle."

"But — "

"Good night, Grossbart." I settled back, and was relieved to feel the springs upbend again as Grossbart rose to leave. I could see him clearly now; his jaw had dropped and he looked like a dazed prizefighter. I noticed for the first time a little paper bag in his hand.

"Grossbart" — I smiled — "my gift?"

"Oh, yes, Sergeant. Here, from all of us." He handed me the bag. "It's egg roll."

"Egg roll?" I accepted the bag and felt a damp grease spot on the bottom. I opened it, sure that Grossbart was joking.

"We thought you'd probably like it. You know, Chinese egg roll. We thought you'd probably have a taste for — "

"Your aunt served egg roll?"

"She wasn't home."

"Grossbart, she invited you. You told me she invited you and your friends."

"I know. I just reread the letter. *Next* week."

I got out of bed and walked to the window. It was black as far off as I could see. "Grossbart," I said. But I was not calling him.

"What?"

"What are you, Grossbart? Honest to God, what are you?"

I think it was the first time I'd asked him a question for which he didn't have an immediate answer.

"How can you do this to people?" I asked.

"Sergeant, the day away did us all a world of good. Fishbein, you should see him, he *loves* Chinese food."

"But the Seder," I said.

"We took second best, Sergeant."

Rage came charging at me. I didn't sidestep — I grabbed it, pulled it in, hugged it to my chest.

"Grossbart, you're a liar! You're a schemer and a crook! You've got no respect for anything! Nothing at all! Not for me, for the truth, not even for poor Halpern! You use us all —"

"Sergeant, Sergeant, I feel for Mickey, honest to God, I do. I *love* Mickey. I try — "

"You try! You feel!" I lurched towards him and grabbed his shirt front. I shook him furiously. "Grossbart, get out. Get out and stay the hell away from me! Because if I see you, I'll make your life miserable. *You understand that?*"

"Yes "

I let him free, and when he walked from the room I
wanted to spit on the floor where he had stood. I couldn't
stop the fury from rising in my heart. It engulfed me,
owned me, till it seemed I could only rid myself of it
with tears or an act of violence. I snatched from the bed
the bag Grossbart had given me and with all my strength
threw it out the window. And the next morning, as the men
policed the area around the barracks, I heard a great cry
go up from one of the trainees who'd been anticipating only
this morning handful of cigarette butts and candy wrap-
pers. "Egg roll!" he shouted. "Holy Christ, Chinese goddam egg roll!"

A week later when I read the orders that had come down
from C & A I couldn't believe my eyes. Every single trainee
was to be shipped to Camp Stoneham, California, and from
there to the Pacific. Every trainee but one: Private Sheldon
Grossbart was to be sent to Fort Monmouth, New Jersey.
I read the mimeographed sheet several times. Dee, Far-
rell, Fishbein, Fuselli, Fylypowycz, Glinicki, Gromke,
Gucwa, Halpern, Hardy, Helebrandt . . . right down to An-
ton Zygadlo, all were to be headed West before the month
was out. All except Grossbart. He had pulled a string and
I wasn't it.

I lifted the phone and called C & A.

The voice on the other end said smartly, "Corporal Shulman, sir."

"Let me speak to Sergeant Wright."

"Who is this calling, sir?"

"Sergeant Marx."

And to my surprise, the voice said, "*Oh.*" Then: "Just
a minute, Sergeant."

Shulman's *oh* stayed with me while I waited for Wright to come to phone. Why *oh*? Who was Shulman? And then, so simply, I knew I'd discovered the string Grossbart had pulled. In fact, I could hear Grossbart the day he'd discovered Shulman, in the PX, or the bowling alley, or maybe even at services. "Glad to meet you. Where you from? Bronx? Me too. Do you know so-and-so? And so-and-so? Me too! You work at C & A? Really? Hey, how's chances of getting East? Could you do something Change something? Swindle, cheat, lie? We gotta help each other, you know ... if the Jews in Germany ..."

At the other end Bob Wright answered. "How are you, Nate? How's the pitching arm?"

"Good. Bob, I wonder if you could do me a favor." I heard clearly my own words and they so reminded me of Grossbart that I dropped more easily than I could have imagined into what I had planned. "This may sound crazy, Bob, but I got a kid here on orders to Monmouth who wants them changed. He had a brother killed in Europe and he's hot to go to the Pacific. Says he'd feel like a coward if he wound up stateside. I don't know, Bob, can anything be done? Put somebody else in the Monmouth slot?"

"Who?" he asked cagily.

"Anybody. First guy on the alphabet. I don't care. The kid just asked if something could be done."

"What's his name?"

"Grossbart, Sheldon."

Wright didn't answer.

"Yeah," I said, "he's a Jewish kid, so he thought I could help him out. You know."

"I guess I can do something," he finally said. "The

Major hasn't been around here for weeks — TDY to the golf course. I'll try, Nate that's all I can say."

"I'd appreciate it, Bob. See you Sunday," and I hung up, perspiring.

And the following day the corrected orders appeared: Fishbein, Fuselli, Fylypowycz, Glinicki, Grossbart, Gucwa, Halpern, Hardy . . . Lucky Private Harley Alton was to go to Fort Monmouth, New Jersey, where for some reason or other, they wanted an enlisted man with infantry training.

After chow that night I stopped back at the orderly room to straighten out the guard duty roster. Grossbart was waiting for me. He spoke first.

"You son of a bitch!"

I sat down at my desk and while he glared down at me I began to make the necessary alterations in the duty roster.

"What do you have against me?" he cried. "Against my family? Would it kill you for me to be near my father, God knows how many months he has left to him."

"Why?"

"His heart," Grossbart said. "He hasn't had enough troubles in a lifetime, you've got to add to them. I curse the day I ever met you, Marx! Shulman told me what happened over there. There's no limit to your anti-Semitism, is there! The damage you've done here isn't enough. You have to make a special phone call! You really want me dead!"

I made the last few notations in the duty roster and got up to leave. "Good night, Grossbart."

"You owe me an explanation!" He stood in my path.

"Sheldon, you're the one who owes explanations."

He scowled. "To *you?*"

"To me, I think so, yes. Mostly to Fishbein and Halpern."

"That's right, twist things around. I owe nobody nothing, I've done all I could do for them. Now I think I've got the right to watch out for myself."

"For each other we have to learn to watch out, Sheldon. You told me yourself."

"You call this watching out for me, what you did?"

"No. For all of us."

I pushed him aside and started for the door. I heard his furious breathing behind me, and it sounded like steam rushing from the engine of his terrible strength.

"You'll be all right," I said from the door. And, I thought, so would Fishbein and Halpern be all right, even in the Pacific, if only Grossbart could continue to see in the obsequiousness of the one, the soft spirituality of the other, some profit for himself.

I stood outside the orderly room, and I heard Grossbart weeping behind me. Over in the barracks, in the lighted windows, I could see the boys in their T-shirts sitting on their bunks talking about their orders, as they'd been doing for the past two days. With a kind of quiet nervousness, they polished shoes, shined belt buckles, squared away underwear, trying as best they could to accept their fate. Behind me, Grossbart swallowed hard, accepting his. And then, resisting with all my will an impulse to turn and seek pardon for my vindictiveness, I accepted my own.

EPSTEIN

Michael, the weekend guest, was to spend the night in one of the twin beds in Herbie's old room, where the baseball pictures still hung on the wall. Lou Epstein lay with his wife in the room with the bed pushed cater-corner. His daughter Sheila's bedroom was empty; she was at a meeting with her fiancé, the folk singer. In the corner of her room a childhood teddy bear balanced on its bottom, a VOTE SOCIALIST button pinned to its left ear; on her bookshelves, where volumes of Louisa May Alcott once gathered dust, were now collected the works of Howard Fast. The house was quiet. The only light burning was downstairs in the dining room where the *shabus* candles flickered in their tall golden holders and Herbie's *jahrzeit* candle trembled in its glass.

Epstein looked at the dark ceiling of his bedroom and let his head that had been bang-banging all day go blank for a moment. His wife Goldie breathed thickly beside him, as though she suffered from eternal bronchitis. Ten minutes before she had undressed and he had watched as she dropped her white nightdress over her head, over the breasts which had funneled down to her middle, over the behind like a bellows, the thighs and calves veined blue like a roadmap. What once could be pinched, what once was small and tight, now could be poked and pulled. Everything hung. He had shut his eyes while she had dressed for sleep and had tried to remember the Goldie of 1927, the Lou Epstein of 1927. Now he rolled his stomach against her backside, remembering, and reached around to hold her breasts. The nipples were dragged down like a cow's, long as his little finger. He rolled back to his own side.

A key turned in the front door — there was whispering, then the door gently shut. He tensed and waited for the noises — it didn't take those Socialists long. At night the noise from the zipping and the unzipping was enough to keep a man awake. "What are they doing down there?" he had screamed at his wife one Friday night, "trying on clothes?" Now, once again, he waited. It wasn't that he was against their playing. He was no puritan, he believed in young people enjoying themselves. Hadn't he been a young man himself? But in 1927 he and his wife were handsome people. Lou Epstein had never resembled that chinless, lazy smart aleck whose living was earned singing folk songs in a saloon, and who once had asked Epstein if it hadn't been "thrilling" to have lived through "a period of great social upheaval" like the thirties.

And his daughter, why couldn't she have grown up to be like — like the girl across the street whom Michael had the date with, the one whose father had died. Now there was a pretty girl. But not his Sheila. What happened, he wondered, what happened to that little pink-skinned baby? What year, what month did those skinny ankles grow thick as logs, the peaches-and-cream turn to pimples? That lovely child was now a twenty-three-year-old woman with "a social conscience"! Some conscience, he thought. She hunts all day for a picket line to march in so that at night she can come home and eat like a horse . . . For her and that guitar plucker to touch each other's unmentionables seemed worse than sinful — it was disgusting. When Epstein tossed in bed and heard their panting and the zipping it sounded in his ears like thunder.

Zip!

They were at it. He would ignore them, think of his other problems. The business . . . here he was a year away from the retirement he had planned but with no heir to Epstein Paper Bag Company. He had built the business from the ground, suffered and bled during the Depression and Roosevelt, only, finally, with the war and Eisenhower to see it succeed. The thought of a stranger taking it over made him sick. But what could be done? Herbie, who would have been twenty-eight, had died of polio, age eleven. And Sheila, his last hope, had chosen as her intended a lazy man. What could he do? Does a man of fifty-nine all of a sudden start producing heirs?

Zip! Pant-pant-pant! Ahh!

He shut his ears and mind, tighter. He tried to recollect things and drown himself in them. For instance, dinner . . .

He had been startled when he arrived home from the shop to find the soldier sitting at his dinner table. Surprised because the boy, whom he had not seen for ten or twelve years, had grown up with the Epstein face, as his son would have, the small bump in the nose, the strong chin, dark skin, and shock of shiny black hair that, one day, would turn gray as clouds.

"Look who's here," his wife shouted at him the moment he entered the door, the day's dirt still under his fingernails. "Sol's boy."

The soldier popped up from his chair and extended his hand. "How do you do, Uncle Louis?"

"A Gregory Peck," Epstein's wife said, "a Monty Clift your brother has. He's been here only three hours already he has a date. And a regular gentleman . . ."

Epstein did not answer.

The soldier stood at attention, square, as though he'd learned courtesy long before the Army. "I hope you don't mind my barging in, Uncle Louis. I was shipped to Monmouth last week and Dad said I should stop off to see you people. I've got the weekend off and Aunt Goldie said I should stay — " He waited.

"Look at him," Goldie was saying, "a Prince!"

"Of course," Epstein said at last, "stay. How is your father?" Epstein had not spoken to his brother Sol since 1945 when he had bought Sol's share of the business and his brother had moved to Detroit, with words.

"Dad's fine," Michael said. "He sends his regards."

"Sure, I send mine too. You'll tell him."

Michael sat down, and Epstein knew that the boy must think just as his father did: that Lou Epstein was a coarse man whose heart beat faster only when he was thinking of Epstein Paper Bag.

When Sheila came home they all sat down to eat, four, as in the old days. Goldie Epstein jumped up and down, up and down, slipping each course under their noses the instant they had finished the one before. "Michael," she said historically, "Michael, as a child you were a very poor eater. Your sister Ruthie, God bless her, was a nice eater. Not a good eater, but a nice eater "

For the first time Epstein remembered his little niece
Ruthie, a little dark-haired beauty, a Bible Ruth. He looked
at his own daughter and heard his wife go on, and on. "No,
Ruthie wasn't such a good eater. But she wasn't a picky
eater. Our Herbie, he should rest in peace, was a picky
eater . . ." Goldie looked towards her husband as though
he would remember precisely what category of eater his
beloved son had been; he stared into his pot roast.

"But," Goldie Epstein resumed, "You should live and
be well, Michael, you turned out to be a good eater . . ."

Ahhh! Ahhh!

The noises snapped Epstein's recollection in two.

Aaahhhh!

Enough was enough. He got out of bed, made certain
that he was tucked into his pajamas, and started down to
the living room. He would give them a piece of his mind.
He would tell them that — that 1927 was not 1957! No,
that was what they would tell him.

But in the living room it was not Sheila and the folk
singer. Epstein felt the cold from the floor rush up the
loose legs of his pajamas and chill his crotch, raising goose
flesh on his thighs. They did not see him. He retreated a
step, back behind the archway to the dining room. His
eyes, however, remained fixed on the living room floor, on
Sol's boy and the girl from across the street.

The girl had been wearing shorts and a sweater. Now
they were thrown over the arm of the sofa. The light from
the candles was enough for Epstein to see that she was
naked. Michael lay beside her, squirming and potent, wearing only his army shoes and khaki socks. The girl's breasts
were like two small white cups. Michael kissed them, and
more. Epstein tingled; he did not dare move, he did not
want to move, until the two, like cars in a railroad yard,

slammed fiercely together, coupled, shook. In their noise
Epstein tiptoed, trembling, up the stairs and back to his
wife's bed.

He could not force himself to sleep for what seemed like
hours, not until the door had opened downstairs and the
two young people had left. When, a minute or so later, he
heard another key turn in the lock he did not know whether
it was Michael returning to go to sleep, or —

Zip!

Now it was Sheila and the folk singer! The whole
world, he thought, the whole young world, the ugly ones
and the pretty ones, the fat and the skinny ones, zipping
and unzipping! He grabbed his great shock of gray hair
and pulled it till his scalp hurt. His wife shuffled, mumbled a noise. "Brrr . . . brrrrr . . ." She captured the blankets and pulled them over her. "Brrr . . ."

Butter! She's dreaming about butter. Recipes she
dreams while the world zips. He closed his eyes and
pounded himself down down into an old man's sleep.

2

How far back must you go to discover the beginning of
trouble? Later, when Epstein had more time he would ask
himself this question. When did it begin? That night he'd
seen those two on the floor? Or the summer night seventeen years before when he had pushed the doctor away
from the bed and put his lips to his Herbie's? Or, Epstein
wondered, was it that night fifteen years ago when instead
of smelling a woman between his sheets he smelled Bab-o?
Or the time when his daughter had first called him "capital-
ist" as though it were a dirty name, as though it were a crime

to be successful? Or was it none of these times? Maybe to look for a beginning was only to look for an excuse. Hadn't the trouble, the big trouble, begun simply when it appeared to, the morning he saw Ida Kaufman waiting for the bus?

And about Ida Kaufman, why in God's name was it a stranger, nobody he loved or ever could love, who had finally changed his life? — she, who had lived across the street for less than a year, and who (it was revealed by Mrs. Katz, the neighborhood Winchell) would probably sell her house now that Mr. Kaufman was dead and move all-year-round into their summer cottage at Barnegat? Until that morning Epstein had not more than noticed the woman: dark, good-looking, a big chest. She hardly spoke to the other housewives, but spent every moment, until a month ago, caring for her cancer-eaten husband. Once or twice Epstein had tipped his hat to her, but even then he had been more absorbed in the fate of Epstein Paper Bag than in the civility he was practicing. Actually then, on that Monday morning it would not have been unlikely for him to have driven right past the bus stop. It was a warm April day, certainly not a bad day to be waiting for a bus. Birds fussed and sang in the elm trees, and the sun glinted in the sky like a young athlete's trophy. But the woman at the bus stop wore a thin dress and no coat, and Epstein saw her waiting, and beneath the dress, the stockings, the imagined underthings he saw the body of the girl on his living room rug, for Ida Kaufman was the mother of Linda Kaufman, the girl Michael had befriended. So Epstein pulled slowly to the curb and, stopping for the daughter, picked up the mother.

"Thank you, Mr. Epstein," she said. "This is kind of you."

"It's nothing," Epstein said. "I'm going to Market Street."

"Market Street will be fine."

He pressed down too hard on the accelerator and the big Chrysler leaped away, noisy as a hot-rodder's Ford. Ida Kaufman rolled down her window and let the breeze waft in; she lit a cigarette. After a while she asked, "That was your nephew, wasn't it, that took Linda out Saturday night?"

"Michael? Yes." Epstein flushed, for reasons Ida Kaufman did not know. He felt the red on his neck and coughed to make it appear that some respiratory failure had caused the blood to rush up from his heart.

"He's a very nice boy, extremely polite," she said.

"My brother Sol's," Epstein said, "in Detroit." And he shifted his thoughts to Sol so that the flush might fade: if there had been no words with Sol it would be Michael who would be heir to Epstein Paper Bag. Would he have wanted that? Was it any better than a stranger . . . ?

While Epstein thought, Ida Kaufman smoked, and they drove on without speaking, under the elm trees, the choir of birds, and the new spring sky unfurled like a blue banner.

"He looks like you," she said.

"What? Who?"

"Michael."

"No," Epstein said, "him, he's the image of Sol."

"No, no, don't deny it — " and she exploded with laughter, smoke dragoning out of her mouth; she jerked her head back mightily, "No, no, no, he's got your face!"

Epstein looked at her, wondering: the lips, big and red,

over her teeth, grinning. Why? Of course — your little boy looks like the iceman, she'd made that joke. He grinned, mostly at the thought of going to bed with his sister-in-law, whose everything had dropped even lower than his wife's.

Epstein's grin provoked Ida Kaufman into more extravagant mirth. What the hell, he decided, he would try a joke himself.

"Your Linda, who does *she* look like?"

Ida Kaufman's mouth straightened; her lids narrowed, killing the light in her eyes. Had he said the wrong thing? Stepped too far? Defiled the name of a dead man, a man who'd had cancer yet? But no, for suddenly she raised her arms in front of her, and shrugged her shoulders as though to say, "Who knows, Epstein, who knows?"

Epstein roared. It was so long since he had been with a woman who had a sense of humor; his wife took everything he said seriously. Not Ida Kaufman, though — she laughed so hard her breasts swelled over the top of her tan dress. They were not cups but pitchers. The next thing Epstein knew he was telling her another joke, and another, in the middle of which a cop screamed up alongside him and gave him a ticket for a red light which, in his joy, he had not seen. It was the first of three tickets he received that day; he earned a second racing down to Barnegat later that morning, and a third speeding up the Parkway at dusk, trying not to be too late for dinner. The tickets cost him $32 in all, but, as he told Ida, when you're laughing so hard you have tears in your eyes, how can you tell the green lights from the red ones, fast from slow?

At seven o'clock that evening he returned Ida to the bus stop on the corner and squeezed a bill into her hands.

"Here," he said, "Here — buy something"; which brought the day's total to fifty-two.

Then he turned up the street, already prepared with a story for his wife: a man interested in buying Epstein Paper Bag had kept him away all day, a good prospect. As he pulled into his driveway he saw his wife's square shape back of the venetian blinds. She ran one hand across a slat, checking for dust while she awaited her husband's home-coming.

3

Prickly heat?

He clutched his pajama trousers around his knees and looked at himself in the bedroom mirror. Downstairs a key turned in the lock but he was too engaged to hear it. Prickly heat is what Herbie always had — a child's complaint. Was it possible for a grown man to have it? He shuffled closer to the mirror, tripping on his half-hoisted pajamas. Maybe it was a sand rash. Sure, he thought, for during those three warm, sunny weeks, he and Ida Kaufman, when they were through, would rest on the beach in front of the cottage. Sand must have gotten into his trousers and irritated him on the drive up the Parkway. He stepped back now and was squinting at himself in the mirror when Goldie walked into the bedroom. She had just emerged from a hot tub — her bones ached, she had said — and her flesh was boiled red. Her entrance startled Epstein, who had been contemplating his blemish with the intensity of a philosopher. When he turned swiftly from his reflection, his feet caught in his pants leg, he tripped, and the pajamas slipped to the floor. So there they were, naked as Adam and Eve, except that Goldie was red all

over, and Epstein had prickly heat, or a sand rash, or —
and it came to him as a first principle comes to a meta-
physician. Of course! His hands shot down to cover his
crotch.

Goldie looked at him, mystified, while Epstein searched
for words appropriate to his posture.

At last: "You had a nice bath?"

"Nice, shmice, it was a bath," his wife mumbled.

"You'll catch a cold," Epstein said. "Put something
on."

"I'll catch a cold? *You'll* catch a cold!" She looked at
the hands laced across his crotch. "Something hurts?"

"It's a little chilly," he said.

"Where?" She motioned towards his protection.
"There?"

"All over."

"Then cover all over."

He leaned over to pick up his pajama trousers; the instant he dropped the fig leaf of his hands Goldie let out a
short airless gasp. "What is *that?*"

"What?"

"That!"

He could not look into the eyes of her face, so concen-
trated instead on the purple eyes of her droopy breasts.
"A sand rash, I think."

"*Vus far* sand!"

"A rash then," he said.

She stepped up closer and reached out her hand, not
to touch but to point. She drew a little circle of the area
with her index finger. "A rash, there?"

"Why not there?" Epstein said. "It's like a rash on the
hand or the chest. A rash is a rash."

"But how come all of a sudden?" his wife said.

"Look, I'm not a doctor," Epstein said. "It's there to-day, maybe tomorrow it'll be gone. How do I know! I probably got it from the toilet seat at the shop. The *shvartzes* are pigs —"

Goldie made a clicking sound with her tongue.

"You're calling me a liar?"

She looked up. "Who said liar?" And she gave her own form a swift looking-over, checked limbs, stomach, breasts, to see if she had perhaps caught the rash from him. She looked back at her husband, then at her own body again, and suddenly her eyes widened. "You!" she screamed.

"Shah," Epstein said, "you'll wake Michael."

"You pig! Who, who was it!"

"I told you, the *shvartzes* —"

"Liar! Pig!" Wheeling her way back to the bed, she flopped onto it so hard the springs squeaked. "Liar!" And then she was off the bed pulling the sheets from it. "I'll burn them, I'll burn every one!"

Epstein stepped out of the pajamas that roped his ankles and raced to the bed. "What are you doing — it's not catching. Only on the toilet seat. You'll buy a little am-monia —"

"Ammonia!" she yelled, "you should *drink* ammonia!"

"No," Epstein shouted, "no," and he grabbed the sheets from her and threw them back over the bed, tucking them in madly. "Leave it be —" He ran to the back of the bed but as he tucked there Goldie raced around and ripped up what he had tucked in the front; so he raced back to the front while Goldie raced around to the back. "Don't touch me," she screamed, "don't come near me, you filthy pig! Go touch some filthy whore!" Then she yanked the sheets off again in one swoop, held them in a ball before her and spat. Epstein grabbed them back and the tug-of-war began, back and forth, back and forth, until they had torn them to shreds. Then for the first time Goldie cried. With white strips looped over her arms she began to sob. "My sheets, my nice clean sheets —" and she threw herself on the bed.

Two faces appeared in the doorway of the bedroom. Sheila Epstein groaned, "Holy Christ!"; the folk singer peeped in, once, twice, and then bobbed out, his feet scuttling down the stairs. Epstein whipped some white strands about him to cover his privates. He did not say a word as his daughter entered.

"Mamma, what's the matter?"

"Your father," the voice groaned from the bed, "he has — a rash!" And so violently did she begin to sob that the flesh on her white buttocks rippled and jumped.

"That's right," Epstein said, "a rash. That's a crime? Get out of here! Let your mother and father get some sleep."

"Why is she crying?" Sheila demanded. "I want an answer!"

"How do I know! I'm a mind reader? This whole family is crazy, who knows what they think!"

"Don't call my mother crazy!"

"Don't you raise your voice to me! Respect your father!" He pulled the white strips tighter around him. "Now get out of here!"

"No!"

"Then I'll throw you out." He started for the door; his daughter did not move, and he could not bring himself to reach out and push her. Instead he threw back his head and addressed the ceiling. "She's picketing my bedroom! Get out, you lummox!" He took a step towards her and growled, as though to scare away a stray cat or dog. With all her one hundred and sixty pounds she pushed her father back; in his surprise and hurt he dropped the sheet. And the daughter looked on the father. Under her lipstick she turned white.

Epstein looked up at her. He pleaded, "I got it from the toilet seat. The *shvartzes* — "

Before he could finish, a new head had popped into the doorway, hair messed and lips swollen and red; it was Michael, home from Linda Kaufman, his regular weekend date. "I heard the noise, is any — " and he saw his aunt naked on the bed. When he turned his eyes away, there was Uncle Lou.

"All of you," Epstein shouted. "Get out!"

But no one obeyed. Sheila blocked the door, politically committed; Michael's legs were rooted, one with shame, the other curiosity.

"Get out!"

Feet now came pounding up the stairs. "Sheila, should I call somebody — " And then the guitar plucker appeared in the doorway, eager, big-nosed. He surveyed the scene and his gaze, at last, landed on Epstein's crotch; the beak opened.

"What's he got? The syph?"

The words hung for a moment, bringing peace. Goldie Epstein stopped crying and raised herself off the bed. The young men in the doorway lowered their eyes. Goldie arched her back, flopped out her breasts, and began to move her lips. "I want . . ." she said. "I want . . ."

"What, Mamma?" Sheila demanded. "What is it?"

"I want...a divorce!" She looked amazed when she said it, though not as amazed as her husband; he smacked his palm to his head.

"Divorce! Are you crazy?" Epstein looked around; to Michael he said, "She's crazy!"

"I want one," she said, and then her eyes rolled up into her head and she passed out across the sheetless mattress.

After the smelling salts Epstein was ordered to bed in Herbie's room. He tossed and turned in the narrow bed which he was unused to; in the twin bed beside him he heard Michael breathing. Monday, he thought, Monday he would seek help. A lawyer. No, first a doctor. Surely in a minute a doctor could take a look and tell him what he already knew — that Ida Kaufman was a clean woman. Epstein would swear by it — he had smelled her flesh! The doctor would reassure him: his blemish resulted simply from their rubbing together. It was a temporary thing, produced by two, not transmitted by one. He was innocent! Unless what made him guilty had nothing to do with some dirty bug. But either way the doctor would prescribe for him. And then the lawyer would prescribe. And by then everyone would know, including, he suddenly realized, his brother Sol who would take special pleasure in thinking the worst. Epstein rolled over and looked to Michael's bed. Pinpoints of light gleamed in the boy's head; he was awake, and wearing the Epstein nose, chin, and brow.

"Michael?"

"Yes."

"You're awake?"

"Yes."

"Me too," Epstein said, and then apologetically, "all the excitement..."

He looked back to the ceiling. "Michael?"

"Yes?"

"Nothing..." But he was curious as well as concerned. "Michael, you haven't got a rash, have you?"

Michael sat up in bed; firmly he said, "No."

"I just thought," Epstein said quickly. " You know, I have this rash..." He dwindled off and looked away from the boy, who, it occurred to him again, might have been heir to the business if that stupid Sol hadn't... But what difference did the business make now. The business had never been for him, but for them. And there was no more them.

He put his hands over his eyes. "The change, the change," he said. "I don't even know when it began. Me, Lou Epstein, with a rash. I don't even feel any more like Lou Epstein. All of a sudden, pffft! and things are changed." He looked at Michael again, speaking slowly now, stressing every word, as though the boy were more than a nephew, more, in fact, than a single person. "All my life I tried. I swear it, I should drop dead on the spot, if all my life I didn't try to do right, to give my family what I didn't have..."

He stopped; it was not exactly what he wanted to say. He flipped on the bedside light and started again, a new way. "I was seven years old, Michael. I came here I was a boy seven years old, and that day, I can remember it like it was yesterday. Your grandparents and me — your father wasn't born yet, this stuff believe me he doesn't know. With your grandparents I stood on the dock, waiting for

Charlie Goldstein to pick us up. He was your grandfather's partner in the old country, the thief. Anyway, we waited, and finally he came to pick us up, to take us where we would live. And when he came he had a big can in his hand. And you know what was in it? Kerosene. We stood there and Charlie Goldstein poured it on all our heads. He rubbed it in, to delouse us. It tasted awful. For a little boy it was awful . . ."

Michael shrugged his shoulder.

"Eh! How can you understand?" Epstein grumbled. "What do you know? Twenty years old . . ."

Michael shrugged again. "Twenty-two," he said softly.

There were more stories Epstein could tell, but he wondered if any of them would bring him closer to what it was he had on his mind but could not find the words for. He got out of bed and walked to the bedroom door. He opened it and stood there listening. On the downstairs sofa he could hear the folk singer snoring. Some night for guests! He shut the door and came back into the room, scratching his thigh. "Believe me, *she's* not losing any sleep . . . She doesn't deserve me. What, she cooks? That's a big deal? She cleans? That deserves a medal? One day I should come home and the house should be a *mess*. I should be able to write my initials in the dust, somewhere, in the basement at least. Michael, after all these years that would be a pleasure!" He grabbed at his gray hair. "How did this happen? My Goldie, that such a woman should become a cleaning machine. Impossible." He walked to the far wall and stared into Herbie's baseball pictures, the long jaw-muscled faces, faded technicolor now, with signatures at the bottom: Charlie Keller, Lou Gehrig, Red Ruffing . . . A long time. How Herbie had loved his Yankees

"One night," Epstein started again, "it was before the Depression even . . . you know what we did, Goldie and me?" He was staring at Red Ruffing now, through him. "You didn't know my Goldie, what a beautiful beautiful woman she was. And that night we took pictures, photos. I set up the camera — it was in the old house — and we took pictures, in the bedroom." He stopped, remembered. "I wanted a picture of my wife naked, to carry with me. I admit it. The next morning I woke up and there was Goldie tearing up the negatives. She said God forbid I should get in an accident one day and the police would take out my wallet for identification, and then oy-oy-oy!" He smiled. "You know, a woman, she worries . . . But at least we took the pictures, even if we didn't develop them. How many people even do that?" He wondered, and then turned away from Red Ruffing to Michael, who was, faintly, at at the corners of his mouth, smiling.

"What, the photos?"

Michael started to giggle.

"Huh?" Epstein smiled. "What, you never had that kind of idea? I admit it. Maybe to someone else it would seem wrong, a sin or something, but who's to say — "

Michael stiffened, at last his father's son. "Somebody's got to say. Some things just aren't right."

Epstein was willing to admit a youthful lapse. "Maybe," he said, "maybe she was even right to tear — "

Michael shook his head vehemently. "No! Some things aren't right. They're just not!"

And Epstein saw the finger pointing not at Uncle Lou the Photographer, but at Uncle Lou the Adulterer. Suddenly he was shouting. "Right, wrong! From you and your father that's all I ever hear. Who are you, what are you, King Solomon!" He gripped the bedposts. "Should

I tell you what else happened the night we took pictures?
That my Herbie was started that night, I'm sure of it.
Over a year we tried and tried till I was *oysgamitched,*
and that was the night. After the pictures, because of the
pictures. Who knows!"

"But — "

"But what! But *this?*" He was pointing at his crotch.
"You're a boy, you don't understand. When they start
taking things away from you, you reach out, you *grab* —
maybe like a pig even, but you grab. And right, wrong, who
knows! With tears in your eyes, who can even see the difference!" His voice dropped now, but in a minor key the
scolding grew more fierce. "Don't call *me* names. I didn't
see you with Ida's girl, there's not a name for that? For
you it's right?"

Michael was kneeling in his bed now. *"You — saw?"*

"I saw!"

"But it's different — "

"Different?" Epstein shouted.

"To be married is different!"

"What's different you don't know about. To have a
wife, to be a father, twice a father — and then they start
taking things away — " and he fell weak-kneed across Michael's bed. Michael leaned back and looked at his uncle,
but he did not know what to do or how to chastise, for
he had never seen anybody over fifteen years old cry before.

4

Usually Sunday morning went like this: at nine-thirty
Goldie started the coffee and Epstein walked to the corner
for the lox and the Sunday *News.* When the lox was on the

table, the bagels in the oven, the rotogravure section of the *News* two inches from Goldie's nose, then Sheila would descend the stairs, yawning, in her toe-length housecoat. They would sit down to eat, Sheila cursing her father for buying the *News* and "putting money in a Fascist's pocket." Outside, the Gentiles would be walking to church. It had always been the same, except, of course, that over the years the *News* had come closer to Goldie's nose and further from Sheila's heart; she had the *Post* delivered.

This Sunday, when he awoke, Epstein smelled coffee bubbling in the kitchen. When he sneaked down the stairs, past the kitchen — he had been ordered to use the basement bathroom until he'd seen a doctor — he could smell lox. And, at last, when he entered the kitchen, shaved and dressed, he heard newspapers rattling. It was as if another Epstein, his ghost, had risen an hour earlier and performed his Sunday duties. Beneath the clock, around the table, sat Sheila, the folk singer, and Goldie. Bagels toasted in the oven, while the folk singer, sitting backwards in a chair, strummed his guitar and sang —

> *I've been down so long*
> *It look like up to me . . .*

Epstein clapped his hands and rubbed them together, preparatory to eating. "Sheila, you went out for this?" He gestured towards the paper and the lox. "Thank you."

The folk singer looked up, and in the same tune, improvised —

> *I went out for the lox . . .*

and grinned, a regular clown.

"Shut up!" Sheila told him.

He echoed her words, plunk! plunk!

"Thank *you*, then, young man," Epstein said.

"His name is Marvin," Sheila said, "for your informa-tion."

"Thank you, Martin."

"Mar*vin*," the young man said.

"I don't hear so good."

Goldie Epstein looked up from the paper. "Syphilis softens the brain."

"What!"

"Syphilis softens the brain..."

Epstein stood up, raging. "Did you tell her that?" he shouted at his daughter. "Who told her that?"

The folk singer stopped plucking his guitar. Nobody answered; a conspiracy. He grabbed his daughter by the shoulders. "You respect your father, you understand!"

She jerked her shoulder away. "You're not *my* father!"

And the words hurled him back — to the joke Ida Kaufman had made in the car, to her tan dress, the spring sky... He leaned across the table to his wife. "Goldie, Goldie, look at me! Look at *me*, Lou!"

She stared back into the newspaper, though she held it far enough from her nose for Epstein to know she could not see the print; with everything else, the optometrist said the muscles in her eyes had loosened. "Goldie," he said, "Goldie, I did the worst thing in the world? Look me in the eyes, Goldie. Tell me, since when do Jewish people get a divorce? Since when?"

She looked up at him, and then at Sheila. "Syphilis makes soft brains. I can't live with a pig!"

"We'll work it out. We'll go to the rabbi — "

"He wouldn't recognize you —"

"But the children, what about the children?"

"What children?"

Herbie was dead and Sheila a stranger; she was right.

"A grown-up child can take care of herself," Goldie said. "If she wants, she can come to Florida with me. I'm thinking I'll move to Miami Beach."

"Goldie!"

"Stop shouting," Sheila said, anxious to enter the brawl. "You'll wake Michael."

Painfully polite, Goldie addressed her daughter. "Michael left early this morning. He took his Linda to the beach for the day, to their place in Belmar."

"Barnegat," Epstein grumbled, retreating from the table.

"What did you say?" Sheila demanded.

"Barnegat." And he decided to leave the house before any further questions were asked.

At the corner luncheonette he bought his own paper and sat alone, drinking coffee and looking out the window beyond which the people walked to church. A pretty young *shiksa* walked by, holding her white round hat in her hand; she bent over to remove her shoe and shake a pebble from it. Epstein watched her bend, and he spilled some coffee on his shirt front. The girl's small behind was round as an apple beneath the close-fitting dress. He looked, and then as though he were praying, he struck himself on the chest with his fist, again and again. "What have I done! Oh, God!"

When he finished his coffee, he took his paper and started up the street. To home? What home? Across the street in her backyard he saw Ida Kaufman, who was wearing shorts and a halter, and was hanging her daughter's underwear on the clothesline. Epstein looked around and saw only the Gentiles walking to church. Ida saw him and smiled. Growing angry, he stepped off the curb and, passionately, began to jaywalk.

At noon in the Epstein house those present heard a siren go off. Sheila looked up from the *Post* and listened; she looked at her watch. "Noon? I'm fifteen minutes slow. This lousy watch, my father's present."

Goldie Epstein was leafing through the ads in the travel section of the *New York Times*, which Marvin had gone out to buy for her. She looked at her watch. "I'm fourteen minutes slow. Also," she said to her daughter, "a watch from him . . ."

The wail grew louder. "God," Sheila said, "it sounds like the end of the world."

And Marvin, who had been polishing his guitar with his red handkerchief, immediately broke into song, a high-pitched, shut-eyed Negro tune about the end of the world.

"Quiet!" Sheila said. She cocked her ear. "But it's Sunday. The sirens are Saturday —"

Goldie shot off the couch. "It's a real air raid? Oy, that's all we need!"

"It's the police," Sheila said, and fiery-eyed she raced to the front door, for she was politically opposed to police. "It's coming up the street — an ambulance!"

She raced out the door, followed by Marvin, whose guitar still hung around his neck. Goldie trailed behind, her feet slapping against her slippers. On the street she suddenly turned back to the house to make sure the door was shut against daytime burglars, bugs, and dust. When she turned again she had not far to run. The ambulance had pulled up across the street in Kaufman's driveway.

Already a crowd had gathered, neighbors in bathrobes, housecoats, carrying the comic sections with them; and too, churchgoers, *shiksas* in white hats. Goldie could not make her way to the front where her daughter and Marvin stood, but even from the rear of the crowd she could see a young doctor leap from the ambulance and race up to the porch, his stethoscope wiggling in his back pocket as he took two steps at a time.

Mrs. Katz arrived. A squat red-faced woman whose stomach seemed to start at her knees, she tugged at Goldie's arm. "Goldie, more trouble here?"

"I don't know, Pearl. All that racket. It sounded like an atomic bomb."

"When it's that, you'll know," Pearl Katz said. She surveyed the crowd, then looked at the house. "Poor woman," she said, remembering that only three months before, on a windy March morning an ambulance had arrived to take Mrs. Kaufman's husband to the nursing home, from which he never returned.

"Troubles, troubles..." Mrs. Katz was shaking her head, a pot of sympathy. "Everybody has their little bundle, believe me. I'll bet she had a nervous breakdown. That's not a good thing. Gallstones, you have them out and they're out. But a nervous breakdown, it's very bad... You think maybe it's the daughter who's sick?"

"The daughter isn't home," Goldie said. "She's away with my nephew, Michael."

Mrs. Katz saw that no one had emerged from the house yet; she had time to gather a little information. "He's who, Goldie? The son of the brother-in-law that Lou doesn't talk to? That's his father?"

"Yes, Sol in Detroit — "

But she broke off, for the front door had opened, though

still no one could be seen. A voice at the front of the crowd was commanding. "A little room here. Please! A little room, damn it!" It was Sheila. "A little room! Marvin, help me!"

"I can't put down my guitar — I can't find a place — "

"Get them back!" Sheila said.

"But my instrument — "

The doctor and his helper were now wiggling and tilting the stretcher through the front door. Behind them stood Mrs. Kaufman, a man's white shirt tucked into her shorts. Her eyes peered out of two red holes; she wore no make-up, Mrs. Katz noted.

"It must be the girl," said Pearl Katz, up on her toes. "Goldie, can you see, who is it — it's the girl?"

"The girl's *away* — "

"Stay back!" Sheila commanded. "Marvin, for crying out loud, help!"

The young doctor and his attendant held the stretcher steady as they walked sideways down the front steps.

Mrs. Katz jumped up and down. "Who *is* it?"

"I can't see," Goldie said. "I can't — " She pushed up on her toes, out of her slippers. "I — oh God! My God!" And she was racing forward, screaming, "Lou! Lou!"

"Mamma, stay back." Sheila found herself fighting off her mother. The stretcher was sliding into the ambulance now.

"Sheila, let me go, it's your father!" She pointed to the ambulance, whose red eye spun slowly on top. For a moment Goldie looked back to the steps. Ida Kaufman stood there yet, her fingers fidgeting at the buttons of the shirt. Then Goldie broke for the ambulance, her daughter beside her, propelling her by her elbows.

"Who are you?" the doctor said. He took a step towards them to stop their forward motion, for it seemed as if they intended to dive right into the ambulance on top of his patient.

"The wife — " Sheila shouted.

The doctor pointed to the porch. "Look, lady — "

"I'm the *wife*," Goldie cried. "Me!"

The doctor looked at her. "Get in."

Goldie wheezed as Sheila and the doctor helped her into the ambulance, and she let out a gigantic gasp when she saw the white face sticking up from the gray blanket; his eyes were closed, his skin grayer than his hair. The doctor pushed Sheila aside, climbed in, and then the ambulance was moving, the siren screaming. Sheila ran after the ambulance a moment, hammering on the door, but then she turned the other way and was headed back through the crowd and up the stairs to Ida Kaufman's house.

Goldie turned to the doctor. "He's dead?"

"No, he had a heart attack."

She smacked her face.

"He'll be all right," the doctor said.

"But a heart attack. Never in his life."

"A man sixty, sixty-five, it happens." The doctor snapped the answers back while he held Epstein's wrist.

"He's only fifty-nine."

"Some only," the doctor said.

The ambulance zoomed through a red light and made a sharp right turn that threw Goldie to the floor. She sat there and spoke. "But how does a healthy man — "

"Lady, don't ask questions. A grown man can't act like a boy."

She put her hands over her eyes as Epstein opened his.

"He's awake now," the doctor said. "Maybe he wants to hold your hand or something."

Goldie crawled to his side and looked at him. "Lou, you're all right? Does anything hurt?"

He did not answer. "He knows it's me?"

The doctor shrugged his shoulders. "Tell him."

"It's me, Lou."

"It's your wife, Lou," the doctor said. Epstein blinked his eyes. "He knows," the doctor said. "He'll be all right. All he's got to do is live a normal life, normal for sixty."

"You hear the doctor, Lou. All you got to do is live a normal life."

Epstein opened his mouth. His tongue hung over his teeth like a dead snake.

"Don't you talk," his wife said. "Don't you worry about anything. Not even the business. That'll work out. Our Sheila will marry Marvin and that'll be that. You won't have to sell, Lou, it'll be in the family. You can retire, rest, and Marvin can take over. He's a smart boy, Marvin, a *mensch.*"

Lou rolled his eyes in his head.

"Don't try to talk. I'll take care. You'll be better soon and we can go someplace. We can go to Saratoga, to the mineral baths, if you want. We'll just go, you and me — " Suddenly she gripped his hand. "Lou, you'll live normal, won't you? *Won't you?*" She was crying. " 'Cause what'll happen, Lou, is you'll kill yourself! You'll keep this up and that'll be the end — "

"All right," the young doctor said, "you take it easy now We don't want two patients on our hands."

The ambulance was pulling down and around into the

side entrance of the hospital and the doctor knelt at the back door.

"I don't know why I'm crying." Goldie wiped her eyes. "He'll be all right? You say so, I believe you, you're a doctor." And as the young man swung open the door with the big red cross painted on the back, she asked, softly, "Doctor, you have something that will cure what else he's got — this rash?" She pointed.

The doctor looked at her. Then he lifted for a moment the blanket that covered Epstein's nakedness.

"Doctor, it's bad?"

Goldie's eyes and nose were running.

"An irritation," the doctor said.

She grabbed his wrist. "You can clean it up?"

"So it'll never come back," the doctor said, and hopped out of the ambulance.

YOU CAN'T
TELL A MAN
BY THE SONG
HE SINGS

I T WAS in a freshman high school class called "Occupations" that, fifteen years ago, I first met the ex-con, Alberto Pelagutti. The first week my new classmates and I were given "a battery of tests" designed to reveal our skills, deficiencies, tendencies, and psyches. At the end of the week, Mr. Russo, the Occupations teacher, would add the skills, subtract the deficiencies, and tell us what jobs best suited our talents; it was all mysterious but scientific. I remember we first took a "Preference Test": "Which would you prefer to do, this, that, or the other thing..." Albie Pelagutti sat one seat behind me and to my left, and while this first day of high school I strolled happily through the test, examining ancient fossils here, defending criminals there, Albie, like the inside of Vesuvius, rose, fell, pitched, tossed, and swelled in his chair. When he finally made a decision, he made it. You could hear his pencil drive the x into the column opposite the activity in which he thought it wisest to prefer to engage. His agony reinforced the legend that had preceded him: he was seventeen; had just left Jamesburg Reformatory; this was his third high school, his third freshman year; but now — I heard another *x* driven home — he had decided "to go straight."

Halfway through the hour Mr. Russo left the room. "I'm going for a drink," he said. Russo was forever at pains to let us know what a square-shooter he was and that, unlike other teachers we might have had, he would not go out the front door of the classroom to sneak around to the back door and observe how responsible we were. And sure enough, when he returned after going for a drink, his lips were wet; when he came back from the men's room, you could smell the soap on his hands. "Take your time, boys," he said, and the door swung shut behind him.

His black wingtipped shoes beat down the marble corridor and five thick fingers dug into my shoulder. I turned around; it was Pelagutti. "What?" I said. "Number twenty-six," Pelagutti said, "What's the answer?" I gave him the truth: "Anything." Pelagutti rose halfway over his desk and glared at me. He was a hippopotamus, big, black, and smelly; his short sleeves squeezed tight around his monstrous arms as though they were taking his own blood pressure — which at that moment was sky-bound: "What's the answer!" Menaced, I flipped back three pages in my question booklet and reread number twenty-six. "Which would you prefer to do: (1) Attend a World Trade Convention. (2) Pick cherries. (3) Stay with and read to a sick friend. (4) Tinker with automobile engines." I looked blank-faced back to Albie, and shrugged my shoulders. "It doesn't matter — there's no right answer. Anything." He almost rocketed out of his seat. "Don't give me that crap! What's the answer!" Strange heads popped up all over the room — thin-eyed glances, hissing lips, shaming grins — and I realized that any minute Russo, wet-lipped, might come back and my first day in high school I would be caught cheating. I looked again at number twenty-six; then back to Albie; and then propelled — as I always was towards him — by anger, pity, fear, love, vengeance, and an instinct for irony that was at the time delicate as a mallet, I whispered, "Stay and read to a sick friend." The volcano subsided, and Albie and I had met.

We became friends. He remained at my elbow throughout the testing, then throughout lunch, then after school. I learned that Albie, as a youth, had done all the things I, under direction, had not: he had eaten hamburgers in strange diners; he had gone out after cold showers, wet-haired, into winter weather; he had been cruel to animals; he had trafficked with whores; he had stolen, he had been caught, and he had paid. But now he told me, as I unwrapped my lunch in the candy store across from school, "Now, I'm through crappin' around. I'm gettin' an education. I'm gonna — " and I think he picked up the figure from a movie musical he had seen the previous afternoon while the rest of us were in English class — "I'm gonna put my best foot forward." The following week when Russo read the results of the testing it appeared that Albie's feet were not only moving forward but finding strange, wonderful paths. Russo sat at his desk, piles of tests stacked before him like ammunition, charts and diagrams mounted huge on either side, and delivered our destinies. Albie and I were going to be lawyers.

Of all that Albie confessed to me that first week, one fact in particular fastened on my brain: I soon forgot the town in Sicily where he was born; the occupation of his father (he either made ice or delivered it); the year and model of the cars he had stolen. I did not forget though that Albie had apparently been the star of the Jamesburg Reformatory baseball team. When I was selected by the gym teacher, Mr. Hopper, to captain one of my gym class's softball teams (we played softball until the World Series was over, then switched to touch football), I knew that I had to get Pelagutti on my side. With those arms he could hit the ball a mile.

The day teams were to be selected Albie shuffled back and forth at my side, while in the lockerroom I changed into my gym uniform — jockstrap, khaki-colored shorts, T-shirt, sweat socks, and sneakers. Albie had already changed: beneath his khaki gym shorts he did not wear a support but retained his lavender undershorts; they hung down three inches below the outer shorts and looked like a long fancy hem. Instead of a T-shirt he wore a sleeveless undershirt; and beneath his high, tar-black sneakers he wore thin black silk socks with slender arrows embroidered up the sides. Naked he might, like some centuries-dead ancestor, have tossed lions to their death in the Colosseum; the outfit, though I didn't tell him, detracted from his dignity.

As we left the lockerroom and padded through the dark basement corridor and up onto the sunny September playing field, he talked continually, "I didn't play sports when I was a kid, but I played at Jamesburg and baseball came to me like nothing." I nodded my head. "What you think of Pete Reiser?" he asked. "He's a pretty good man," I said. "What you think of Tommy Henrich?" "I don't know," I answered, "he's dependable, I guess." As a Dodger fan I preferred Reiser to the Yankees' Henrich; and besides, my tastes have always been a bit baroque, and Reiser, who re-

peatedly bounced off outfield walls to save the day for
Brooklyn, had won a special trophy in the Cooperstown of
my heart. "Yeh," Albie said, "I like all them Yankees."

I didn't have a chance to ask Albie what he meant by
that, for Mr. Hopper, bronzed, smiling, erect, was flipping
a coin; I looked up, saw the glint in the sun, and I was calling "heads." It landed tails and the other captain had first
choice. My heart flopped over when he looked at Albie's
arms, but calmed when he passed on and chose first a tall,
lean, first-baseman type. Immediately I said, "I'll take
Pelagutti." You don't very often see smiles like the one that
crossed Albie Pelagutti's face that moment: you would
think I had paroled him from a life sentence.

The game began. I played shortstop — left-handed —
and batted second; Albie was in center field and, at his
wish, batted fourth. Their first man grounded out, me to
the first baseman. The next batter hit a high, lofty fly ball
to center field. The moment I saw Albie move after it I
knew Tommy Henrich and Pete Reiser were only names
to him; all he knew about baseball he'd boned up on the
night before. While the ball hung in the air, Albie jumped
up and down beneath it, his arms raised upward directly
above his head; his wrists were glued together, and his two
hands flapped open and closed like a butterfly's wings,
begging the ball toward them.

"C'mon," he was screaming to the sky, "c'mon you bastard . . ." And his legs bicycle-pumped up and down, up
and down. I hope the moment of my death does not take
as long as it did for that damn ball to drop. It hung, it
hung, Albie cavorting beneath like a Holy Roller. And then
it landed, smack into Albie's chest. The runner was round-

ing second and heading for third while Albie twirled all around, looking, his arms down now, stretched out, as though he were playing ring-around-a-rosy with two invisible children. "Behind you, Pelagutti!" I screamed. He stopped moving. "What?" he called back to me. I ran halfway out to center field. "Behind you — relay it!" And then, as the runner rounded third, I had to stand there defining "relay" to him.

At the end of the first half of the first inning we came to bat behind, 8–0 — eight home runs, all relayed in too late by Pelagutti.

Out of a masochistic delight I must describe Albie at the plate: first, he *faced* the pitcher; then, when he swung at the ball — and he did, at every one — it was not to the side but down, as though he were driving a peg into the ground. Don't ask if he was right-handed or left-handed. I don't know.

While we changed out of our gym uniforms I was silent. I boiled as I watched Pelagutti from the corner of my eye. He kicked off those crazy black sneakers and pulled his pink gaucho shirt on over his undershirt — there was still a red spot above the U front of the undershirt where the first fly ball had hit him. Without removing his gym shorts he stuck his feet into his gray trousers — I watched as he hoisted the trousers over the red splotches where ground balls had banged off his shins, past the red splotches where pitched balls had smacked his knee caps and thighs.

Finally I spoke. "Damn you, Pelagutti, you wouldn't know Pete Reiser if you fell over him!" He was stuffing his sneakers into his locker; he didn't answer. I was talking to his mountainous pink shirt back. "Where do you come off telling me you played for that prison team?" He mumbled something. "What?" I said. "I did," he grumbled. "Bull-shit!" I said. He turned and, black-eyed, glared at me: "I did!" "That must've been some team!" I said. We did not speak as we left the lockerroom. As we passed the gym office on our way up to Occupations, Mr. Hopper looked up from his desk and winked at me. Then he motioned his head at Pelagutti to indicate that he knew I'd picked a lemon, but how could I have expected a bum like Pelagutti to be an All-American boy in the first place? Then Mr. Hopper turned his sun-lamped head back to his desk.

"Now," I said to Pelagutti as we turned at the second floor landing, "now I'm stuck with you for the rest of the term." He shuffled ahead of me without answering; his oxlike behind should have had a tail on it to flick the flies away — it infuriated me. "You goddamn liar!" I said.

He spun around as fast as an ox can. "You ain't stuck with nobody." We were at the top of the landing headed into the locker-lined corridor; the kids who were piling up the stairs behind stopped, listened. "No you ain't, you snot-ass!" And I saw five hairy knuckles coming right at my mouth. I moved but not in time, and heard a crash inside the bridge of my nose. I felt my hips dip back, my legs and head come forward, and, curved like the letter c, I was swept fifteen feet backward before I felt cold marble beneath the palms of my hands. Albie stepped around me and into the Occupations room. Just then I looked up to see Mr. Russo's black wingtipped shoes enter the room. I'm almost sure he had seen Albie blast me but I'll never know. Nobody, including Albie and myself, ever mentioned it again. Perhaps it had been a mistake for me to call Albie a liar, but if he had starred at baseball, it was in some league I did not know.

By way of contrast I want to introduce Duke Scarpa, another ex-con who was with us that year. Neither Albie nor the Duke, incidentally, was a typical member of my high school community. Both lived at the other end of Newark, "down neck," and they had reached us only after the Board of Education had tried Albie at two other schools and the Duke at four. The Board hoped finally, like Marx, that the higher culture would absorb the lower.

Albie and Duke had no particular use for each other; where Albie had made up his mind to go straight, one always felt that the Duke, in his oily quietness, his boneless grace, was planning a job. Yet, though affection never lived between them, Duke wandered after Albie and me, aware, I suspect, that if Albie despised him it was because he was able to read his soul — and that such an associate was easier to abide than one who despises you because he does not know your soul at all. Where Albie was a hippopotamus, an ox, Duke was reptilian. Me? I don't know; it is easy to spot the animal in one's fellows.

During lunch hour, the Duke and I used to spar with each other in the hall outside the cafeteria. He did not know a hook from a jab and disliked having his dark skin roughened or his hair mussed; but he so delighted in moving, bobbing, coiling, and uncoiling, that I think he would have paid for the privilege of playing the serpent with me. He hypnotized me, the Duke; he pulled some slimy string inside me — where Albie Pelagutti sought and stretched a deeper and, I think, a nobler cord.

But I make Albie sound like peaches-and-cream. Let me tell you what he and I did to Mr. Russo.

Russo believed in his battery of tests as his immigrant parents (and Albie's, and maybe Albie himself) believed in papal infallibility. If the tests said Albie was going to be a lawyer then he was going to be a lawyer. As for Albie's past, it seemed only to increase Russo's devotion to the prophecy: he approached Albie with salvation in his eyes. In September, then, he gave Albie a biography to read, the life of Oliver Wendell Holmes; during October, once a week, he had the poor fellow speak impromptu before the class; in November he had him write a report on the Constitution, which I wrote; and then in December, the final indignity, he sent Albie and me (and two others who displayed a legal bent) to the Essex County Court House where we could see "real lawyers in action."

It was a cold, windy morning and as we flicked our cigarettes at the Lincoln statue on the courtyard plaza, and started up the long flight of white cement steps, Albie suddenly did an about-face and headed back across the plaza and out to Market Street. I called to him but he shouted back that he had seen it all before, and then he was not walking, but running towards the crowded downtown streets, pursued not by police, but by other days. It wasn't that he considered Russo an ass for having sent him to visit the Court House — Albie respected teachers too much for that; rather I think he felt Russo had tried to rub his nose in it.

No surprise, then, when the next day after gym Albie announced his assault on the Occupations teacher; it was the first crime he had planned since his decision to go straight back in September. He outlined the action to me and indicated that I should pass the details on to the other members of the class. As liaison between Albie and the well-

behaved, healthy nonconvicts like myself who made up the
rest of the class, I was stationed at the classroom door and
as each member passed in I unfolded the plot into his ear:
"As soon after ten-fifteen as Russo turns to the black-
board, you bend over to tie your shoelace." If a classmate
looked back at me puzzled, I would motion to Pelagutti
hulking over his desk; the puzzled expression would vanish
and another accomplice would enter the room. The only
one who gave me any trouble was the Duke. He listened to
the plan and then scowled back at me with the look of a
man who's got his own syndicate, and, in fact, has never
even heard of yours.

Finally the bell rang; I closed the door behind me and
moved noiselessly to my desk. I waited for the clock to
move to a quarter after; it did; and then Russo turned to
the board to write upon it the salary range of aluminum
workers. I bent to tie my shoelaces —beneath all the desks
I saw other upside-down grinning faces. To my left behind
me I heard Albie hissing; his hands fumbled about his
black silk socks, and the hiss grew and grew until it was a
rush of Sicilian, muttered, spewed, vicious. The exchange
was strictly between Russo and himself. I looked to the
front of the classroom, my fingers knotting and unknotting
my shoelaces, the blood pumping now to my face. I saw
Russo's legs turn. What a sight he must have seen — where
there had been twenty-five faces, now there was nothing.
Just desks. "Okay," I heard Russo say, "okay." And then
he gave a little clap with his hands. "That's enough now,
fellas. The joke is over. Sit up." And then Albie's hiss
traveled to all the blood-pinked ears below the desks;
it rushed about us like a subterranean stream — "Stay
down!"

While Russo asked us to get up we stayed down. And we did not sit up until Albie told us to; and then under his direction we were singing —

> *Don't sit under the apple tree*
> *With anyone else but me,*
> *Anyone else but me,*
> *Anyone else but me,*
> *Oh, no, no, don't sit under the apple tree . . .*

And then in time to the music we clapped. What a noise!

Mr. Russo stood motionless at the front of the class, listening, astonished. He wore a neatly pressed dark blue pin-striped suit, a tan tie with a collie's head in the center, and a tieclasp with the initials R.R. engraved upon it; he had on the black wingtipped shoes; they glittered. Russo, who believed in neatness, honesty, punctuality, planned destinies — who believed in the future, in Occupations! And next to me, behind me, inside me, all over me — Albie! We looked at each other, Albie and I, and my lungs split with joy: "*Don't sit under the apple tree —* " Albie's monotone boomed out, and then a thick liquid crooner's voice behind Albie bathed me in sound: it was the Duke's; he clapped to a tango beat.

Russo leaned for a moment against a visual aids chart — "Skilled Laborers: Salaries and Requirements" — and then scraped back his chair and plunged down into it, so far down it looked to have no bottom. He lowered his big head to the desk and his shoulders curled forward like the ends of wet paper; and that was when Albie pulled his coup. He stopped singing "Don't Sit Under the Apple Tree"; we all stopped. Russo looked up at the silence; his eyes black and baggy, he stared at our leader, Alberto Pelagutti. Slowly

Russo began to shake his head from side to side: this was no Capone, this was a Garibaldi! Russo waited, I waited, we all waited. Albie slowly rose, and began to sing *"Oh, say can you see, by the dawn's early light, what so proudly we hailed —"* And we all stood and joined him. Tears sparkling on his long black lashes, Mr. Robert Russo dragged himself wearily up from his desk, beaten, and as the Pelagutti basso boomed disastrously behind me, I saw Russo's lips begin to move, *"the bombs bursting in air, gave proof —"* God, did we sing!

Albie left school in June of that year — he had passed only Occupations — but our comradeship, that strange vessel, was smashed to bits at noon one day a few months earlier. It was a lunch hour in March, the Duke and I were sparring in the hall outside the cafeteria, and Albie, who had been more hospitable to the Duke since the day his warm, liquid voice had joined the others — Albie had decided to act as our referee, jumping between us, separating our clinches, warning us about low blows, grabbing out for the Duke's droopy crotch, in general having a good time. I remember that the Duke and I were in a clinch; as I showered soft little punches to his kidneys he squirmed in my embrace. The sun shone through the window behind him, lighting up his hair like a nest of snakes. I fluttered his sides, he twisted, I breathed hard through my nose, my eyes registered on his snaky hair, and suddenly Albie wedged between and knocked us apart — the Duke plunged sideways, I plunged forward, and my fist crashed through the window that Scarpa had been using as his corner. Feet pounded; in a second a wisecracking, guiltless, chewing crowd was gathered around me, just me. Albie and the Duke were gone. I cursed them both, the honorless bastards! The crowd did not drift back to lunch until the head dietitian, a huge, varicose-veined matron in a laundry-stiff white uniform had written down my name and led me to the nurse's office to have the glass picked out of my knuckles. Later in the afternoon I was called for the first and only time to the office of Mr. Wendell, the Principal.

Fifteen years have passed since then and I do not know what has happened to Albie Pelagutti. If he is a gangster he was not one with notoriety or money enough for the Kefauver Committee to interest itself in several years ago. When the Crime Committee reached New Jersey I followed their investigations carefully but never did I read in the papers the name Alberto Pelagutti or even Duke Scarpa — though who can tell what name the Duke is known by now. I do know, however, what happened to the Occupations teacher, for when another Senate Committee swooped through the state a while back it was discovered that Robert Russo — among others — had been a Marxist while attending Montclair State Teachers' College circa 1935. Russo refused to answer some of the Committee's questions, and the Newark Board of Education met, chastised, and dismissed him. I read now and then in the Newark *News* that Civil Liberties Union attorneys are still trying to appeal his case, and I have even written a letter to the Board of Education swearing that if anything subversive was ever done to my character, it wasn't done by my ex-high school teacher, Russo; if he was a Communist I never knew it. I could not decide whether or not to include in the letter a report of the "Star-Spangled Banner" incident: who knows what is and is not proof to the crotchety ladies and chainstore owners who sit and die on Boards of Education?

And if (to alter an Ancient's text) a man's history is
his fate, who knows whether the Newark Board of Education will ever attend to a letter written to them by me. I
mean, have fifteen years buried that afternoon I was called
to see the Principal?

... He was a tall, distinguished gentleman and as I entered his office he rose and extended his hand. The same
sun that an hour earlier had lit up snakes in the Duke's hair
now slanted through Mr. Wendell's blinds and warmed his
deep green carpet. "How do you do?" he said. "Yes," I
answered, non sequiturly, and ducked my bandaged hand
under my unbandaged hand. Graciously he said, "Sit
down, won't you?" Frightened, unpracticed, I performed
an aborted curtsy and sat. I watched Mr. Wendell go to
his metal filing cabinet, slide one drawer open, and take
from it a large white index card. He set the card on his desk
and motioned me over so I might read what was typed on
the card. At the top, in caps, was my whole name — last,
first, and middle; below the name was a Roman numeral
one, and beside it, "Fighting in corridor; broke window
(3/19/42)." Already documented. And on a big card with
plenty of space.

I returned to my chair and sat back as Mr. Wendell told
me that the card would follow me through life. At first I
listened, but as he talked on and on the drama went out
of what he said, and my attention wandered to his filing
cabinet. I began to imagine the cards inside, Albie's card
and the Duke's, and then I understood — just short of forgiveness — why the two of them had zoomed off and left
me to pay penance for the window by myself. Albie, you
see, had always known about the filing cabinet and these
index cards; I hadn't; and Russo, poor Russo, has only
recently found out.

ELI,

THE

FANATIC

Leo Tzuref stepped out from back of a white column to welcome Eli Peck. Eli jumped back, surprised; then they shook hands and Tzuref gestured him into the sagging old mansion. At the door Eli turned, and down the slope of lawn, past the jungle of hedges, beyond the dark, untrampled horse path, he saw the street lights blink on in Woodenton. The stores along Coach House Road tossed up a burst of yellow — it came to Eli as a secret signal from his townsmen: "Tell this Tzuref where we stand, Eli. This is a modern community, Eli, we have our families, we pay taxes . . ." Eli, burdened by the message, gave Tzuref a dumb, weary stare.

"You must work a full day," Tzuref said, steering the attorney and his briefcase into the chilly hall.

Eli's heels made a racket on the cracked marble floor, and he spoke above it. "It's the commuting that's killing," he said, and entered the dim room Tzuref waved open for him. "Three hours a day . . . I came right from the train." He dwindled down into a harp-backed chair. He expected it would be deeper than it was and consequently jarred himself on the sharp bones of his seat. It woke him, this shiver of the behind, to his business. Tzuref, a bald shaggy-browed man who looked as if he'd once been very fat, sat back of an empty desk, halfway hidden, as though he were settled on the floor. Everything around him was empty. There were no books in the bookshelves, no rugs on the floor, no draperies in the big casement windows. As Eli began to speak Tzuref got up and swung a window back on one noisy hinge. "May and it's like August," he said, and with his back to Eli, he revealed the black circle on the back of his head. The crown of his head was missing! He returned through the dimness — the lamps had no bulbs — and Eli realized all he'd seen was a skullcap. Tzuref struck a match and lit a candle, just as the half-dying shouts of children at play rolled in through the open window. It was as though Tzuref had opened it so Eli could hear them.

"Aah, now," he said. "I received your letter."

Eli poised, waiting for Tzuref to swish open a drawer and remove the letter from his file. Instead the old man leaned forward onto his stomach, worked his hand into his pants pocket, and withdrew what appeared to be a week-old handkerchief. He uncrumpled it; he unfolded it; he ironed it on the desk with the side of his hand. "So," he said.

Eli pointed to the grimy sheet which he'd gone over word-by-word with his partners, Lewis and McDonnell. "I expected an answer," Eli said. "It's a week."

"It was so important, Mr. Peck, I knew you would come."

Some children ran under the open window and their mysterious babble — not mysterious to Tzuref, who smiled — entered the room like a third person. Their noise caught up against Eli's flesh and he was unable to restrain a shudder. He wished he had gone home, showered and eaten dinner, before calling on Tzuref. He was not feeling as professional as usual — the place was too dim, it was too late. But down in Woodenton they would be waiting, his clients and neighbors. He spoke for the Jews of Woodenton, not just himself and his wife.

"You understood?" Eli said.

"It's not hard."

"It's a matter of zoning . . ." and when Tzuref did not answer, but only drummed his fingers on his lips, Eli said, "We didn't make the laws . . ."

"You respect them."

"They protect us . . . the community."

"The law is the law," Tzuref said.

"Exactly!" Eli had the urge to rise and walk about the room.

"And then of course " — Tzuref made a pair of scales in the air with his hands —"The law is not the law. When is the law that is the law not the law?" He jiggled the scales. "And vice versa."

"Simply," Eli said sharply. "You can't have a boarding school in a residential area." He would not allow Tzuref to cloud the issue with issues. "We thought it better to tell you before any action is undertaken."

"But a house in a residential area?"

"Yes. That's what residential means." The DP's English was perhaps not as good as it seemed at first. Tzuref spoke slowly, but till then Eli had mistaken it for craft — or even wisdom. "Residence means home," he added.

"So this is my residence."

"But the children?"

"It is their residence."

"*Seventeen* children?"

"Eighteen," Tzuref said.

"But you *teach* them here."

"The Talmud. That's illegal?"

"That makes it school."

Tzuref hung the scales again, tipping slowly the balance.

"Look, Mr. Tzuref, in America we call such a place a boarding school."

"Where they teach the Talmud?"

"Where they teach period. You are the headmaster, they are the students."

Tzuref placed his scales on the desk. "Mr. Peck," he said, "I don't believe it . . ." but he did not seem to be referring to anything Eli had said.

"Mr. Tzuref, that is the law. I came to ask what you intend to do."

"What I *must* do?"

"I hope they are the same."

"They are." Tzuref brought his stomach into the desk. "We stay." He smiled. "We are tired. The headmaster is tired. The students are tired."

Eli rose and lifted his briefcase. It felt so heavy packed with the grievances, vengeances, and schemes of his clients. There were days when he carried it like a feather — in Tzuref's office it weighed a ton.

"Goodbye, Mr. Tzuref."

"Sholom," Tzuref said.

Eli opened the door to the office and walked carefully down the dark tomb of a corridor to the door. He stepped out on the porch and, leaning against a pillar, looked down across the lawn to the children at play. Their voices whooped and rose and dropped as they chased each other round the old house. The dusk made the children's game look like a tribal dance. Eli straightened up, started off the porch, and suddenly the dance was ended. A long piercing scream trailed after. It was the first time in his life anyone had run at the sight of him. Keeping his eyes on the lights of Woodenton, he headed down the path.

And then, seated on a bench beneath a tree, Eli saw him. At first it seemed only a deep hollow of blackness — then the figure emerged. Eli recognized him from the description. There he was, wearing the hat, that hat which was the very cause of Eli's mission, the source of Woodenton's upset. The town's lights flashed their message once again: "Get the one with the hat. What a nerve, what a nerve . . ."

Eli started towards the man. Perhaps he was less stubborn than Tzuref, more reasonable. After all, it was the law. But when he was close enough to call out, he didn't. He was stopped by the sight of the black coat that fell down below the man's knees, and the hands which held each other in his lap. By the round-topped, wide-brimmed Talmudic hat, pushed onto the back of his head. And by the beard, which hid his neck and was so soft and thin it fluttered away and back again with each heavy breath he took. He was asleep, his sidelocks curled loose on his cheeks. His face was no older than Eli's.

Eli hurried towards the lights.

The note on the kitchen table unsettled him. Scribblings on bits of paper had made history this past week. This one, however, was unsigned. "Sweetie," it said, "I went to sleep. I had a sort of Oedipal experience with the baby today. Call Ted Heller."

She had left him a cold soggy dinner in the refrigerator. He hated cold soggy dinners, but would take one gladly in place of Miriam's presence. He was ruffled, and she never helped that, not with her infernal analytic powers. He loved her when life was proceeding smoothly — and that was when she loved him. But sometimes Eli found being a lawyer surrounded him like quicksand — he couldn't get his breath. Too often he wished he were pleading for the other side; though if he were on the other side, then he'd wish he were on the side he was. The trouble was that sometimes the law didn't seem to be the answer, *law* didn't seem to have anything to do with what was aggravating everybody. And that, of course, made him feel foolish and unnecessary . . . Though that was not the situation here — the townsmen had a case. But not *exactly*, and if Miriam were awake to see Eli's upset, she would set about explaining his distress to him, understanding him, forgiving him, so as to get things back to Normal, for Normal was where they loved one another. The difficulty with Miriam's efforts was they only upset him more; not only did they explain little to him about himself or his predicament, but they convinced him of *her* weakness. Neither Eli nor Miriam, it turned out, was terribly strong. Twice before he'd faced this fact, and on both occasions had found solace in what his neighbors forgivingly referred to as "a nervous breakdown."

Eli ate his dinner with his briefcase beside him. Halfway through, he gave in to himself, removed Tzuref's notes, and put them on the table, beside Miriam's. From time to time he flipped through the notes, which had been carried into town by the one in the black hat. The first note, the incendiary:

To whom it may concern:

Please give this gentleman the following: Boys shoes with rubber heels and soles.

5 prs size 6c

3 prs size 5c

3 prs size 5b

2 prs size 4a

3 prs size 4c

1 pr size 7b

1 pr size 7c

Total 18 prs. boys shoes. This gentleman has a check already signed. Please fill in correct amount.

L. TZUREF

Director, Yeshivah of

Woodenton, N.Y.

(5/8/48)

"Eli, a regular greenhorn," Ted Heller had said. "He didn't say a word. Just handed me the note and stood there, like in the Bronx the old guys who used to come around selling Hebrew trinkets."

"A Yeshivah!" Artie Berg had said. "Eli, in Woodenton, a Yeshivah! If I want to live in Brownsville, Eli, I'll live in Brownsville."

"Eli," Harry Shaw speaking now, "the old Puddington place. Old man Puddington'll roll over in his grave. Eli, when I left the city, Eli, I didn't plan the city should come to me."

Note number two:

Dear Grocer:

Please give this gentleman ten pounds of sugar. Charge it to our account, Yeshivah of Woodenton, NY — which we will now open with you and expect a bill each month. The gentleman will be in to see you once or twice a week.

L. Tzuref, Director

(5/10/48)

P.S. Do you carry kosher meat?

"He walked right by my window, the greenie," Ted had said, "and he nodded, Eli. He's my *friend* now."

"Eli," Artie Berg had said, "he handed the damn thing to a *clerk* at Stop N' Shop — and in that hat yet!"

"Eli," Harry Shaw again, "it's not funny. Someday, Eli, it's going to be a hundred little kids with little *yamalkahs* chanting their Hebrew lessons on Coach House Road, and then it's not going to strike you funny."

"Eli, what goes on up there — my kids hear strange sounds."

"Eli, this is a modern community."

"Eli, we pay taxes."

"Eli."

"Eli!"

"*Eli!*"

At first it was only another townsman crying in his ear; but when he turned he saw Miriam, standing in the doorway, behind her belly.

"Eli, sweetheart, how was it?"

"He said no."

"Did you see the other one?" she asked.

"Sleeping, under a tree."

"Did you let him know how people feel?"

"He was sleeping."

"Why didn't you wake him up? Eli, this isn't an every-day thing."

"He was tired!"

"Don't shout, please," Miriam said.

" 'Don't shout. I'm pregnant. The baby is heavy.' " Eli found he was getting angry at nothing she'd said yet; it was what she was going to say.

"He's a very heavy baby the doctor says," Miriam told him.

"Then sit *down* and make my dinner." Now he found himself angry about her not being present at the dinner which he'd just been relieved that she wasn't present at. It was as though he had a raw nerve for a tail, that he kept stepping on. At last Miriam herself stepped on it.

"Eli, you're upset. I understand."

"You *don't* understand."

She left the room. From the stairs she called, "I do, sweetheart."

It was a trap! He would grow angry knowing she would be "understanding." She would in turn grow more under-standing seeing his anger. He would in turn grow angrier ... The phone rang.

"Hello," Eli said.

"Eli, Ted. So?"

"So nothing."

"Who is Tzuref? He's an American guy?"

"No. A DP. German."

"And the kids?"

"DP's too. He teaches them."

"What? What subjects?" Ted asked.

"I don't know."

"And the guy with the hat, you saw the guy with the hat?"

"Yes. He was sleeping."

"Eli, he sleeps with the *hat?*"

"He sleeps with the hat."

"Goddam fanatics," Ted said. "This is the twentieth century, Eli. Now it's the guy with the hat. Pretty soon all the little Yeshivah boys'll be spilling down into town."

"Next thing they'll be after our daughters."

"Michele and Debbie wouldn't look at them."

"Then," Eli mumbled, "you've got nothing to worry about, Teddie," and he hung up.

In a moment the phone rang. "Eli? We got cut off. We've got nothing to worry about? You worked it out?"

"I have to see him again tomorrow. We can work something out."

"That's fine, Eli. I'll call Artie and Harry."

Eli hung up.

"I thought you said *nothing* worked out." It was Miriam.

"I did."

"Then why did you tell Ted *something* worked out?"

"It did."

"Eli, maybe you should get a little more therapy."

"That's enough of that, Miriam."

"You can't function as a lawyer by being neurotic. That's no answer."

"You're ingenious, Miriam."

She turned, frowning, and took her heavy baby to bed.

The phone rang.

"Eli, Artie. Ted called. You worked it out? No trouble?"

"Yes."

"When are they going?"

"Leave it to me, will you, Artie? I'm tired. I'm going to sleep."

In bed Eli kissed his wife's belly and laid his head upon it to think. He laid it lightly, for she was that day entering the second week of her ninth month. Still, when she slept, it was a good place to rest, to rise and fall with her breathing and figure things out. "If that guy would take off that crazy hat. I know it, what eats them. If he'd take off that crazy hat everything would be all right."

"What?" Miriam said.

"I'm talking to the baby."

Miriam pushed herself up in bed. "Eli, please, baby, shouldn't you maybe stop in to see Dr. Eckman, just for a little conversation?"

"I'm fine."

"Oh, sweetie!" she said, and put her head back on the pillow.

"You know what your mother brought to this marriage — a sling chair and a goddam New School enthusiasm for Sigmund Freud."

Miriam feigned sleep, he could tell by the breathing.

"I'm telling the kid the truth, aren't I, Miriam? A sling chair, three months to go on a *New Yorker* subscription, and *An Introduction to Psychoanalysis*. Isn't that right?"

"Eli, must you be aggressive?"

"That's all you worry about, is your insides. You stand in front of the mirror all day and look at yourself being pregnant."

"Pregnant mothers have a relationship with the fetus that fathers can't understand."

"Relationship my ass. What is my liver doing now? What is my small intestine doing now? Is my island of Langerhans on the blink?"

"Don't be jealous of a little fetus, Eli."

"I'm jealous of your island of Lagerhans!"

"Eli, I can't argue with you when I know it's not me you're really angry with. Don't you see, sweetie, you're angry with yourself."

"You and Eckman."

"Maybe he could help, Eli."

"Maybe he could help you. You're practically lovers as it is."

"You're being hostile again," Miriam said.

"What do you care — it's only *me* I'm being hostile towards."

"Eli, we're going to have a beautiful baby, and I'm going to have a perfectly simple delivery, and you're going to make a fine father, and there's absolutely no reason to be obsessed with whatever is on your mind. All we have to worry about — " she smiled at him " — is a name."

Eli got out of bed and slid into his slippers. "We'll name the kid Eckman if it's a boy and Eckman if it's a girl."

"Eckman Peck sounds terrible."

"He'll have to live with it," Eli said, and he went down to his study where the latch on his briefcase glinted in the moonlight that came through the window.

He removed the Tzuref notes and read through them all again. It unnerved him to think of all the flashy reasons his wife could come up with for his reading and rereading the notes. "Eli, why are you so *preoccupied* with Tzuref?" "Eli, stop getting *involved*. Why do you think you're getting *involved*, Eli?" Sooner or later, everybody's wife finds their weak spot. His goddam luck he had to be neurotic! Why couldn't he have been born with a short leg.

He removed the cover from his typewriter, hating Miriam for the edge she had. All the time he wrote the letter, he could hear what she would be saying about his not being *able* to let the matter drop. Well, her trouble was that she wasn't *able* to face the matter. But he could hear her answer already: clearly, he was guilty of "a reaction formation." Still, all the fancy phrases didn't fool Eli: all she wanted really was for Eli to send Tzuref and family on their way, so that the community's temper would quiet, and the calm circumstances of their domestic happiness return. All she wanted were order and love in her private world. Was she so wrong? Let the world bat its brains out —in Woodenton there should be peace. He wrote the letter anyway:

Dear Mr. Tzuref:

Our meeting this evening seems to me inconclusive. I don't think there's any reason for us not to be able to come up with some sort of compromise that will satisfy the Jewish community of Woodenton and the Yeshivah and yourself. It seems to me that what most disturbs my neighbors are the visits to town by the gentleman in the black hat, suit, etc. Woodenton is a progressive suburban community whose members, both Jewish and Gentile, are anxious that their families live in comfort and beauty and serenity. This is, after all, the twentieth century, and we do not think it too much to ask that the members of our community dress in a manner appropriate to the time and place.

Woodenton, as you may not know, has long been the home of well-to-do Protestants. It is only since the war that Jews have been able to buy property here, and for Jews and Gentiles to live beside each other in amity. For this adjustment to be made, both Jews and Gentiles alike have had to give up some of their more extreme practices in order not to threaten or offend the other. Certainly such amity is to be desired. Perhaps if such conditions had existed in prewar Europe, the persecution of the Jewish people, of which you and those 18 children have been victims, could not have been carried out with such success — in fact, might not have been carried out at all.

Therefore, Mr. Tzuref, will you accept the following conditions? If you can, we will see fit not to carry out legal action against the Yeshivah for failure to comply with township Zoning ordinances No. 18 and No. 23. The conditions are simply:

1. The religious, educational, and social activities of the Yeshivah of Woodenton will be confined to the Yeshivah grounds.

2. Yeshivah personnel are welcomed in the streets and stores of Woodenton provided they are attired in clothing usually associated with American life in the 20th century.

If these conditions are met, we see no reason why the Yeshivah of Woodenton cannot live peacefully and satisfactorily with the Jews of Woodenton — as the Jews of Woodenton have come to live with the Gentiles of Woodenton. I would appreciate an immediate reply.

Sincerely,

ELI PECK, Attorney

Two days later Eli received his immediate reply:

Mr. Peck:
The suit the gentleman wears is all he's got.
                              Sincerely,
                              LEO TZUREF, Headmaster

Once again, as Eli swung around the dark trees and onto
the lawn, the children fled. He reached out with his briefcase as if to stop them, but they were gone so fast all he saw
moving was a flock of skullcaps.

"Come, come . . ." a voice called from the porch. Tzuref
appeared from behind a pillar. Did he *live* behind those
pillars? Was he just watching the children at play? Either
way, when Eli appeared, Tzuref was ready, with no fore-
warning.

"Hello," Eli said.

"Sholom."

"I didn't mean to frighten them."

"They're scared, so they run."

"I didn't do anything."

Tzuref shrugged. The little movement seemed to Eli
strong as an accusation. What he didn't get at home, he
got here.

Inside the house they took their seats. Though it was
lighter than a few evenings before, a bulb or two would
have helped. Eli had to hold his briefcase towards the window for the last gleamings. He removed Tzuref's letter
from a manila folder. Tzuref removed Eli's letter from his
pants pocket. Eli removed the carbon of his own letter
from another manila folder. Tzuref removed Eli's first letter from his back pocket. Eli removed the carbon from his

briefcase. Tzuref raised his palms. "... It's all I've got..."

Those upraised palms, the mocking tone — another accusation. It was a crime to keep carbons! Everybody had an edge on him — Eli could do no right.

"I offered a compromise, Mr. Tzuref. You refused."

"Refused, Mr. Peck? What is, is."

"The man could get a new suit."

"That's all he's got."

"So you told me," Eli said.

"So I told you, so you know."

"It's not an insurmountable obstacle, Mr. Tzuref. We have stores."

"For that too?"

"On Route 12, a Robert Hall —"

"To take away the one thing a man's got?"

"Not take away, *replace*."

"But I tell you he has nothing. *Nothing*. You have that word in English? *Nicht*? *Gornisht*?"

"Yes, Mr. Tzuref, we have the word."

"A mother and a father?" Tzuref said. "No. A wife? No. A baby? A little ten-month-old baby? No! A village full of friends? A synagogue where you knew the feel of every seat under your pants? Where with your eyes closed you could smell the cloth of the Torah?" Tzuref pushed out of his chair, stirring a breeze that swept Eli's letter to the floor. At the window he leaned out, and looked, beyond Woodenton. When he turned he was shaking a finger at Eli. "And a medical experiment they performed on him yet! That leaves nothing, Mr. Peck. Absolutely nothing!"

"I misunderstood."

"No news reached Woodenton?"

"About the suit, Mr. Tzuref. I thought he couldn't afford another."

"He can't."

They were right where they'd begun. "Mr. Tzuref!" Eli demanded. *"Here?"* He smacked his hand to his billfold.

"Exactly!" Tzuref said, smacking his own breast.

"Then we'll buy him one!" Eli crossed to the window and taking Tzuref by the shoulders, pronounced each word slowly. "We-will-pay-for-it. All right?"

"Pay? What, diamonds!"

Eli raised a hand to his inside pocket, then let it drop. Oh stupid! Tzuref, father to eighteen, had smacked not what lay under his coat, but deeper, under the ribs.

"Oh . . ." Eli said. He moved away along the wall. "The suit is all he's got then."

"You got my letter," Tzuref said.

Eli stayed back in the shadow, and Tzuref turned to his chair. He swished Eli's letter from the floor, and held it up. "You say too much . . . all this reasoning . . . all these conditions . . ."

"What can I do?"

"You have the word 'suffer' in English?"

"We have the word suffer. We have the word law too."

"Stop with the law! You have the word suffer. Then try it. It's a little thing."

"They won't," Eli said.

"But you, Mr. Peck, how about you?"

"I am them, they are me, Mr. Tzuref."

"Aach! You are us, we are you!"

Eli shook and shook his head. In the dark he suddenly felt that Tzuref might put him under a spell. "Mr. Tzuref, a little light?"

Tzuref lit what tallow was left in the holders. Eli was

afraid to ask if they couldn't afford electricity. Maybe candles were all they had left.

"Mr. Peck, who made the law, may I ask you that?"

"The people."

"No."

"Yes."

"Before the people."

"No one. Before the people there was no law." Eli didn't care for the conversation, but with only candle-light, he was being lulled into it.

"Wrong," Tzuref said.

"We make the law, Mr. Tzuref. It is our community. These are my neighbors. I am their attorney. They pay me. Without law there is chaos."

"What you call law, I call shame. The heart, Mr. Peck, the heart is law! God!" he announced.

"Look, Mr. Tzuref, I didn't come here to talk meta-physics. People use the law, it's a flexible thing. They protect what they value, their property, their well-being, their happiness —"

"Happiness? They hide their shame. And you, Mr. Peck, you are shameless?"

"We do it," Eli said, wearily, "for our children. This is the twentieth century . . ."

"For the goyim maybe. For me the Fifty-eighth." He pointed at Eli. "That is too old for shame."

Eli felt squashed. Everybody in the world had evil rea-sons for his actions. Everybody! With reasons so cheap, who buys bulbs. "Enough wisdom, Mr. Tzuref. Please. I'm exhausted."

"Who isn't?" Tzuref said.

He picked Eli's papers from his desk and reached up with them. "What do you intend for us to do?"

"What you must," Eli said. "I made the offer."

"So he must give up his suit?"

"Tzuref, Tzuref, leave me be with that suit! I'm not the only lawyer in the world. I'll drop the case, and you'll get somebody who won't talk compromise. Then you'll have no home, no children, nothing. Only a lousy black suit! Sacrifice what you want. I know what I would do."

To that Tzuref made no answer, but only handed Eli his letters.

"It's not me, Mr. Tzuref, it's them."

"They are you."

"No," Eli intoned, "I am me. They are them. You are you."

"You talk about leaves and branches. I'm dealing with under the dirt."

"Mr. Tzuref, you're driving me crazy with Talmudic wisdom. This is that, that is the other thing. Give me a straight answer."

"Only for straight questions."

"Oh, God!"

Eli returned to his chair and plunged his belongings into his case. "Then, that's all," he said angrily.

Tzuref gave him the shrug.

"Remember, Tzuref, you called this down on yourself."

"I did?"

Eli refused to be his victim again. Double-talk proved nothing.

"Goodbye," he said.

But as he opened the door leading to the hall, he heard Tzuref.

"And your wife, how is she?"

"Fine, just fine." Eli kept going.

"And the baby is due when, any day?"

Eli turned. "That's right."

"Well," Tzuref said, rising. "Good luck."

"You know?"

Tzuref pointed out the window — then, with his hands, he drew upon himself a beard, a hat, a long, long coat. When his fingers formed the hem they touched the floor. "He shops two, three times a week, he gets to know them."

"He *talks* to them?"

"He sees them."

"And he can tell which is my wife?"

"They shop at the same stores. He says she is beautiful. She has a kind face. A woman capable of love . . . though who can be sure."

"*He* talks about *us*, to *you*?" demanded Eli.

"You talk about us, to her?"

"Goodbye, Mr. Tzuref."

Tzuref said, "Sholom. And good luck — I know what it is to have children. Sholom," Tzuref whispered, and with the whisper the candles went out. But the instant before, the flames leaped into Tzuref's eyes, and Eli saw it was not luck Tzuref wished him at all.

Outside the door, Eli waited. Down the lawn the children were holding hands and whirling around in a circle. At first he did not move. But he could not hide in the shadows all night. Slowly he began to slip along the front of the house. Under his hands he felt where bricks were out. He moved in the shadows until he reached the side. And then, clutching his briefcase to his chest, he broke across the darkest spots of the lawn. He aimed for a distant glade of woods, and when he reached it he did not stop, but ran through until he was so dizzied that the trees seemed to be running beside him, fleeing not towards Woodenton but away. His lungs were nearly ripping their seams as he burst into the yellow glow of the Gulf station at the edge of town.

"Eli, I had pains today. Where were you?"

"I went to Tzuref."

"Why didn't you call? I was worried."

He tossed his hat past the sofa and onto the floor. "Where are my winter suits?"

"In the hall closet. Eli, it's May."

"I need a strong suit." He left the room, Miriam behind him.

"Eli, talk to me. Sit down. Have dinner. Eli, what are you doing? You're going to get moth balls all over the carpet."

He peered out from the hall closet. Then he peered in again — there was a zipping noise, and suddenly he swept a greenish tweed suit before his wife's eyes.

"Eli, I love you in that suit. But not now. Have something to eat. I made dinner tonight — I'll warm it."

"You've got a box big enough for this suit?"

"I got a Bonwit's box, the other day. Eli, *why?*"

"Miriam, you see me doing something, let me do it."

"You haven't eaten."

"I'm *doing* something." He started up the stairs to the bedroom.

"Eli, would you please tell me what it is you want, and why?"

He turned and looked down at her. "Suppose this time you give me the reasons *before* I tell you what I'm doing. It'll probably work out the same anyway."

"Eli, I want to help."

"It doesn't concern you."

"But I want to help *you*," Miriam said.

"Just be quiet, then."

"But you're upset," she said, and she followed him up the stairs, heavily, breathing for two.

"Eli, what now?"

"A shirt." He yanked open all the drawers of their new teak dresser. He extracted a shirt.

"Eli, batiste? With a tweed suit?" she inquired.

He was at the closet now, on his knees. "Where are my cordovans?"

"Eli, why are you doing this so compulsively? You look like you *have* to do something."

"Oh, Miriam, you're supersubtle."

"Eli, stop this and talk to me. Stop it or I'll call Dr. Eckman."

Eli was kicking off the shoes he was wearing. "Where's the Bonwit box?"

"Eli, do you want me to have the baby right *here!*"

Eli walked over and sat down on the bed. He was draped not only with his own clothing, but also with the greenish tweed suit, the batiste shirt, and under each arm a shoe. He raised his arms and let the shoes drop onto the bed. Then he undid his necktie with one hand and his teeth and added that to the booty.

"Underwear," he said. "He'll need underwear."

"Who!"

He was slipping out of his socks.

Miriam kneeled down and helped him ease his left foot out of the sock. She sat with it on the floor. "Eli, just lie back. Please."

"Plaza 9-3103."

"What?"

"Eckman's number," he said. "It'll save you the trouble."

"Eli —"

"You've got that goddam tender 'You need help' look in your eyes, Miriam, don't tell me you don't."

"I don't."

"I'm not flipping," Eli said.

"I know, Eli."

"Last time I sat in the bottom of the closet and chewed on my bedroom slippers. That's what I did."

"I know."

"And I'm not doing that. This is not a nervous break-down, Miriam, let's get that straight."

"Okay," Miriam said. She kissed the foot she held. Then, softly, she asked, "What *are* you doing?"

"Getting clothes for the guy in the hat. Don't tell me why, Miriam. Just let me do it."

"That's all?" she asked.

"That's all."

"You're not leaving?"

"No."

"Sometimes I think it gets too much for you, and you'll just leave."

"What gets too much?"

"I don't *know*, Eli. Something gets too much. When-ever everything's peaceful for a long time, and things are nice and pleasant, and we're expecting to be even happier. Like now. It's as if you don't think we *deserve* to be happy."

"Damn it, Miriam! I'm giving this guy a new suit, is that all right? From now on he comes into Woodenton like everybody else, is that all right with you?"

"And Tzuref moves?"

"I don't even know if he'll take the suit, Miriam! What do you have to bring up moving!"

"Eli, I didn't bring up moving. Everybody did. That's what everybody wants. Why make everybody un*happy*. It's even a law, Eli."

"Don't tell me what's the law."

"All right, sweetie. I'll get the box."

"*I'll* get the box. Where is it?"

"In the basement."

When he came up from the basement, he found all the clothes neatly folded and squared away on the sofa: shirt, tie, shoes, socks, underwear, belt, and an old gray flannel suit. His wife sat on the end of the sofa, looking like an anchored balloon.

"Where's the green suit?" he said.

"Eli, it's your loveliest suit. It's my favorite suit. Whenever I think of you, Eli, it's in that suit."

"Get it out."

"Eli, it's a Brooks Brothers suit. You say yourself how much you love it."

"Get it out."

"But the gray flannel's more practical. For shopping."

"Get it out."

"You go overboard, Eli. That's your trouble. You won't do anything in moderation. That's how people destroy themselves."

"I do *everything* in moderation. That's my trouble. The suit's in the closet again?"

She nodded, and began to fill up with tears. "Why does it have to be *your* suit? Who are you even to decide to give a suit? What about the others?" She was crying openly, and holding her belly. "Eli, I'm going to have a baby. Do we need all *this?*" and she swept the clothes off the sofa to the floor.

At the closet Eli removed the green suit. "It's a J. Press," he said, looking at the lining.

"I hope to hell he's happy with it!" Miriam said, sobbing.

A half hour later the box was packed. The cord he'd found in the kitchen cabinet couldn't keep the outfit from popping through. The trouble was there was too much: the gray suit *and* the green suit, an oxford shirt as well as the batiste. But let him have two suits! Let him have three, four, if only this damn silliness would stop! And a hat — of course! God, he'd almost forgotten the hat. He took the stairs two at a time and in Miriam's closet yanked a hatbox from the top shelf. Scattering hat and tissue paper to the floor, he returned downstairs, where he packed away the hat he'd worn that day. Then he looked at his wife, who lay outstretched on the floor before the fireplace. For the third time in as many minutes she was saying, "Eli, this is the real thing."

"Where?"

"Right under the baby's head, like somebody's squeezing oranges."

Now that he'd stopped to listen he was stupefied. He said, "But you have two more weeks..." Somehow he'd really been expecting it was to go on not just another two weeks, but another nine months. This led him to suspect, suddenly, that his wife was feigning pain so as to get his mind off delivering the suit. And just as suddenly he resented himself for having such a thought. God, what had he become! He'd been an unending bastard towards her since this Tzuref business had come up — just when her pregnancy must have been most burdensome. He'd allowed her no access to him, but still, he was sure, for good reasons: she might tempt him out of his confusion with her easy answers. He could be tempted all right, it was why he fought so hard. But now a sweep of love came over him at the thought of her contracting womb, and his child. And yet he would not indicate it to her. Under such splendid marital conditions, who knows but she might extract some promise from him about his concern with the school on the hill.

Having packed his second bag of the evening, Eli sped his wife to Woodenton Memorial. There she proceeded not to have her baby, but to lie hour after hour through the night having at first oranges, then bowling balls, then basketballs, squeezed back of her pelvis. Eli sat in the waiting room, under the shattering African glare of a dozen rows of fluorescent bulbs, composing a letter to Tzuref.

Dear Mr. Tzuref:
The clothes in this box are for the gentleman in the hat. In a life of sacrifice what is one more? But in a life of no sacrifices even one is impossible. Do you see what I'm saying, Mr. Tzuref? I am not a Nazi who would drive eighteen children, who are probably frightened at the sight of a firefly, into homelessness. But if you want a home here, you must accept what we have to offer. The world is the world, Mr. Tzuref. As you would say, what is, is. All we say to this man is change your clothes. Enclosed are two suits and two shirts, and everything else he'll need, including a new hat. When he needs new clothes let me know.

We await his appearance in Woodenton, as we await friendly relations with the Yeshivah of Woodenton.

He signed his name and slid the note under a bursting flap and into the box. Then he went to the phone at the end of the room and dialed Ted Heller's number.

"Hello."

"Shirley, it's Eli."

"Eli, we've been calling all night. The lights are on in your place, but nobody answers. We thought it was burglars."

"Miriam's having the baby."

"At home?" Shirley said. "Oh, Eli, what a fun-idea!"

"Shirley, let me speak to Ted."

After the ear-shaking clatter of the phone whacking the floor, Eli heard footsteps, breathing, throat-clearing, then Ted. "A boy or a girl?"

"Nothing yet."

"You've given Shirley the bug, Eli. Now she's going to have *our* next one at home."

"Good."

"That's a terrific way to bring the family together, Eli."

"Look, Ted, I've settled with Tzuref."

"When are they going?"

"They're not exactly going, Teddie. I settled it — you won't even know they're there."

"A guy dressed like 1000 B.C. and I won't know it? What are you thinking about, pal?"

"He's changing his clothes."

"Yeah, to what? Another funeral suit?"

"Tzuref promised me, Ted. Next time he comes to town, he comes dressed like you and me."

"What! Somebody's kidding somebody, Eli."

Eli's voice shot up. "If he says he'll do it, he'll do it!"

"And, Eli," Ted asked, "he said it?"

"He said it." It cost him a sudden headache, this invention.

"And suppose he doesn't change, Eli. Just suppose. I mean that *might* happen, Eli. This might just be some kind of stall or something."

"No," Eli assured him.

The other end was quiet a moment. "Look, Eli," Ted said, finally, "he changes. Okay? All right? But they're still up there, aren't they? *That* doesn't change."

"The point is you won't know it."

Patiently Ted said, "Is this what we asked of you, Eli? When we put our faith and trust in you, is that what we were asking? We weren't concerned that this guy should become a Beau Brummel, Eli, believe me. We just don't think this is the community for them. And, Eli, we isn't me. The Jewish members of the community appointed me, Artie, and Harry to see what could be done. And we appointed you. And what's happened?"

Eli heard himself say, "What happened, happened."

"Eli, you're talking in crossword puzzles."

"My wife's having a baby," Eli explained, defensively.

"I realize that, Eli. But this is a matter of zoning, isn't it? Isn't that what we discovered? You don't abide by the ordinance, you go. I mean I can't raise mountain goats, say, in my backyard —"

"This isn't so simple, Ted. People are involved—"

"People? Eli, we've been through this and through this. We're not just dealing with people — these are religious fanatics is what they are. Dressing like that. What I'd really like to find out is what goes on up there. I'm getting more and more skeptical, Eli, and I'm not afraid to admit it. It smells like a lot of hocus-pocus abracadabra stuff to me. Guys like Harry, you know, they think and they think and they're afraid to admit what they're thinking. I'll tell you. Look, I don't even know about this Sunday school business. Sundays I drive my oldest kid all the way to Scarsdale to learn Bible stories . . . and you know what she comes up with? This Abraham in the Bible was going to kill his own *kid* for a sacrifice. She gets nightmares from it, for God's sake! You call that religion? Today a guy like that they'd lock him up. This is an age of science, Eli. I size people's feet with an X-ray machine, for God's sake. They've disproved all that stuff, Eli, and I refuse to sit by and watch it happening on my own front lawn."

"Nothing's happening on your front lawn, Teddie. You're exaggerating, nobody's sacrificing their kid."

"You're damn right, Eli — I'm not sacrificing mine. You'll see when you have your own what it's like. All the place is, is a hideaway for people who can't face life. It's a matter of *needs*. They have all these superstitions, and why do you think? Because they can't face the world, because they can't take their place in society. That's no environment to bring kids up in, Eli."

"Look, Ted, see it from another angle. We can convert them," Eli said, with half a heart.

"What, make a bunch of Catholics out of them? Look, Eli — pal, there's a good healthy relationship in this town because it's modern Jews and Protestants. That's the point, isn't it, Eli? Let's not kid each other, I'm not Harry. The way things are now are fine — like human beings. There's going to be no pogroms in Woodenton. Right? 'Cause there's no fanatics, no crazy people —" Eli winced, and closed his eyes a second — "just people who respect each other, and leave each other be. Common sense is the ruling thing, Eli. I'm for common sense. Moderation."

"Exactly, exactly, Ted. I agree, but common sense, maybe, says make this guy change his clothes. Then maybe —"

"Common sense says that? Common sense says to me they go and find a nice place somewhere else, Eli. New York is the biggest city in the world, it's only 30 miles away — why don't they go there?"

"Ted, give them a chance. Introduce them to common sense."

"Eli, you're dealing with *fanatics*. Do they display common sense? Talking a dead language, that makes sense? Making a big thing out of suffering, so you're going oy-oy-oy all your life, that's common sense? Look, Eli, we've been through all this. I don't know if you know — but there's talk that *Life* magazine is sending a guy out to the Yeshivah for a story. With pictures."

"Look, Teddie, you're letting your imagination get inflamed. I don't think *Life's* interested."

"But I'm interested, Eli. And we thought you were supposed to be."

"I am," Eli said, "I am. Let him just change the clothes, Ted. Let's see what happens."

"They live in the medieval ages, Eli — it's some superstition, some *rule*."

"Let's just *see*," Eli pleaded.

"Eli, every day —"

"One more day," Eli said. "If he doesn't change in one more day. . . ."

"What?"

"Then I get an injunction first thing Monday. That's that."

"Look, Eli — it's not up to me. Let me call Harry —"

"You're the spokesman, Teddie. I'm all wrapped up here with Miriam having a baby. Just give me the day — them the day."

"All right, Eli. I want to be fair. But tomorrow, that's all. Tomorrow's the judgment day, Eli, I'm telling you."

"I hear trumpets," Eli said, and hung up. He was shaking inside — Teddie's voice seemed to have separated his bones at the joints. He was still in the phone booth when the nurse came to tell him that Mrs. Peck would positively not be delivered of a child until the morning. He was to go home and get some rest, he looked like *he* was having the baby. The nurse winked and left.

But Eli did not go home. He carried the Bonwit box out into the street with him and put it in the car. The night was soft and starry, and he began to drive the streets of Woodenton. Square cool windows, apricot-colored, were all one could see beyond the long lawns that fronted the homes of the townsmen. The stars polished the permanent baggage carriers atop the station wagons in the driveways. He drove slowly, up, down, around. Only his tires could be heard taking the gentle curves in the road.

What peace. What incredible peace. Have children ever been so safe in their beds? Parents — Eli wondered — so full in their stomachs? Water so warm in its boilers? Never. Never in Rome, never in Greece. Never even did walled cities have it so good! No wonder then they would keep things just as they were. Here, after all, were peace and safety — what civilization had been working toward for centuries. For all his jerkiness, that was all Ted Heller was asking for, peace and safety. It was what his parents had asked for in the Bronx, and his grandparents in Poland, and theirs in Russia or Austria, or wherever else they'd fled to or from. It was what Miriam was asking for. And now they had it — the world was at last a place for families, even Jewish families. After all these centuries, maybe there just had to be this communal toughness — or numbness — to protect such a blessing. Maybe that was the trouble with the Jews all along — too soft. Sure, to live takes guts . . . Eli was thinking as he drove on beyond the train station, and parked his car at the darkened Gulf station. He stepped out, carrying the box.

At the top of the hill one window trembled with light. What *was* Tzuref doing up there in that office? Killing babies — probably not. But studying a language no one understood? Practicing customs with origins long forgotten? Suffering sufferings already suffered once too often? Teddie was right — why keep it up! However, if a man chose to be stubborn, then he couldn't expect to survive. The world is give-and-take. What sense to sit and brood over a suit. Eli would give him one last chance.

He stopped at the top. No one was around. He walked slowly up the lawn, setting each foot into the grass, listening to the shh shhh shhhh his shoes made as they bent the wetness into the sod. He looked around. Here there was nothing. Nothing! An old decaying house — and a suit.

On the porch he slid behind a pillar. He felt someone was watching him. But only the stars gleamed down. And at his feet, off and away, Woodenton glowed up. He set his package on the step of the great front door. Inside the cover of the box he felt to see if his letter was still there. When he touched it, he pushed it deeper into the green suit, which his fingers still remembered from winter. He should have included some light bulbs. Then he slid back by the pillar again, and this time there was something on the lawn. It was the second sight he had of him. He was facing Woodenton and barely moving across the open space towards the trees. His right fist was beating his chest. And then Eli heard a sound rising with each knock on the chest. What a moan! It could raise hair, stop hearts, water eyes. And it did all three to Eli, plus more. Some feeling crept into him for whose deepness he could find no word. It was strange. He listened — it did not hurt to hear this moan. But he wondered if it hurt to make it. And so, with only stars to hear, he tried. And it did hurt. Not the bumble-bee of noise that turned at the back of his throat and winged out his nostrils. What hurt buzzed down. It stung and stung inside him, and in turn the moan sharpened. It became a scream, louder, a song, a crazy song that whined through the pillars and blew out to the grass, until the strange hatted creature on the lawn turned and threw his arms wide, and looked in the night like a scarecrow.

Eli ran, and when he reached the car the pain was only a bloody scratch across his neck where a branch had whipped back as he fled the greenie's arms.

The following day his son was born. But not till one in the afternoon, and by then a great deal had happened.

First, at nine-thirty the phone rang. Eli leaped from the sofa — where he'd dropped the night before — and picked it screaming from the cradle. He could practically smell the hospital as he shouted into the phone, "Hello, yes!"

"Eli, it's Ted. Eli, he *did* it. He just walked by the store. I was opening the door, Eli, and I turned around and I swear I thought it was you. But it was him. He still walks like he did, but the clothes, Eli, the clothes."

"Who?"

"The greenie. He has on man's regular clothes. And the suit, it's a beauty."

The suit barreled back into Eli's consciousness, pushing all else aside. "What color suit?"

"Green. He's just strolling in the green suit like it's a holiday. Eli . . . is it a Jewish holiday?"

"Where is he now?"

"He's walking straight up Coach House Road, in this damn tweed job. Eli, it worked. You were right."

"We'll see."

"What next?"

"We'll see."

He took off the underwear in which he'd slept and went into the kitchen where he turned the light under the coffee. When it began to perk he held his head over the pot so it would steam loose the knot back of his eyes. It still hadn't when the phone rang.

"Eli, Ted again. Eli, the guy's walking up and down every street in town. Really, he's on a tour or something. Artie called me, Herb called me. Now Shirley calls that he just walked by our house. Eli, go out on the porch you'll see."

Eli went to the window and peered out. He couldn't see past the bend in the road, and there was no one in sight.

"Eli?" He heard Ted from where he dangled over the telephone table. He dropped the phone into the hook, as a few last words floated up to him — "Eliyousawhim . . . ?" He threw on the pants and shirt he'd worn the night before and walked barefoot on to his front lawn. And sure enough, his apparition appeared around the bend: in a brown hat a little too far down on his head, a green suit too far back on the shoulders, an unbuttoned-down button-down shirt, a tie knotted so as to leave a two-inch tail, trousers that cascaded onto his shoes — he was shorter than that black hat had made him seem. And moving the clothes was that walk that was not a walk, the tiny-stepped shlumpy gait. He came round the bend, and for all his strangeness — it clung to his whiskers, signaled itself in his locomotion — he looked as if he belonged. Eccentric, maybe, but he belonged. He made no moan, nor did he invite Eli with wide-flung arms. But he did stop when he saw him. He stopped and put a hand to his hat. When he felt for its top, his hand went up too high. Then it found the level and fiddled with the brim. The fingers fiddled, fumbled, and when they'd finally made their greeting, they traveled down the fellow's face and in an instant seemed to have touched each one of his features. They dabbed the eyes, ran the length of the nose, swept over the hairy lip, until they found their home in the hair that hid a little of his collar. To Eli the fingers said, *I have a face, I have a face at least.* Then his hand came through the beard and when it stopped at his chest it was like a pointer — and the eyes asked a question as tides of water shifted over them. *The face is all right, I can keep it?* Such a look was in those eyes that Eli was still seeing them when he turned his head away. They were the hearts of his jonquils, that only last week had appeared — they were the leaves on his birch, the bulbs in his coach lamp, the droppings on his lawn: those eyes were the eyes in his head. They were his, he had made them. He turned and went into his house and when he peeked out the side of the window, between shade and molding, the green suit was gone.

The phone.

"Eli, Shirley."

"I saw him, Shirley," and he hung up.

He sat frozen for a long time. The sun moved around the windows. The coffee steam smelled up the house. The phone began to ring, stopped, began again. The mailman came, the cleaner, the bakery man, the gardener, the ice cream man, the League of Women Voters lady. A Negro woman spreading some strange gospel calling for the revision of the Food and Drug Act knocked at the front, rapped the windows, and finally scraped a half-dozen pamphlets under the back door. But Eli only sat, without underwear, in last night's suit. He answered no one.

Given his condition, it was strange that the trip and crash at the back door reached his inner ear. But in an instant he seemed to melt down into the crevices of the chair, then to splash up and out to where the clatter had been. At the door he waited. It was silent, but for a fluttering of damp little leaves on the trees. When he finally opened the door, there was no one there. He'd expected to see green, green, green, big as the doorway, topped by his hat, waiting for him with those eyes. But there was no one out there, except for the Bonwit's box which lay bulging at his feet. No string tied it and the top rode high on the bottom.

The coward! He couldn't do it! He couldn't!

The very glee of that idea pumped fuel to his legs. He tore out across his back lawn, past his new spray of forsythia, to catch a glimpse of the bearded one fleeing naked through yards, over hedges and fences, to the safety of his hermitage. In the distance a pile of pink and white stones — which Harriet Knudson had painted the previous day — tricked him. "Run," he shouted to the rocks, "Run, you . . ." but he caught his error before anyone else did, and though he peered and craned there was no hint anywhere of a man about his own size, with white, white, terribly white skin (how white must be the skin of his body!) in cowardly retreat. He came slowly, curiously, back to the door. And while the trees shimmered in the light wind, he removed the top from the box. The shock at first was the shock of having daylight turned off all at once. Inside the box was an eclipse. But black soon sorted from black, and shortly there was the glassy black of lining, the coarse black of trousers, the dead black of fraying threads, and in the center the mountain of black: the hat. He picked the box from the doorstep and carried it inside. For the first time in his life he *smelled* the color of blackness: a little stale, a little sour, a little old, but nothing that could overwhelm you. Still, he held the package at arm's length and deposited it on the dining room table.

Twenty rooms on a hill and they store their old clothes with me! What am I supposed to do with them? Give them to charity? That's where they came from. He picked up the hat by the edges and looked inside. The crown was smooth as an egg, the brim practically threadbare. There is nothing else to do with a hat in one's hands but put it on, so Eli dropped the thing on his head. He opened the door to the hall closet and looked at himself in the full-length mirror. The hat gave him bags under the eyes. Or perhaps he had not slept well. He pushed the brim lower till a shadow touched his lips. Now the bags under his eyes had inflated to become his face. Before the mirror he unbuttoned his shirt, unzipped his trousers, and then, shedding his clothes, he studied what he was. What a silly disappointment to see yourself naked in a hat. Especially in that hat. He sighed, but could not rid himself of the great weakness that suddenly set on his muscles and joints, beneath the terrible weight of the stranger's strange hat.

He returned to the dining room table and emptied the box of its contents: jacket, trousers, and vest (*it* smelled deeper than blackness). And under it all, sticking between the shoes that looked chopped and bitten, came the first gleam of white. A little fringed serape, a gray piece of semi-underwear, was crumpled at the bottom, its thready border twisted into itself. Eli removed it and let it hang free. What is it? For warmth? To wear beneath underwear in the event of a chest cold? He held it to his nose but it did not smell from Vick's or mustard plaster. It was something special, some Jewish thing. Special food, special language, special prayers, why not special BVD's? So fearful was he that he would be tempted back into wearing his traditional clothes — reasoned Eli — that he had carried and buried in Woodenton everything, including the special underwear. For that was how Eli now understood the box of clothes. The greenie was saying, Here, I give up. I refuse even to be tempted. We surrender. And that was how Eli continued to understand it until he found he'd slipped the white fringy surrender flag over his hat and felt it clinging to his chest. And now, looking at himself in the mirror, he was momentarily uncertain as to who was tempting who into what. Why *did* the greenie leave his clothes? Was it even the greenie? Then who was it? And why? But, Eli, for Christ's sake, in an age of science things don't happen like that. Even the goddam pigs take drugs . . .

Regardless of who was the source of the temptation, what was its end, not to mention its beginning, Eli, some moments later, stood draped in black, with a little white underneath, before the full-length mirror. He had to pull down on the trousers so they would not show the hollow of his ankle. The greenie, didn't he wear socks? Or had he forgotten them? The mystery was solved when Eli mustered enough courage to investigate the trouser pockets. He had expected some damp awful thing to happen to his fingers should he slip them down and out of sight — but when at last he jammed bravely down he came up with a khaki army sock in each hand. As he slipped them over his toes, he invented a genesis: a G.I.'s present in 1945. Plus everything else lost between 1938 and 1945, he had also lost his socks. Not that he had lost the socks, but that he'd had to stoop to accepting these, made Eli almost cry. To calm himself he walked out the back door and stood looking at his lawn.

On the Knudson back lawn, Harriet Knudson was giving her stones a second coat of pink. She looked up just as Eli stepped out. Eli shot back in again and pressed himself against the back door. When he peeked between the curtain all he saw were paint bucket, brush, and rocks scattered on the Knudsons' pink-spattered grass. The phone rang. Who was it — Harriet Knudson? Eli, there's a Jew at your door. *That's me.* Nonsense, Eli, I saw him with my own eyes. *That's me, I saw you too, painting your rocks pink.* Eli, you're having a nervous breakdown again. Jimmy, Eli's having a nervous breakdown again. Eli, this is Jimmy, hear you're having a little breakdown, anything I can do, boy? Eli, this is Ted, Shirley says you need help. Eli, this is Artie, you need help. Eli, Harry, you need help you need help . . . The phone rattled its last and died.

"God helps them who help themselves," intoned Eli, and once again he stepped out the door. This time he walked to the center of his lawn and in full sight of the trees, the grass, the birds, and the sun, revealed that it was he, Eli, in the costume. But nature had nothing to

say to him, and so stealthily he made his way to the hedge
separating his property from the field beyond and he cut
his way through, losing his hat twice in the underbrush.
Then, clamping the hat to his head, he began to run, the
threaded tassels jumping across his heart. He ran through
the weeds and wild flowers, until on the old road that
skirted the town he slowed up. He was walking when he
approached the Gulf station from the back. He supported
himself on a huge tireless truck rim, and among tubes,
rusted engines, dozens of topless oil cans, he rested. With
a kind of brainless cunning, he readied himself for the last
mile of his journey.

"How are you, Pop?" It was the garage attendant, rub-
ing his greasy hands on his overalls, and hunting among
the cans.

Eli's stomach lurched and he pulled the big black coat
round his neck.

"Nice day," the attendant said and started around to the
front.

"Sholom," Eli whispered and zoomed off towards the
hill.

The sun was directly overhead when Eli reached the
top. He had come by way of the woods, where it was
cooler, but still he was perspiring beneath his new suit.
The hat had no sweatband and the cloth clutched his
head. The children were playing. The children were always playing, as if it was that alone that Tzuref had to
teach them. In their shorts, they revealed such thin legs
that beneath one could see the joints swiveling as they ran.
Eli waited for them to disappear around a corner before
he came into the open. But something would not let him

wait — his green suit. It was on the porch, wrapped around the bearded fellow, who was painting the base of a pillar. His arm went up and down, up and down, and the pillar glowed like white fire. The very sight of him popped Eli out of the woods onto the lawn. He did not turn back, though his insides did. He walked up the lawn, but the children played on; tipping the black hat, he mumbled, "Shhh . . . shhhh," and they hardly seemed to notice.

At last he smelled paint.

He waited for the man to turn to him. He only painted. Eli felt suddenly that if he could pull the black hat down over his eyes, over his chest and belly and legs, if he could shut out all light, then a moment later he would be home in bed. But the hat wouldn't go past his forehead. He couldn't kid himself — he was there. No one he could think of had forced him to do this.

The greenie's arm flailed up and down on the pillar. Eli breathed loudly, cleared his throat, but the greenie wouldn't make life easier for him. At last, Eli had to say "Hello."

The arm swished up and down; it stopped — two fingers went out after a brush hair stuck to the pillar.

"Good day," Eli said.

The hair came away; the swishing resumed.

"Sholom," Eli whispered and the fellow turned.

The recognition took some time. He looked at what Eli wore. Up close, Eli looked at what he wore. And then Eli had the strange notion that he was two people. Or that he was one person wearing two suits. The greenie looked to be suffering from a similar confusion. They stared long at one another. Eli's heart shivered, and his brain was momentarily in such a mixed-up condition that his hands went out to button down the collar of his shirt that somebody else was wearing. What a mess! The greenie flung his arms over his face.

"What's the matter..." Eli said. The fellow had picked up his bucket and brush and was running away. Eli ran after him.

"I wasn't going to hit..." Eli called. "Stop..." Eli caught up and grabbed his sleeve. Once again, the greenie's hands flew up to his face. This time, in the violence, white paint spattered both of them.

"I only want to..." But in that outfit Eli didn't really know what he wanted. "To talk..." he said finally. "For you to look at me. Please, just *look* at me..."

The hands stayed put, as paint rolled off the brush onto the cuff of Eli's green suit.

"Please... please," Eli said, but he did not know what to do. "Say something, speak *English*," he pleaded.

The fellow pulled back against the wall, back, back, as though some arm would finally reach out and yank him to safety. He refused to uncover his face.

"Look," Eli said, pointing to himself. "It's your suit. I'll take care of it."

No answer — only a little shaking under the hands, which led Eli to speak as gently as he knew how.

"We'll... we'll moth-proof it. There's a button missing" — Eli pointed — "I'll have it fixed. I'll have a zipper put in... Please, please — just look at me..." He was talking to himself, and yet how could he stop? Nothing he said made any sense — that alone made his heart swell. Yet somehow babbling on, he might babble something that would make things easier between them. "Look..." He reached inside his shirt to pull the frills of underwear into the light. "I'm wearing the special underwear, even

... Please," he said, "*please, please, please*" he sang, as as if it were some sacred word. "Oh, *please*..."

Nothing twitched under the tweed suit — and if the eyes watered, or twinkled, or hated, he couldn't tell. It was driving him crazy. He had dressed like a fool, and for what? For this? He reached up and yanked the hands away.

"There!" he said — and in that first instant all he saw of the greenie's face were two white droplets stuck to each cheek.

"Tell me — " Eli clutched his hands down to his sides — "Tell me, what can I do for you, I'll do it..."

Stiffly, the greenie stood there, sporting his two white tears.

"Whatever I can do . . . Look, look, what I've done *already*." He grabbed his black hat and shook it in the man's face.

And in exchange, the greenie gave him an answer. He raised one hand to his chest, and then jammed it, finger first, towards the horizon. And with what a pained look! As though the air were full of razors! Eli followed the finger and saw beyond the knuckle, out past the nail, Woodenton.

"What do you want?" Eli said. "I'll bring it!"

Suddenly the greenie made a run for it. But then he stopped, wheeled, and jabbed that finger at the air again. It pointed the same way. Then he was gone.

And then, all alone, Eli had the revelation. He did not question his understanding, the substance or the source. But with a strange, dreamy elation, he started away.

On Coach House Road, they were double-parked. The

Mayor's wife pushed a grocery cart full of dog food from Stop N' Shop to her station wagon. The President of the Lions Club, a napkin around his neck, was jamming pennies into the meter in front of the Bit-in-Teeth Restaurant. Ted Heller caught the sun as it glazed off the new Byzantine mosaic entrance to his shoe shop. In pinkened jeans, Mrs. Jimmy Knudson was leaving Halloway's Hardware, a paint bucket in each hand. Roger's Beauty Shoppe had its doors open — women's heads in silver bullets far as the eye could see. Over by the barbershop the pole spun, and Artie Berg's youngest sat on a red horse, having his hair cut; his mother flipped through *Look*, smiling: the greenie had changed his clothes.

And into this street, which seemed paved with chromium, came Eli Peck. It was not enough, he knew, to walk up one side of the street. That was not enough. Instead he walked ten paces up one side, then on an angle, crossed to the other side, where he walked ten more paces, and crossed back. Horns blew, traffic jerked, as Eli made his way up Coach House Road. He spun a moan high up in his nose as he walked. Outside no one could hear him, but he felt it vibrate the cartilage at the bridge of his nose.

Things slowed around him. The sun stopped rippling on spokes and hubcaps. It glowed steadily as everyone put on brakes to look at the man in black. They always paused and gaped, whenever he entered the town. Then in a minute, or two, or three, a light would change, a baby squawk, and the flow continue. Now, though lights changed, no one moved.

"He shaved his beard," Eric the barber said.

"Who?" asked Linda Berg.

"The . . . the guy in the suit. From the place there."

Linda looked out the window.

"It's Uncle Eli," little Kevin Berg said, spitting hair.

"Oh, God," Linda said, "Eli's having a nervous break-down."

"A nervous breakdown!" Ted Heller said, but not imme-diately. Immediately he had said "Hoooly . . ."

Shortly, everybody in Coach House Road was aware that Eli Peck, the nervous young attorney with the pretty wife, was having a breakdown. Everybody except Eli Peck. He knew what he did was not insane, though he felt every inch of its strangeness. He felt those black clothes as if they were the skin of his skin — the give and pull as they got used to where he bulged and buckled. And he felt eyes, every eye on Coach House Road. He saw headlights screech to within an inch of him, and stop. He saw mouths: first the bottom jaw slides forward, then the tongue hits the teeth, the lips explode, a little thunder in the throat, and they've said it: Eli Peck Eli Peck Eli Peck Eli Peck. He began to walk slowly, shifting his weight down and forward with each syllable: E–li–Peck–E–li–Peck–E–li–Peck. Heavily he trod, and as his neighbors ut-tered each syllable of his name, he felt each syllable shak-ing all his bones. He knew who he was down to his mar-row — they were telling him. Eli Peck. He wanted them to say it a thousand times, a million times, he would walk forever in that black suit, as adults whispered of his strange-ness and children made "Shame . . . shame" with their fingers.

"It's going to be all right, pal . . ." Ted Heller was mo-tioning to Eli from his doorway. "C'mon, pal, it's going to be all right . . ."

Eli saw him, past the brim of his hat. Ted did not move from his doorway, but leaned forward and spoke with his hand over his mouth. Behind him, three customers peered through the doorway. "Eli, it's Ted, remember Ted . . ."

Eli crossed the street and found he was heading directly towards Harriet Knudson. He lifted his neck so she could see his whole face.

He saw her forehead melt down to her lashes. "Good morning, Mr. Peck."

"Sholom," Eli said, and crossed the street where he saw the President of the Lions.

"Twice before . . ." he heard someone say, and then he crossed again, mounted the curb, and was before the bakery, where a delivery man charged past with a tray of powdered cakes twirling above him. "Pardon me, Father," he said, and scooted into his truck. But he could not move it. Eli Peck had stopped traffic.

He passed the Rivoli Theater, Beekman Cleaners, Harris' Westinghouse, the Unitarian Church, and soon he was passing only trees. At Ireland Road he turned right and started through Woodenton's winding streets. Baby carriages stopped whizzing and creaked — "Isn't that . . ." Gardeners held their clipping. Children stepped from the sidewalk and tried the curb. And Eli greeted no one, but raised his face to all. He wished passionately that he had white tears to show them . . . And not till he reached his own front lawn, saw his house, his shutters, his new jonquils, did he remember his wife. And the child that must have been born to him. And it was then and there he had the awful moment. He could go inside and put on his clothes and go to his wife in the hospital. It was not irrevocable, even the walk wasn't. In Woodenton memories are long but fury short. Apathy works like forgiveness. Besides, when you've flipped, you've flipped — it's Mother Nature.

What gave Eli the awful moment was that he turned

away. He knew exactly what he could do but he chose not to. To go inside would be to go halfway. There was more . . . So he turned and walked towards the hospital and all the time he quaked an eighth of an inch beneath his skin to think that perhaps he'd chosen the crazy way. To think that he'd *chosen* to be crazy! But if you chose to be crazy, then you weren't crazy. It's when you didn't choose. No, he wasn't flipping. He had a child to see.

"Name?"

"Peck."

"Fourth floor." He was given a little blue card.

In the elevator everybody stared. Eli watched his black shoes rise four floors.

"Four."

He tipped his hat, but knew he couldn't take it off.

"Peck," he said. He showed the card.

"Congratulations," the nurse said. ". . . the grandfather?"

"The father. Which room?"

She led him to 412. "A joke on the Mrs?" she said, but he slipped in the door without her.

"Miriam?"

"Yes?"

"Eli."

She rolled her white face towards her husband. "Oh, Eli . . . Oh, Eli."

He raised his arms. "What could I do?"

"You have a son. They called all morning."

"I came to see him."

"Like *that!*" she whispered harshly. "Eli, you can't go around like that."

"I have a son. I want to see him."

"Eli, why are you doing this to me!" Red seeped back

into her lips. *"He's* not your fault," she explained. "Oh, Eli, sweetheart, why do you feel guilty about everything. Eli, change your clothes. I forgive you."

"Stop forgiving me. Stop understanding me."

"But I love you."

"That's something else."

"But, sweetie, you *don't* have to dress like that. You didn't do anything. You don't have to feel guilty because ... because everything's all right. Eli, can't you see that?"

"Miriam, enough reasons. Where's my son?"

"Oh, please, Eli, don't flip now. I need you now. Is that why you're flipping — because I need you?"

"In your selfish way, Miriam, you're very generous. I want my son."

"Don't flip now. I'm afraid, now that he's out." She was beginning to whimper. "I don't know if I love him, now that he's out. When I look in the mirror, Eli, he won't be there ... Eli, Eli, you look like you're going to your own funeral. Please, can't you leave well enough *alone?* Can't we just have a family?"

"No."

In the corridor he asked the nurse to lead him to his son. The nurse walked on one side of him, Ted Heller on the other.

"Eli, do you want some help? I thought you might want some help."

"No."

Ted whispered something to the nurse; then to Eli he whispered, "Should you be walking around like this?"

"Yes."

In his ear Ted said, "You'll ... you'll frighten the kid ..."

"There," the nurse said. She pointed to a bassinet in the second row and looked, puzzled, to Ted. "Do I go in?" Eli said.

"No," the nurse said. "She'll roll him over." She rapped on the enclosure full of babies. "Peck," she mouthed to the nurse on the inside.

Ted tapped Eli's arm. "You're not thinking of doing something you'll be sorry for . . . are you, Eli? Eli — I mean you know you're still Eli, don't you?"

In the enclosure, Eli saw a bassinet had been wheeled before the square window.

"Oh, Christ. . . ." Ted said. "You don't have this Bible stuff on the brain — " And suddenly he said, "You wait, pal." He started down the corridor, his heels tapping rapidly.

Eli felt relieved — he leaned forward. In the basket was what he'd come to see. Well, now that he was here, what did he think he was going to say to it? I'm your father, Eli, the Flipper? I am wearing a black hat, suit, and fancy underwear, all borrowed from a friend? How could he admit to this reddened ball — *his* reddened ball — the worst of all: that Eckman would shortly convince him he wanted to take off the whole business. He couldn't admit it! He wouldn't do it!

Past his hat brim, from the corner of his eye, he saw Ted had stopped in a doorway at the end of the corridor. Two interns stood there smoking, listening to Ted. Eli ignored it.

No, even Eckman wouldn't make him take it off! No! He'd wear it, if he chose to. He'd make the kid wear it! Sure! Cut it down when the time came. A smelly hand-me-down, whether the kid liked it or not!

Only Teddie's heels clacked; the interns wore rubber soles — for they were there, beside him, unexpectedly. Their white suits smelled, but not like Eli's.

"Eli," Ted said, softly, "visiting time's up, pal."

"How are you feeling, Mr. Peck? First child upsets everyone. . . ."

He'd just pay no attention; nevertheless, he began to perspire, thickly, and his hat crown clutched his hair.

"Excuse me — Mr. Peck. . . ." It was a new rich bass voice. "Excuse me, rabbi, but you're wanted . . . in the temple." A hand took his elbow, firmly; then another hand, the other elbow. Where they grabbed, his tendons went taut.

"Okay, rabbi. Okay okay okay okay okay okay. . . ." He listened; it was a very soothing word, that okay. "Okay okay everything's going to be okay." His feet seemed to have left the ground some, as he glided away from the window, the bassinet, the babies. "Okay easy does it everything's all right all right — "

But he rose, suddenly, as though up out of a dream, and flailing his arms, screamed: *I'm the father!*

But the window disappeared. In a moment they tore off his jacket — it gave so easily, in one yank. Then a needle slid under his skin. The drug calmed his soul, but did not touch it down where the blackness had reached.

MERIDIAN BOOKS

published by The World Publishing Company
2231 West 110 Street, Cleveland 2, Ohio

MERIDIAN FICTION

MF1 THE MANDARINS *by Simone de Beauvoir*
MF2 PICTURES FROM AN INSTITUTION *by Randall Jarrell*
MF3 THE COLLECTED STORIES *by Isaac Babel*
MF4 A LEGACY *by Sybille Bedford*
MF5 GOODBYE, COLUMBUS *by Philip Roth*
MF6 THE MIDDLE AGE OF MRS. ELIOT *by Angus Wilson*
MF7 A LONG DAY'S DYING *by Frederick Buechner*
MF8 THE TOWERS OF TREBIZOND *by Rose Macaulay*
MF9 DANGLING MAN *by Saul Bellow*
MF10 BEASTS AND MEN *and* THE SEED *by Pierre Gascar*
MF11 THE ACCEPTANCE WORLD *by Anthony Powell*
MF12 MEMENTO MORI *by Muriel Spark*
MF13 CARDS OF IDENTITY *by Nigel Dennis*
MF14 THE LITTLE DISTURBANCES OF MAN *by Grace Paley*
MF15 TEMPO DI ROMA *by Alexis Curvers*
MF16 LOVE AND LIKE *by Herbert Gold*
MF17 GOLK *by Richard G. Stern*
MF18 PASSAGE FROM HOME *by Isaac Rosenfeld*
MF19 THE CHARIOTEER *by Mary Renault*
MF20 THE RECOGNITIONS *by William Gaddis*
MF21 AN AMERICAN TRAGEDY *by Theodore Dreiser, introduction by Robert Penn Warren*

MERIDIAN BOOKS

published by The World Publishing Company
2231 West 110 Street, Cleveland 2, Ohio

MERIDIAN BOOKS

published by The World Publishing Company
2231 West 110 Street, Cleveland 2, Ohio

MERIDIAN GIANTS

MG1 MYSTICISM *by Evelyn Underhill*

MG2 MEDIEVAL PANORAMA *by G. G. Coulton*

MG3 PROLEGOMENA TO THE STUDY OF GREEK RELIGION *by Jane Harrison*

MG4 MY LIFE IN ART *by Constantin Stanislavski*

MG5 THE ROMANTIC AGONY *by Mario Praz*

MG6 PHILOSOPHIES OF INDIA *by Heinrich Zimmer*

MG7 PLATO: THE MAN AND HIS WORK *by A. E. Taylor*

MG8 FRANCE AGAINST HERSELF *by Herbert Luethy*

MG9 THE LITERATURE OF THE SPANISH PEOPLE *by Gerald Brenan*

MG10 FILM FORM *and* THE FILM SENSE *by Sergei Eisenstein*

MG11 LITERATURE IN AMERICA *edited by Philip Rahv*

MG12 THE DISSOCIATION OF A PERSONALITY *by Morton Prince*

MG13 A TREASURY OF YIDDISH STORIES *edited by Irving Howe and Eliezer Greenberg*

MG14 CHINESE CIVILIZATION *by Marcel Granet*

MG15 THE ORIGINS OF TOTALITARIANISM *by Hannah Arendt*

MG16 THE PHILOSOPHY OF SPINOZA *by Harry Austryn Wolfson*

MG17 THE MAN OF THE RENAISSANCE *by Ralph Roeder*

MG18R NEW YORK PLACES & PLEASURES: REVISED EDITION *by Kate Simon*

MG19 THE PLACE OF VALUE IN A WORLD OF FACTS *by Wolfgang Köhler*

MG20 FROM THE N.R.F. *edited by Justin O'Brien*

MG21 JAIL KEYS MADE HERE AND OTHER SIGNS *photographs by Lee Boltin*

MG22 FRANK LLOYD WRIGHT: WRITINGS AND BUILDINGS *selected by Edgar Kaufmann and Ben Raeburn*

MG23 THE CHILDHOOD OF MAN *by Leo Frobenius*

MG24 THE MYSTIC ROSE *by Ernest Crawley*

MG25 WEBSTER'S NEW WORLD DICTIONARY OF THE AMERICAN LANGUAGE (CONCISE EDITION)

MG26A A HISTORY OF THE EARLY CHURCH, Vol. I *by Hans Lietzmann*

MG26B A HISTORY OF THE EARLY CHURCH, Vol. II *by Hans Lietzmann*

MG27 FOLKSONGS AND FOOTNOTES: AN INTERNATIONAL SONGBOOK *by Theodore Bikel*

MERIDIAN BOOKS

published by The World Publishing Company
2231 West 110 Street, Cleveland 2, Ohio

LIVING AGE BOOKS